INVERTEBRATE TISSUE CULTURE

Volume I

ADVISORY BOARD

INVERTEBRATE TISSUE CULTURE

Edited by C. Vago

STATION DE RECHERCHES CYTOPATHOLOGIQUES
INRA-CNRS, SAINT-CHRISTOL,
UNIVERSITÉ DES SCIENCES
MONTPELLIER, FRANCE

VOLUME I

ACADEMIC PRESS   New York and London   1971

ACADEMIC PRESS, INC.
111 Fifth Avenue, New York, New York 10003

United Kingdom Edition published by
ACADEMIC PRESS, INC. (LONDON) LTD.
24/28 Oval Road, London NW1 7DD

LIBRARY OF CONGRESS CATALOG CARD NUMBER: 75-154371

PRINTED IN THE UNITED STATES OF AMERICA

CONTENTS

I. METHODS IN INVERTEBRATE TISSUE CULTURE

1 Cell Culture Media and Methods

James L. Vaughn

v

2   Organ Culture Methods

N. Le Douarin

3   Electron Microscopy of Cell and Organ Cultures of Invertebrates

G. Devauchelle

4   Aseptic Rearing of Invertebrates for Tissue Culture

G. Meynadier

II. CELL CULTURES

5   The Morphology and Physiology of Cultured Invertebrate Cells

T. D. C. Grace

6   Cell Culture of Lepidoptera

K. Aizawa

7   Cell Culture of Diptera

Silvana Dolfini

8   Cell Culture of Coleoptera, Orthoptera and Dictyoptera

J. M. Quiot

9   Cell Culture of Hymenoptera

A. Giauffret

10   Cell Culture of Hemiptera

Hiroyuki Hirumi and Karl Maramorosch

11 Cell Cultures of Crustacea, Arachnida, and Merostomacea

F. Peponnet and J. M. Quiot

12 Cell Culture of Mollusks

O. Flandre

13 Cell Culture of Invertebrates Other Than Mollusks and Arthropods

Michel Rannou

LIST OF CONTRIBUTORS

Numbers in parentheses indicate the pages on which the authors' contributions begin.

K. Aizawa, Institute of Biological Control, Faculty of Agriculture, Kyushu University, Fukuoka, Japan (211)

G. Devauchelle, Laboratoire de Biologie Animale, Université d'Amiens, Amiens, France (115)

Silvana Dolfini, Istituto di Genetica, Università di Milano, Milan, Italy (247)

O. Flandre, Laboratoire de Thérapeutique, Faculté de Médecine, Université de Montpellier, Montpellier, France (361)

A. Giauffret, Laboratoire de Recherches Vétérinaires et Apicoles, Nice, France (295)

T. D. C. Grace, Division of Entomology, C. S. I. R. O., Canberra, Australia (171)

Hiroyuki Hirumi, Boyce Thompson Institute for Plant Research, Yonkers, New York (307)

N. LE DOUARIN, Laboratoire d'Embryologie, Université de Nantes, Nantes, France (41)

KARL MARAMOROSCH, Boyce Thompson Institute for Plant Research, Yonkers, New York (307)

G. MEYNADIER, Station de Recherches Cytopathologiques, INRA-CNRS, Saint-Christol, Université des Sciences, Montpellier, France (141)

F. PEPONNET, Station de Recherches Cytopathologiques, INRA-CNRS, Saint-Christol, Université des Sciences, Montpellier, France (341)

J. M. QUIOT, Station de Recherches Cytopathologiques, INRA-CNRS, Saint-Christol, Université des Sciences, Montpellier, France (267, 341)

MICHEL RANNOU, Pêches Outre-Mer, Muséum National d'Histoire Naturelle, Paris, France (385)

JAMES L. VAUGHN, Entomology Research Division, Agriculture Research Service, United States Department of Agriculture, Beltsville, Maryland (3)

PREFACE

The contribution of cell and tissue culture to the development of medical and biological sciences is universally known. Most of the recent progress in cellular biology and pathology has been achieved by *in vitro* investigations. Fifteen years ago this was true for biological experimentation dealing with man and other vertebrates. The use of tissue culture in invertebrate research in physiology and pathology was being considered, but only a few attempts were made to achieve such cultures, and then in only a small number of insect and mollusk species.

The First International Colloquium on Invertebrate Tissue Culture held in 1962 in Montpellier (France) enabled us to evaluate results of previous research and opened new vistas for future research. Since then rapid advances have occurred in cell and organ culture of invertebrates—Arthropoda, Mollusca, Echinoderma, Nematoda, and Coelenterata. Such cultures, often barely developed, were also used in studies involving genetics, physiology, and pathology.

At present, investigations and results are so numerous and diversified that the publication of a treatise to collate this material seemed desirable. With the aid of the foremost specialists in the field of invertebrate cell and organ culture, this two-volume treatise was made possible.

xi

This work was organized so that the techniques utilized and their applications to the various biological disciplines are developed, accompanied by the results and characteristics of the resulting cultures. Some overlap was necessary to ensure linkage of information from chapter to chapter.

Volume I includes general methodology concerning both cell and organ cultures and their preparation from aseptic conditions. Methods for the examination of cultures are also developed, particularly those concerning ultrastructure studies by electron microscopy. Cell cultures obtained from different groups of invertebrates are then discussed with emphasis on peculiarities specific to each group.

Organ cultures of different invertebrates are the subject of several chapters in Volume II, including an important section on the use of cell and organ cultures in physiology, genetics, and pathology. The study of the effect of pathogens is distinguished from that of microorganisms transmitted by vectors.

I wish to thank the members of the advisory board—C. Barigozzi, P. Buchner, J. de Wilde, M. Florkin, E. Hadorn, P. Lepine, K. Maramorosch, N. Oker-Blom, R. C. Parker, G. Ubrizsy, and E. Wolff—for their aid in the preparation of this treatise. The continuous assistance of M. Laporte is gratefully acknowledged.

It is hoped that this treatise will not only evaluate the present state of research and the problems in invertebrate tissue culture but will also serve as a guide to those working in this field and as a technical and scientific introduction to those intending to culture invertebrate tissues or to use cultures in pathology, physiology, or other biological disciplines.

C. Vago

CONTENTS OF VOLUME II

I

Methods in Invertebrate Tissue Culture

1

CELL CULTURE MEDIA AND METHODS

James L. Vaughn

I. DESIGN OF CELL CULTURE MEDIA*

A. Introduction

The principle underlying the design of any suitable media for the growth of cells *in vitro* is to provide an environment in which the cell metabolism approximates, as closely as possible, that occurring in similar cells of an intact animal. The success achieved in approximating the normal *in vivo* metabolism depends to a large extent on the understanding of the factors controlling this metabolism in the intact animal. Since the environment of animal cells *in vivo* is the body fluid which bathes them, it was natural for tissue culturists to attempt to duplicate this fluid when designing culture media. However, the investigators who first attempted to grow invertebrate cells *in vitro* had very little information about the composition of the invertebrate hemolymphs. The importance of a proper balance of inorganic ions for maintaining tissue and organ function *in vitro* had been empirically established, and some balanced salt solutions had been developed. These were the major, if not the only, components of the early culture media.

Early workers found that filtered seawater served as a good balanced salt solution, permitting the survial of many tissues from marine invertebrates. Thus, much was learned about the behavior of these tissues *in vitro* before it was possible to grow the cells. For example, studies with the tissues of sponges (Wilson, 1907) revealed that in the absence of calcium these tissues dissociated into single cells which would reaggregate when calcium was restored to the medium. Balanced salt solutions, with or without hemolymph added, were also used in studies on the survival of insect tissue *in vitro*. Goldschmidt (1915) used a simple salt solution plus cecropia hemolymph to demonstrate division in cecropia

---

* Since the composition of media varies considerably from one group of invertebrates to another, it will be treated separately in chapters concerning each group.

spermatocytes *in vitro*. For the next 40 years most of the research on growth of invertebrate tissues *in vitro* was done with this simple type of medium, and survival was nearly all that was achieved. Mitosis was found in maturing germ cells, but explants of other tissues produced only migrating cells which did not divide.

In 1935, Trager reported the first observation of mitosis in cells other than germ cells cultured *in vitro*. The medium he used consisted of a balanced salt solution plus maltose, egg albumin digest, and silkworm hemolymph. Since this medium does not differ significantly from that used by other investigators, it may have been that factors other than medium contributed to his success. In 1938, Trager successfully cultured mosquito tissue in a medium similar to that which he used for silkworm tissue. From mosquito ovaries, he obtained small outgrowths of cells which contained some mitotic figures. Cultures of other tissues, e.g., midgut, brain, and appendages, survived for periods up to 47 days but did not produce free cells that divided by mitosis.

These two studies were probably the most successful attempts to culture invertebrate tissue during this entire period. For a more complete description of this early work, interested readers are referred to the review of insect tissue culture by Day and Grace (1959) or to the review of invertebrate tissue culture by Jones (1966).

By the early 1950's a great deal more information on the composition of invertebrate hemolymphs had accumulated. In 1956, using this accumulated knowledge, S. S. Wyatt developed a more complex medium for the culture of insect tissue. In addition to the inorganic salts and sugars used in the earlier media, Wyatt's medium contained organic and amino acids. The levels of these compounds in the medium corresponded to the levels found in the hemolymph of several Lepidoptera. With this medium, Wyatt obtained cultures superior to any previously reported. The cells were more numerous and could be maintained in a healthy condition for extended periods. The time required for completion of mitosis from the metaphase stage was reduced from 50 minutes in Trager's medium to 20–25 minutes in the new medium.

This medium was subsequently modified by numerous workers to produce even better growth (Grace, 1958a; Vago and Chastang, 1958a). Jones and Cunningham (1961) reported that replacement of the amino acids and the B-vitamin group with lactalbumin hydrolysate and yeast extract, respectively, not only simplified the media preparation but provided equal or somewhat better cell division. Other workers have since devised media equally suited for the culture of tissues from other insects: Hirumi and Maramorosch (1964b) and Chiu and Black (1967) for leafhoppers, Carlson (1961) for grasshoppers, Ting and Brooks (1965) and Landureau (1968) for cockroaches, Echalier et al. (1965) for *Drosophila,* and Schneider (1969) for mosquitoes.

The development of suitable media for the culture of tissues from other invertebrates also has made progress within the last few years. Vago and Chastang (1960a) established cultures of cells from the cardiac tissue of oysters in a medium composed of an isotonic salt solution, glucose, and amino acids, and supplemented with oyster serum. Although some mitosis was observed, the medium did not permit sufficient growth for subculture of these cells. Cultures of cells from several species of snails have also been made (Flandre and Vago, 1963; Burch and Cuadros, 1965). Mitosis was observed in the cells, and a limited number of subcultures were made. Necco and Martin (1963) cultured the white body cells of the octopus in Parker's medium 199 to which NaCl was added to raise the osmotic pressure. They were able to determine the mitotic index and the percentage of cells in prophase, metaphase, anaphase, and telophase at intervals up to 20 hours *in vitro.* No attempts to subculture these cells were reported.

Thus, within the last 10 years media have been developed in which cells from many different invertebrates could be grown. Some of these media were formulated from the known composition of the hemolymph of a particular invertebrate; others were prepared by combining components from media used for the growth of other cells, both invertebrate and vertebrate. The only medium in which the levels of any of the individual components have been established after studies on the requirements of invertebrate cells in culture is that of Landureau (1969).

The levels of the various components in invertebrate tissue culture media and the effect of variation in these levels will be discussed in the remaining parts of this section. Wherever possible the concentration of the components in the media will be compared with that found in the hemolymph of various invertebrates. It is hoped that this will provide some guidelines for those investigators wishing to develop media for the culture of cells from invertebrates other than those used by previous workers.

B. Inorganic Salts

The hemolymph of all invertebrates is the source of the inorganic ions required for the growth and function of the animal's cells and tissues. In addition, the inorganic salts have some role in regulating the osmotic pressure and the pH of the hemolymph. The degree to which the inorganic ions regulate these last two functions varies with different animals. In insects the inorganic ions exert less of an effect on osmotic pressure and pH than in vertebrates because organic acids, amino acids, and other organic molecules are of considerable importance in the regulation of these factors (Florkin and Jeuniaux, 1964).

The invertebrates are a large and diverse group and any generalizations cannot cover all situations. However, some useful generalizations concerning the levels of inorganic ions in hemolymph can be made. For example, the overall ionic balance in the hemolymph of invertebrates differs from that in the blood of vertebrates in that the ratio of Na + K to Ca + Mg is in the range of 10–25 in blood and only 5–10 in hemolymph (Lockwood, 1961). The concentration of individual ions in the body fluids of marine invertebrates generally corresponds to that of seawater, regarding both the levels of ions and the ratios of one ion to another, e.g., Na to K. Hemolymphs of freshwater invertebrates maintain similar ratios, but the individual ion concentrations are lower. Except for certain groups of insects this is also true of terrestrial invertebrates (Prosser, 1950). Among the insects, it has been suggested that the mole ratio of sodium to potassium is correlated with, but not dependent upon, the food of the insect: Phytophagous insects have a ratio of less than 1, zoophagous insects greater than 1, and omnivorous insects close to 1 (Buck, 1953). However, this is not true for all insects, and Florkin and Jeuniaux (1964) have suggested a phylogenetic grouping with the most primitive insects having Na to K ratios nearer those of other animals (that is, greater than 1). They suggest that the more specialized insects, such as the Lepidoptera and the Hymenoptera, have developed other regulating mechanisms involving a different ionic pattern. The specific analyses of many invertebrate hemolymphs are given in the articles by Buck, Lockwood, Florkin and Jeuniaux, and Prosser cited above. Such analyses provide an estimate of the ionic concentrations that can be tolerated by tissues from an animal and are most useful in preparing balanced salt solutions. It should be noted, however, that all cells appear to be able to regulate selectively their internal ion levels, and therefore, it is not necessary to duplicate exactly the ion content of the hemolymph to get cell growth *in vitro*.

The inorganic salts which are included in most tissue culture media are $NaCl$, KCl, $MgCl_2$, $CaCl_2$, $MgSO_4$, NaH_2PO_4, $NaHCO_3$, and KH_2PO_4. Table I lists the balanced salt portions of several media used to culture invertebrate tissues. These media were chosen because they supported cell division by mitosis rather than just tissue or cell maintenance. The balanced salt portions of two media commonly used for vertebrate cell culture are included for comparison. The data from within a

TABLE I

Representative Balanced Salt Portions of Invertebrate Tissue Culture Medium

mg/100 ml

NaCl	KCl	CaCl₂	MgCl₂	MgSO₄	NaH₂PO₄	NaHCO₃	KH₂PO₄	Tissue source	Reference
87.5	—	11.1	9.6	—	18.0	—	26.3	Lepidoptera	Trager (1935)
—	298.0	81.0	161.5	180.7	110.0	—	—	Lepidoptera	S. S. Wyatt (1956)
—	300.0	50.0	140.1	171.0	110.0	—	—	Lepidoptera	Vago and Chastang (1958a)
—	300.0	100.0	140.6	171.0	100.0	—	—	Lepidoptera	Vago and Chastang (1958b)
—	300.0	74.5	140.6	195.4	104.4	—	—	Lepidoptera	Vago and Chastang (1960b)
—	224.0	100.0	106.8	135.8	84.4	35.0	—	Lepidoptera	Grace (1962)
160.0	128.0	32.6	57.3	79.1	44.5	125.0	1.2	Lepidoptera	Mitsuhashi (1965b)
450.0	250.0	302.0	187.3	195.3	153.8	—	—	Lepidoptera and Diptera	Converse and Nagle (1967)
78.8	6.0	15.5	—	—	12.0	—	56.0	Diptera	Trager (1938)
90.0	300.0	80.0	—	180.7	95.7	—	—	Diptera	Trager (1959)
700.0	20.0	1.5	4.7	—	16.4	5.0	—	Diptera	Horikawa and Kurada (1959)
700.0	20.0	1.5	46.9	—	17.4	35.0	—	Diptera	Horikawa and Fox (1964)
900.0	20.0	20.0	—	180.7	10.0	—	—	Diptera	Peleg (1965)
300.0	110.0	40.0	53.4	19.5	—	—	—	Diptera	Schneider (1969)

								Taxon	Reference
—	—	14.9	4.7	—	80.0	50.0	—	Orthoptera	Shaw (1956)
409.0	14.9	22.2	9.5	—	24.0	102.0	—	Orthoptera	Carlson (1961)
100.0	40.0	50.0	7.7	—	50.0	20.0	—	Orthoptera	Marks and Reinecke (1965)[a]
1100.0	140.0	110.0	—	61.5	6.0	—	—	Orthoptera	Ting and Brooks (1965)
850.0	105.0	49.0	—	59.7	—	36.0	—	Orthoptera	Landureau and Jollès (1969)[b]
377.8	177.8	31.8	39.1	—	36.8	122.2	—	Homoptera	Hirumi and Maramorosch (1964c)
700.0	20.0	14.9	4.7	2.0	17.4	12.0	—	Homoptera	Mitsuhashi and Maramorosch (1964)
416.0	16.0	10.0	1.9	90.3	10.8	49.0	—	Homoptera	Mitsuhashi (1965a)
105.0	80.0	30.0	—	102.6	—	35.0	30.0	Homoptera	Chiu and Black (1967)
340.0	170.0	47.2	70.2	10.0	58.3	110.0	—	Ticks	Rehacek (1962)
30.0	—	—	—	—	420.0	—	260.0	Snails	Burch and Cuadros (1965)
650.0	14.0	12.0	—	0.2	1.0	20.0	—	Snails	Vago and Chastang (1958a)
7.2	0.4	0.3	—	—	0.2	5.5	—	Snails	Flandre and Vago (1963)
2580.0	64.0	64.0	144.0	9.8	8.0	20.0	2.0	Octopus	Necco and Martin (1963)
680.0	40.0	20.0	—	—	14.0	220.0	—	Vertebrates	TC 199 in Parker (1961)[c]
680.0	40.0	20.0	9.4	—	15.0	200.0	—	Vertebrates	Eagles in Parker (1961)

[a] Contains 20 mg of Na_2SO_4.
[b] Contains 58.1 mg of $MnSO_4$ and 90 mg of H_3PO_3.
[c] Contains $Fe(NO_3)_3 \cdot 9H_2O$ in trace amounts.

limited group, e.g., those media used for cells from Lepidoptera, show a considerable range of salt concentrations which permit growth of the cells from those insects. The NaCl concentration ranges from 450 mg/100 ml to none. A similar range of concentrations exists for other salts in this group and within other groups as well.

The range of salt concentrations shown in Table I clearly indicates that invertebrate cells *in vitro,* as *in vivo,* can tolerate some variation in the inorganic salt levels. Ting and Brooks (1965) studied the effect of different Na/K ratios on the growth of cells from the cockroach, *Blatella germanica* Linnaeus. They found that Trager's medium for the culture of tsetse-fly tissue did not support the growth of cockroach tissue until the Na/K ratio was raised from 0.57 to 10.0 to correspond more closely to that of cockroach hemolymph. Other media designed for the growth of cells from Lepidoptera and having a Na/K ratio of less than 1 were not suitable for growth of cockroach tissue. Growth of this tissue was not obtained in TC 199, Hank's, or Eagle's media which have a Na/K ratio of 25 or 26. Neither did growth occur in White's medium for plant tissue which has a Na/K ratio of 1. As pointed out by the authors, caution must be used in interpreting these latter results because factors other than the Na/K ratio may have caused the lack of growth. However, the establishment of a Na/K ratio of 10 for the growth of cockroach tissue agrees with the findings of Marks and Reinecke (1964) that the medium of Grace would support the growth of cells from the cockroach, *Leucophaea maderae* Fabricius only after the Na/K ratio had been changed from 0.25 to 10.0. These two studies have established some limits on the Na/K ratio which cockroach cells can tolerate *in vitro.* Unfortunately, no similar studies have been done with cells from other invertebrates.

There has been very little investigation of the anion requirements of invertebrate cells *in vitro.* Generally invertebrate hemolymphs are low in Cl ion and so Shaw (1956) substituted glutamate and glycine for NaCl and KCl in his culture medium for grasshopper tissue. Thus, he was able to maintain the Na/K ratio and also bring the Cl ion level and the organic acid levels closer to that found in the hemolymph. The effects of such changes have not been investigated with other invertebrate culture media. Other anions such as HCO_3, PO_4, and SO_4 have received no study in invertebrate tissue culture media, and their importance other than as components of buffer systems is not known.

These are some examples of balanced salt solutions which have been used successfully in media for the culture of invertebrate cells. For those investigators having to prepare balanced salt solutions for other invertebrates, it would seem that, wherever possible, an approximation of the inorganic salt content of the hemolymph of the animal should be adequate. When an analysis of the hemolymph is not available, the general features of invertebrate hemolymphs given at the beginning of this section can be used as guides: a general inorganic salt level corresponding to a hemolymph from a similar type of invertebrate, i.e., marine, freshwater, or terrestrial, with particular attention to the Na/K ratio and to maintaining a low ratio of Na + K to Ca + Mg.

C. Organic Acids

Unlike the bloods of most animals, the hemolymph of insects contain free organic acids of the type associated with the tricarboxylic acid cycle. Citrate, α-ketoglutarate, malate, fumarate, succinate, oxaloacetate, and pyruvate, in amounts ranging from a few tenths of a millimole to 25–35 mmoles are found in the hemolymphs of both the larval and the adult stages of many insects. They play an important role in the cation balance of the hemolymph by binding large amounts of the inorganic ions present there (Florkin and Jeuniaux, 1964).

The organic acids were first used in the insect tissue culture medium formulated by S. S. Wyatt in 1956. This medium contained 67 mg of malic acid, 37 mg of α-ketoglutaric acid, 6 mg of succinic acid and 5.5 mg of fumaric acid per 100 ml of medium. Media based on the Wyatt formulation have been designed by other workers using some or all of these organic acids in similar amounts (e.g., Trager, 1959; Grace, 1962, and Schneider, 1969). The function of these compounds in tissue culture is not known, but they probably contribute to the ionic balance by binding cations as they do in the hemolymph. In addition, they may contribute to the osmotic pressure and to the buffering capacity of the media. However, other media, which contain no organic acids or only small amounts of sodium citrate, have been used successfully to culture insect cells (Vago and Chastang, 1960b; Mitsuhashi, 1965a; Mitsuhashi and Maramorosch, 1964). Thus, the organic acids are probably not an essential ingredient in insect tissue culture media.

The medium of Necco and Martin (1963) for the culture of the white body cells of the octopus contained 150 mg of malic acid and 105 mg of fumaric acid per 100 ml of medium. Since most other media for the culture of invertebrate cells do not contain organic acids, they are probably not essential for these invertebrates either.

D. Amino Acids

Insect hemolymphs characteristically contain high levels of free amino acids, which may contribute as high as 40% of the total blood osmotic

pressure (Martignoni, 1960). The total free amino acids in insect hemolymph varies widely (300–2100 mg/100 ml), but the highest levels are
found in the hemolymphs of the Coleoptera, the Lepidoptera, and the Hymenoptera. The amounts of the individual amino acids vary among different species and within a single species during successive phases of development. Generally free aspartic acid, phenylalanine, leucine, and isoleucine
are found in the lowest amounts. Glutamic acid and proline are among
those found in the largest amounts. The remainder occur at intermediate
levels, which may vary with the species (Florkin and Jeuniaux, 1964).

The unusually high level of free amino acids in the hemolymph of
insects is reflected in the composition of culture media designed for insect cells. The medium for silkworm cells formulated by Wyatt, on the
basis of the analysis of silkworm hemolymph, contained 22 amino acids
and had a total free amino acid concentration of 1040.5 mg/100 ml medium (Table II). Tryptophan, cystine, and cysteine were found beneficial
to cell growth and were included even though they were not found in the
hemolymph. The ratio of aspartic and glutamic acids to their amides
was increased over that found in hemolymph to promote the removal of
ammonia from the medium (S. S. Wyatt, 1956).

The amino acids in the hemolymph are usually of the L configuration.
However, the D configuration of alanine has been found in *Oncopeltus
fasciatus* Dallas, and D-serine has been found in the hemolymph of some
Lepidoptera (Corrigan and Srinivasan, 1966). In the Lepidoptera, D-
serine may account for up to 70% of the total free serine (Florkin and
Jeuniaux, 1964). Normally only the L-amino acids are added to tissue

TABLE II
Amino Acids in Wyatt's
Insect Tissue Culture Medium[a]

Amino acid	mg/100 ml	Amino acid	mg/100 ml
L-Arginine–HCl	70	L-Proline	35
DL-Lysine–HCl	125	L-Tyrosine	5
L-Histidine	250	DL-Threonine	35
L-Aspartic Acid	35	DL-Methionine	10
L-Asparagine	35	L-Phenylalanine	15
L-Glutamic Acid	60	DL-Valine	20
L-Glutamine	60	DL-Isoleucine	10
Glycine	65	DL-Leucine	15
DL-Serine	110	L-Tryptophan	10
DL-Alanine	45	L-Cystine	2.5
β-Alanine	20	Cysteine–HCl	8

[a] From S. S. Wyatt (1956).

culture media although some, e.g., lysine, serine, and alanine, are added as mixtures of both forms (Table II). This mixture of free amino acids has sometimes been altered to more closely resemble the hemolymph analysis of a particular insect. For example, Marks and Reinecke (1965), in developing a medium for grasshopper tissue, added L-taurine and altered the levels of many of the amino acids common to their medium and Wyatt's.

Vago and Chastang (1958a) substituted 10% lactalbumin hydrolysate for the individual amino acids and obtained satisfactory growth of cells from several Lepidoptera. Similar results have been obtained with media for cells from the cockroach (Ting and Brooks, 1965), locust (Miciarelli et al., 1967), and leafhoppers (Mitsuhashi and Maramorosch, 1964). Higher levels, 17.5% (Horikawa and Fox, 1964) and 20% (Echalier et al., 1965) have been used for the cultivation of cells from Drosophila melanogaster Meigen. In some media the content of specific amino acids has been increased by adding the pure amino acid in addition to the lactalbumin hydrolysate. Vago (1959) obtained improved growth when he added histidine (100 mg/100 ml) to his medium containing 10% lactalbumin hydrolysate, but the addition of other amino acids produced no noticeable effect. The medium of Horikawa and Fox (1964) contained L-tryptophan (10 mg/100 ml) and L-cysteine hydrochloride (2.5 mg/100 ml) in addition to the 17.5% lactalbumin hydrolysate.

As with most of the other constituents of insect cell culture media, the levels of the amino acids were chosen on the basis of hemolymph composition. Few studies have been made on the amino acid requirements of insect cells in culture. Such studies are difficult with all invertebrate cells because of the need to supplement the chemically defined media with some serum. However, Grace and Brzostowski (1966) studied the depletion of amino acids in their culture medium during growth of the Antheraea cell line. The medium contained an amino acid mixture similar to that of Wyatt's except that the DL-amino acids (DL-serine excepted) were replaced by L-amino acids at one-half the level shown in Table II. This medium was supplemented with 3% heat-treated (60° for 10 minutes) Antheraea pernyi (Guerin) hemolymph. After seven days of cell growth, the medium contained no aspartic acid, less than 25% of the original glutamine, and less than 50% of the glutamic acid, leucine–isoleucine, cystine, and tyrosine. Phenylalanine and methionine showed a reduction of between 30 and 50%. Proline, β-alanine, arginine, and valine showed a reduction from 5 to 20%. Alanine increased approximately fourfold.

The amino acid requirements of cells from a cockroach line have been studied using a minimal medium similar in amino acid content to Grace's but containing only human albumin (Cohn Fract. V) and α_2-macroglobulin as protein supplements (Landureau and Jollès, 1969). Analysis of the residual amino acid levels after seven days of cell growth showed only 8.7% of the glutamic acid and less than 50% of the aspartic acid, cysteine, and methionine remained. Of the remaining 15 amino acids used, none showed a reduction of more than 25% and only proline was reduced by more than 20%. Alanine showed a fivefold increase.

Landureau and Jollès also observed the effect of the deletion of individual amino acids from the medium on the growth of the cockroach cells. They found that proline, cysteine, glycine, phenylalanine, methionine, valine, leucine, tryptophan, histidine, tyrosine, and arginine were essential for continued growth of the cells. Lysine, threonine, serine, and isoleucine were necessary for optimum growth of the cells.

From the standpoint of the nutrition of insect cells in culture these two studies indicate several important points. First, the amino acids depleted from the medium by both the moth cells and the cockroach cells were similar. Aspartic acid and glutamic acid were heavily depleted by both cell lines, but Landureau and Jollès found evidence for active transamination reactions involving these two amino acids in cockroach cells; so perhaps their main use was as precursors for other amino acids. The second important finding in both studies was that the sulfur-containing amino acids (methionine, cysteine, and cystine) and proline were depleted by 50% or more and are apparently important for the growth of insect cells in culture. Finally, many of the amino acids were depleted less than 25% even though Landureau and Jollès reported that they were required for good cell growth. Thus, it appears that these media, which were formulated from data on the amino acid levels in hemolymph, contain an excess amount of many amino acids.

In comparing those amino acids listed by Landureau and Jollès as essential for cells in culture with those listed by House (1965) as required by several insects reared on artificial diets, one finds general agreement. However, the cells in culture require proline, serine, glycine, and tyrosine in addition to the 10 normally required by insects.

There is very little information available concerning the amino acid requirements of invertebrate cells other than insect cells *in vitro*. Flandre and Vago (1963) used 10% lactalbumin hydrolysate as the amino acid source in their medium for cells from *Helix aspersa* Muller. Burch and Cuadros (1965) used a 1:2 dilution of medium TC 199 supplemented with peptone and trypticase for the culture of cells from several snails. The white body cells from the octopus have been grown in short-term cultures using TC 199 medium without any additional amino acid supplements (Necco and Martin, 1963). The actual amino acid components of these media have thus been chosen empirically, and no experimental data exists on the requirements for free amino acids by the cells from these animals.

E. Carbohydrates

The energy requirements of cells growing *in vitro* are usually met by the addition of one or more sugars to the media. Culture media for vertebrate cells generally contain only glucose but often at levels higher than those normally found in the blood of these animals. The cells are not harmed by the increased glucose, and the energy reserve is greatly extended.

When compared to the sugar levels in the bloods of higher animals, the levels of glucose and total fermentable sugars in the hemolymphs of insects are unusually low. Normally, the total fermentable sugar in the hemolymph of immature insects is less than 100 mg/100 ml and consists of varying proportions of glucose and fructose. Sucrose and glycogen are present only in very small amounts or not at all (Florkin and Jeuniaux, 1964).

Even though the sugar levels of bloods and insect hemolymphs are quite different, the choice of sugars and the levels used have been dictated either by past experience in the culture of vertebrate cells or by the analysis of the hemolymph of the invertebrate from which the tissue was taken. As a result, media for the culture of invertebrate cells have contained a variety of carbohydrates at widely differing levels.

In media where the choice of carbohydrate reflects the experience of the culture of vertebrate cells, only glucose was used. Such media has been used to culture tissue from Lepidoptera (Vago and Chastang, 1958a,b; Mitsuhashi, 1965b), Homoptera (Mitsuhashi and Maramorosch, 1964; Mitsuhashi, 1965a), and Diptera (Trager, 1938; Echalier *et al.*, 1965). The concentrations ranged from 100 mg/100 ml used by Vago and Chastang to 5400 mg/100 ml used by Trager. However, most of the media contained about 200 mg/100 ml or about double the level generally reported for insect hemolymphs.

Glucose has also been the only carbohydrate in several media used for the culture of tissues from some invertebrates other than insects. As with insect cells, these cells apparently will tolerate a wide range of glucose concentrations. Flandre and Vago (1963) used a concentration of 500 mg/100 ml for the culture of snail cells, but Burch and Cuadros (1965) obtained satisfactory cultures with medium containing only 75 mg of glucose/100 ml of medium.

In media designed from the analysis of hemolymph, combinations of sugars have been used. S. S. Wyatt (1956) used glucose, fructose, and sucrose in her medium for cells from the silkworm. These three sugars occur in silkworm hemolymph in low levels; however, to increase the energy reserve in the medium the levels were increased to a total of 150 mg/100 ml, consisting of 70 mg of glucose, 40 mg of fructose, and 40 mg of sucrose. Hirumi and Maramorosch (1964b) used a medium with the same carbohydrate composition for the culture of embryonic tissue from leafhoppers. Marks and Reinecke (1965) obtained their best results with cockroach tissue in a medium containing the three sugars in a total concentration of 1200 mg/100 ml, consisting of 400 mg of glucose, 200 mg of fructose, and 600 mg of sucrose. Grace (1962) was able to increase the total carbohydrate concentration even higher by increasing the sucrose level to 2668 mg/100 ml, giving a total concentration of 2778 mg/100 ml. This medium is now widely used to culture the established cell lines derived from moth tissues and from mosquito tissues. Similar high levels of sugar were used by Horikawa and Fox (1964) in their medium for the culture of embryonic tissue from *Drosophila melanogaster*. This medium contained 1380 mg of glucose and 1380 mg of sucrose/100 ml. However, in a later medium (Horikawa *et al.*, 1966) this was reduced to 550 mg/100 ml of each of the two sugars.

In most of the media above, the total carbohydrate level exceeds the level of fermentable sugars found in insect hemolymph. When G. R. Wyatt and Kalf (1957) identified the nonreducing disaccharide, trehalose, as a major sugar in insect hemolymph, the true sugar level in insect hemolymph was established. This level corresponded more closely to that of other animals and to the total carbohydrate level used in tissue culture media. It also raised the possibility that trehalose had some special role as an energy reserve for insect tissue. Grace (1958a) obtained normal migration of free cells from insect tissue when one of the three sugars, glucose, fructose, or sucrose, in Wyatt's medium was replaced by trehalose. However, when trehalose replaced all three sugars, no migrations occurred unless an extract of endocrine organs was also added. Vago and Chastang (1960b) obtained normal growth of the silkworm cells in a medium in which trehalose was the only sugar added. Both Wyatt's medium, used by Grace, and the medium of Vago and Chastang were supplemented with insect hemolymph, but the medium of Vago and Chastang contained 1.1% lactalbumin hydrolysate and was further supplemented with 12% calf serum. These two materials may have contributed other sugars which were not in Wyatt's chemically defined medium, and therefore, the complete medium supported growth with trehalose alone, whereas Wyatt's did not. The media of Ting and

Brooks (1965) for cockroach cells, of Miciarelli *et al.* (1967) for cells of the desert locust, and of Trager (1959) for tsetse-fly tissue all contained trehalose in combination with other sugars and gave some growth of cells from the respective tissue. However, no information was given by these authors as to whether trehalose alone would support growth. Thus, it has not been established whether or not trehalose alone will support cell growth. It does appear certain that its presence in a medium is of no special benefit.

The use of carbohydrates other than glucose, fructose, sucrose, and trehalose has been investigated only on a limited basis. Trager (1935) obtained growth of silkworm cells *in vitro* in a medium which contained only maltose. Gottschewski (cited in Martignoni, 1962) found that fructose, glucose, and mannose were utilized in cultures of *Drosophila* organs but that ribose, arabinose, xylose, galactose, glucosamine, sucrose, lactose, maltose, glycogen, and starch were not.

The study by Grace and Brzostowski (1966) on the utilization of glucose, fructose, and sucrose by cells from the established moth line indicates a sequential use of these carbohydrates. Sixty percent of the glucose was removed from the medium within the first two days. During this time less than 20% of the fructose and none of the sucrose was depleted. After the second day the uptake of sucrose began, and by the seventh day 23% of the sucrose as well as 90% of the glucose had been removed from the medium. In actual weight, however, this corresponds to a loss of 63 mg/100 ml of glucose and 614 mg/100 ml of sucrose. Fructose was utilized at an intermediate rate until the fourth day, after which there was a decline in use. Grace reports that rapid cell division began after the second day; thus, during the period of rapid cell division, sucrose appears to have been a major source of carbohydrates.

The utilization of sugars by cells of the Grace *Antheraea* line has also been investigated using ^{14}C-labeled sugars (Clements and Grace, 1967). In these tests each sugar was added to the medium separately and utilization was measured by trapping the radioactive CO_2 and measuring the level of activity. Clements and Grace found that the monosaccharides, glucose and trehalose, were metabolized at approximately the same rate over the three-day test period. The addition of extracts from the corpora cardiaca did not increase the rate of trehalose metabolism. Sucrose was not metabolized when it was tested under the same conditions.

Grace and his co-workers concluded that in media containing combinations of sugars, the monosaccharides would be utilized in preference to sucrose until they were reduced to a restrictive level. Since the medium used by Clements and Grace contained 4% hemolymph, which added 32 mg of trehalose/100 ml of medium, this could account for their negative results with sucrose. Thus, it appears that insect cells have no special requirements for sugars. Unless further study indicates otherwise, media containing only glucose are probably adequate for insect cell cultures.

F. Vitamins

The only vitamins which have been shown to be essential for insects are the water-soluble type, particularly those of the B-vitamin group. For immature insects nicotinic acid, pantothenic acid, pyridoxine, riboflavine, and thiamine can be considered essential; and biotin, choline, and folic acid are at least beneficial. Ascorbic acid is also essential for many insects (House, 1965).

The early insect tissue culture media did not include any of the vitamins. Grace (1958a) was the first to demonstrate an improvement in cell growth when they were added. He found that thiamine, riboflavine, pyridoxine, niacin, pantothenic acid, biotin, folic acid, p-aminobenzoic acid, choline, and $meso$-inositol, each at 1 μg/100 ml, increased the number of cells that migrated from an explant but did not increase either the number of mitoses in these cells or their survival time. Choline at 10 mg/100 ml, $meso$-inositol at 0.2 mg/100 ml, and all others at 1 mg/100 ml were detrimental to cell growth. Grace's medium (1962) for his established $Antheraea$ cell line contain thiamine hydrochloride, riboflavin, calcium pantothenate, pyridoxine hydrochloride, p-aminobenzoic acid, folic acid, niacin, and isoinositol at 0.002 mg/100 ml, biotin at 0.001 mg/100 ml, and choline hydrochloride at 0.02 mg/100 ml. This combination of water-soluble vitamins has been included, at slightly different levels, in the medium of Horikawa and Kurada (1959) for tissue from $Drosophila$ and by Marks and Reinecke (1965) for cockroach tissue.

Ascorbic acid has also been included in some media (Ting and Brooks, 1965; Horikawa and Fox, 1964). The value of this vitamin for promoting growth is uncertain, although it is useful in reducing the oxidation–reduction potential of media (Martignoni and Scallion, 1961).

The necessary B-vitamin group may also be added to insect tissue culture media as yeast hydrolysate. Jones and Cunningham (1961) used TC Yeastolate at 100 mg/ml in their culture medium for Lepidoptera tissue. TC Yeastolate at a concentration of 200 mg/100 ml was used by Ting and Brooks (1965) for the culture of cockroach tissue and by Horikawa and Fox (1964) for the culture of $Drosophila$ tissue.

The stimulation of individual members of the B-vitamin group on primary cultures of cynthia moth tissue was reported by Sanborn and Haskell (1961). In this work, individual vitamins were omitted from the medium and the effect on growth recorded. In a second test the individual vitamin was omitted and the corresponding analog added to block the action of any vitamins which occurred in the explant or in hemolymph supplement. Sanborn and Haskell found that each of the vitamins used by Grace were required for maximum growth but that folic acid, riboflavin, niacinamide, thiamine, p-aminobenzoic acid, and pyridoxine were present in the hemolymph-supplemented medium and the explant in sufficient amounts for maximum migration of free cells. Additional choline, biotin, and *meso*-inositol were required. The addition of calcium pantothenate at the level of 1 μg/100 ml inhibited growth of free cells, but when the level was reduced to 0.1 μg/100 ml, growth was not inhibited.

The vitamin requirements for established insect cell lines have been studied only with EPa (cockroach) cells (Landureau, 1969). This study was done in a chemically defined medium, supplemented with purified α_2-macroglobulin and was thus presumably free of vitamins from unidentified sources. The complete medium contained, in milligrams per liter, ascorbic acid 10.0, folic acid 0.01, p-aminobenzoic acid 0.02, biotin 0.01, choline hydrochloride 0.40, inositol 0.05, nicotinamide 0.10, calcium pantothenate 0.10, pyridoxine hydrochloride 0.03, riboflavin 0.05, thiamine hydrochloride 0.01, and cyanocobalamine 0.005.

Each vitamin was studied for its effect on the long-term survival of the culture and the facility of transfer in the absence of the vitamin. Landureau found that calcium pantothenate, riboflavin, inositol, cyanocobalamine, and thiamine were essential for continued growth of the EPa cell line. Choline, pyridoxine, folic acid, nicotinic acid, and biotin were required to obtain optimum growth. Ascorbic acid and p-aminobenzoic acid were not required. The requirement for cyanocobalamine was only detected in the absence of any serum. Landureau and Stienbuch (1969) demonstrated that the cell requirement for serum or the albumin fraction of serum was, in part, a requirement for the cyanocobalamine normally bound to such proteins.

The level of choline in Landureau's medium is double the level used in Grace's medium. Nagle (1969) tested the effect of various levels of choline on the growth of Grace's *Aedes* cells and found that growth was stimulated by levels of choline up to 50 mg/liter. At 200 mg/liter some inhibition was detected. The choline tests were made in a medium containing 5% fetal bovine serum, and some growth was obtained in a medium containing no added choline, indicating the presence of choline in the serum. The stimulating effect of such comparatively high levels of choline would seem to indicate that this compound has a metabolic function different from that of most other water-soluble vitamins.

G. Nucleotides, Sterols, and Miscellaneous Additives

The inorganic salts, amino acids, organic acids, carbohydrates, and
vitamins discussed in the preceding sections, when combined in the
proper proportions, constitute the minimal tissue culture media. Generally
the minimal media are supplemented with one or more complex, chemically undefined materials to obtain maximum growth. Several investigators
have attempted to design chemically defined, complete media which
would support optimum growth of vertebrate cells, e.g., TC 199, NCTC-
109, and CMRL 1066. These media contain fat-soluble vitamins, a
variety of purines and pyrimidines, nucleosides and nucleotides, lipids,
and some enzymes in addition to the components of the minimal media.
For a description of these media and a discussion of the value of the
individual compounds, the reader is referred to the chapter on synthetic
media in "Methods of Tissue Culture" by Parker (1961).

Some investigators have added certain of these compounds to media
for culturing invertebrate cells to try to stimulate mitosis in these cells.
Grace (1958a) added yeast ribonucleic acid and thymus nucleic acid
(separately and together) in several concentrations without any noticeable
effect on cultures of silkworm cells. He also obtained no stimulation of
growth when cholesterol, at sufficient concentration (3 mg/100 ml) to
produce a saturated solution, was added to his basic medium. The medium
of Horikawa and Fox (1964) for cells from *Drosophila* contained 0.5
mg/100 ml of nicotinamide-adenine dinucleotide. B. M. Martin and
Nishiitsutsuji-Uwo (1967) included diphosphopyridine nucleotide and
triphosphopyridine nucleotide in their medium for the culture of tracheal
tissue from the locust. However, neither of them reported a specific effect
caused by these materials.

Maramorosch and co-workers have used TC 199 in their medium for
the cultivation of leafhopper tissues, but again, no effects specifically
attributable to the presence of this complex medium were reported
(Hirumi and Maramorosch, 1964b; Mitsuhashi and Maramorosch, 1964).
Thus, although the sterols, nucleic acids, and related compounds are of
importance in chemically defined media for vertebrate cells, the very
limited evidence so far available from cultured invertebrate cells does
not indicate any importance for growth of these cells. It must be noted,
however, that all of the tests with invertebrate cells have been done in
media supplemented with sera which may have contributed sufficient
amounts of these compounds.

Antibiotics, although of no nutritional value, are nevertheless an important part of nearly all media for establishing primary cultures of

invertebrate cells because of the difficulty in obtaining tissue free of microbial contamination. Penicillin and streptomycin are routinely added to invertebrate cell culture media with no adverse effect. Mycostatin and other fungicides have been used to inhibit the growth of fungi. However, the fungicides must be used with care since there is some evidence that at least those compounds containing Amphotericin B as the active ingredient are toxic for the cells of the Grace *Antheraea* line and the Grace *Aedes* line (Stanley and Vaughn, 1967).

Normally, antibiotics are not used in culturing established vertebrate cell lines, and the established insect cell lines can be grown in medium free of antibiotics. It is advisable to avoid the routine use of antibiotics in media for the culture of these cells.

H. Naturally Occurring Compounds as Supplements

Hemolymph is the only body fluid present in invertebrates, and the serum portion has been used extensively as a supplement for various minimal media. However, when the untreated insect hemolymph is exposed to air, toxic quinones are formed as the result of reactions involving the enzyme polyphenol oxidase. This enzymatic reaction can be avoided by diluting the hemolymph with medium; however, this limits the concentration of hemolymph to an undesirably low level. To overcome this problem various inhibitors of this enzyme have been used with some degree of success. Phenylthiourea was used by S. S. Wyatt (1956) but found to be slightly toxic to silkworm cells. Wyatt also tried *p*-aminobenzoic acid, ascorbic acid, glutathione, and disodium ethylenediaminetetraacetate. The best of these, ascorbic acid and glutathione, prevented melaninization of the hemolymph for only four days. Martignoni and Scallion (1961) found that ascorbic acid would prevent the formation of quinones in blood cells for longer periods if the cells were cultured in an atmosphere of 1% oxygen, 3% carbon dioxide, and 96% nitrogen.

Since none of the chemical treatments provided permanent inhibition of the enzyme, a heat treatment was devised which precipitated the enzyme without removing the nutrient value of the hemolymph (S. S. Wyatt, 1956). In this treatment, the hemolymph was heated to 60° for five minutes, chilled, and the precipitated protein, including the polyphenol oxidase, removed by centrifugation. Heat-treated hemolymph will remain nontoxic indefinitely and can be stored frozen for long periods. This method is now routinely used to prepare hemolymph for supplementing insect tissue culture media.

Hemolymph has been used at levels ranging from 2% (Grace, 1958a) to 25% (Trager, 1935), but the most common levels used are 5 to 10%. Usually the hemolymph used is homologous with the cells to be cultured; however, this is not a necessity. Sen Gupta (1964) demonstrated that hemolymph from *Galleria mellonella* Linnaeus, *Antheraea pernyi*, or *Melolontha melolontha* Linnaeus were suitable supplements for the culture of not only homologous cells but of cells from either of the other two species as well. Thomson and Grace (1963) reported that cells from the Grace *Antheraea* line would grow in a medium supplemented with homologous hemolymph from either *Antheraea pernyi* or *Antheraea helena* White. Grace (1966) grew the *Aedes aegypti* line cells first in a medium supplemented with *Antheraea eucalypti* hemolymph and, later *Antheraea pernyi* hemolymph. Attempts to adapt the *Antheraea* cell line to lobster hemolymph were partially successful, but growth was never equal to that of the cells growing on insect hemolymph (Yunker *et al.*, 1967).

The need to supplement invertebrate tissue culture media with invertebrate sera was soon recognized as a severe handicap to the extensive culture of invertebrate cells, particularly insect cells. For very small insects, e.g., mosquitoes, it was not possible to obtain hemolymph for this purpose. Even when the hemolymph from a larger insect was used, as was done by Grace, large numbers of these insects had to be reared or collected to provide the necessary amounts of hemolymph. Therefore, attempts were made to substitute sera from vertebrates for at least part of the invertebrate sera required. Vago and Chastang (1962a) tested several combinations of calf serum and insect hemolymph and found that primary cultures of ovarian tissue grew almost as well on 13% calf serum and 2% insect hemolymph as did control cultures on 15% insect hemolymph alone. Hukuhara (1966) was able to culture the cells of the Grace *Antheraea* cell line in a medium minimally supplemented with only 1% calf serum and 1% *Antheraea pernyi* hemolymph.

Other workers have succeeded in replacing insect hemolymph entirely with sera from vertebrates. Trager (1938) obtained limited growth of cells from midgut and ovarian mosquito tissue in a medium supplemented with 50% guinea pig or chicken plasma and 10% egg albumin digest. Later, using an improved minimal medium, he was able to get some growth and extended tissue survival with 2% sheep serum as a supplement (Trager, 1959). Peleg and Trager (1963) obtained growth of cells from the imaginal discs of mosquito larvae and from the ovaries of the cynthia moth in minimal medium plus 2% calf serum. They reported that growth from cynthia ovaries was not improved by the further addition of homologous hemolymph to the medium. The addition of chick embryo extract did increase the number of mosquito explants which showed cellular outgrowths, but had no effect on the development of the cynthia cultures. Peleg (1965) increased the level of calf serum to 20% and this improved substantially the growth of cells from mosquito tissue.

The culture of tissue from various ticks has also been possible, using supplements of vertebrate origin instead of the homologous hemolymph which is difficult to obtain from these small arthropods. Rehacek (1962) has cultured tissue from *Dermacentor* species in medium supplemented with 0.1% of an albumin fraction prepared from dried calf serum and with 5% dextran. Neumann grew cells from the tick *Rhipicephalus appendiculatus* in culture for over 150 days in medium supplemented with 20% of serum (H. M. Martin and Vidler, 1962).

Tissues from *Drosophila*, another insect too small to provide homologous hemolymph, have been cultured in minimal media supplemented with vertebrate sera. Horikawa and Fox (1964) supplemented their medium for the culture of embryonic cells with 10% newborn calf serum and obtained limited growth. Fetal bovine serum, at a final concentration of 15%, was used by Echalier *et al.* (1965) to culture embryonic cells for extended periods of time.

Another group of insects whose size prohibits the collection of hemolymph is the leafhoppers (Cicadellidae). The growth of cells from tissue explants of the six-spotted leafhopper has been reported by Hirumi and Maramorosch (1964b) in medium containing fetal bovine serum (17%) as the only supplement. Mitsuhashi and Maramorosch (1964) tested chicken serum, horse serum, and calf serum as supplements and found that with each of these sera few cells migrated from the explants and within a few days the explants detached from the glass. The medium supplemented with 20% fetal bovine serum supported both cell migration and cell division. When the fetal bovine serum was replaced with newborn calf serum, normal cell migration occurred, but growth was retarded and the cells became granulated within two weeks.

Although most Lepidoptera are large enough to enable investigators to collect hemolymph, the use of vertebrate sera has many advantages, the main one being that it frees the investigator from dependence upon a supply of healthy insects. Several studies have been made to find vertebrate serum supplements suitable for the culture of tissue from Lepidoptera. Vago and Chastang (1962b) were able to maintain growing cultures of fibroblasts from several Lepidoptera in medium supplemented with 0.6% chick embryo extract. For the first 20 days the growth compared favorably with that in medium supplemented with hemolymph, but after that the cultures containing the embryo extract began to deteriorate. Similar results were obtained with cultures of ovarian tissue and of blood cells from the monarch butterfly cultured in a medium supplemented with 23% fetal bovine serum (Hirumi and Maramorosch, 1964a). Martignoni and Scallion (1961) maintained short-term cultures of blood cells using 30% fetal bovine serum as a medium supplement and Mitsuhashi (1966) cultured blood cells from the rice stem borer (*Chilo suppressalis* Walker) for over 12 months using 20% fetal bovine serum as a supplement. The addition of either homologous hemolymph or *Bombyx mori* hemolymph improved neither the appearance nor the rate of mitosis in these cultures. However, when added to older cultures, hemolymph stimulated the recovery of degenerating cells. Short-term (three months) cultures of ovarian tissues were also obtained using this medium (Mitsuhashi, 1965b).

The development of cell lines from moth and mosquito tissue by Grace represented a considerable step forward in insect cell culture. For the first time, investigators had an invertebrate cell culture system in which sufficient growth occurred to permit some quantitative measurements of the changes that occur in invertebrate cell systems during growth. However, the increased growth possible with these cells accentuated the problem of hemolymph supply. The need to incorporate 5 to 10% hemolymph in the medium for these cultures prohibited their use by many investigators. This problem was overcome by developing strains of the Grace cell lines adapted to growth in medium which did not contain insect hemolymph. Yunker *et al.* (1967) developed a subline of the Grace *Antheraea* cell line which grew well in medium supplemented with 10% heat-inactivated fetal bovine serum (FBS), 10% whole egg ultrafiltrate, and 1% bovine serum albumin (Fraction V). Several authors have reported strains of the Grace *Aedes* line adapted to hemolymph-free medium (Converse and Nagle, 1967; Hsu *et al.*, 1969; and Sohi, 1969). Chiu and Black (1967) developed lines from primary cultures of leafhopper tissues using a medium supplemented with 2.5% hemolymph and 17.5% FBS only during the early passages. In later passages, and for growth of the line, a medium supplemented with only 17.5 to 20% FBS was used successfully.

The value of FBS as a substitute for insect hemolymph was more firmly established when Singh (1967) developed lines of *Aedes albopictus* and *A. aegypti* cells from primary cultures grown in medium supplemented only with 20% FBS. Subsequently, fetal bovine serum, in concentrations of from 10 to 20%, was used to establish cell lines from *Periplaneta americana* (Landureau, 1968), *Anopheles stephensi* (Schneider, 1969), and *Drosophila melanogaster* (Echalier and Ohanessian, 1969). Peleg (1969) developed an established cell line from *Aedes aegypti* in medium supplemented with 10% FBS and 1% chick embryo extract.

Although these results do establish that the growth-promoting factors originally found in insect hemolymph are not restricted to such hemolymph, the actual nutrient factors remain to be identified. The studies of

Hsu et al. (1969) indicated that at least a critical part of the nutritional factors in FBS are not diffusable through a dialysis membrane with a pore radius of 24 Å. This would indicate that proteins may be one of the growth-stimulating factors. One of the characteristics of FBS is the high level of the protein fetuin that it contains compared to other bovine sera. To determine if fetuin was one of the stimulating factors, FBS was replaced by an equal volume of a 0.02% solution of fetuin, but the growth of leafhopper cell cultures was not improved as compared to serum-free controls (Mitsuhashi, 1969). Unpublished data obtained with the Grace *Antheraea* cell line in this author's laboratory supports Mitsuhashi's findings and would seem to rule out fetuin as a vital factor for insect cell growth.

Still, the serum proteins may be involved in cell nutrition as carriers of growth-stimulating compounds. The work of Landureau and Steinbuck (1969) with a line of cockroach cells established that cyanocobalamine (vitamin B_{12}) was one important growth factor bound to the serum albumins.

Because vertebrate sera can be used to supplement most insect tissue culture media, it does not seem likely that the insect hormones are required to stimulate cell division in those cells now cultured from insect tissue. Investigators have been trying for some time to determine what substances will stimulate insect cells to divide *in vitro*. The successful use of chick embryo extract to stimulate growth of vertebrate cells led to the preparation and testing of many insect tissue extracts in hopes of finding a similar substance. Insect embryo extracts, which may contain an extract of egg as well, have been tried by several authors. S. S. Wyatt (1956) prepared a 50% aqueous extract of silkworm eggs in which some development of the embryo had occurred. The addition of a "small amount," less than 1%, of this extract produced noticeable improvement in the cultures. However, Grace (1958a) reported that 2.5% of an embryo extract, free of egg material, produced heavy granulation in migrated cells within four days. If the extract was heated to precipitate some of the protein, the onset of granulation was delayed for a few days but eventually developed in nearly all of the migrated cells. Extracts of mosquito eggs had no apparent beneficial effect on the growth of imaginal discs from *Aedes aegypti* larvae although some improvement in these cultures was obtained by adding 10% chick embryo extract (Peleg and Trager, 1963). Gaulden and Kokomoor (1955) found that there was an increase in the number of mitoses in grasshopper neuroblasts corresponding to an increase in the amount of egg yolk added, up to a certain level. When more yolk was added the mitotic index was lowered. They believe this decline was caused by the effect of the additional yolk on the osmotic pressure of the medium. Miciarelli et al. (1967) found that the addition of 8.3% embryo extract to their medium delayed the deterioration of integument tissue for one week but did not stimulate mitosis. On the basis of these limited observations one can only conclude that the addition of embryo (egg) extract improves the general condition of insect cells *in vitro* but that it has a stimulating effect on the division of such cells only in certain specific situations. Because the effect is minimal and the preparation difficult, embryo extracts have not been used routinely in insect tissue culture media.

Extracts of other tissues or whole animal extracts have also been tested for possible growth stimulating effects. Grace (1958a) tested aqueous extracts prepared from ring glands of last instar *Lucilia cuprina* Wiedemann larvae and from prothoracic glands of last-stage nymphs of *Periplaneta americana* Linnaeus on cultures of silkworm larval ovary and found that the overall health of the culture was improved and that there was a slight increase in the number of divisions that occurred. The most obvious change he noted was the increase in cell migration. Extracts of whole mosquitoes at various stages of growth did not have any effect on the cultures of imaginal discs from mosquito larvae (Peleg and Trager, 1963). Extracts of moth gonads, a very good source of cells for culture, did have a stimulating effect on the growth of mosquito cells according to these authors. Thus, there appears to be some beneficial effect when certain tissue extracts are added to culture media.

There are now available purified preparations of some of the known insect hormones, thus overcoming the difficulty of preparing extracts.

Most of the results reported with these purified hormones have been from tests on organ cultures and are thus outside the scope of this chapter. However, Judy (1969) has reported that ecdysterone (β-ecdysone) at concentrations of 2.5 to 25 μg/ml caused a noticeable increase in membrane activity, including pinocytosis, of isolated migrant cells from pupal gut tissue of the tobacco hornworm.

No mitosis was observed in the cells, either before treatment or after treatment. The hormone had a similar "exciting" effect on primary cultures of larval and pupal hemocytes. However, cultures of the Grace *Antheraea* cell line, adapted to hemolymph-free medium, did not respond to the hormone.

I. pH and Osmotic Pressure

The hydrogen ion content of most tissue culture media, whether for vertebrate or for invertebrate cells, has been chosen, at least initially, on the basis of the pH of the body fluid in the animal from which the cells were taken. The pH of the blood of most land vertebrates is near 7.4. The blood pH of most marine animals is between 7.2 and 7.8 (Prosser, 1950). Insects are unique in this respect as their hemolymph is generally slightly acidic. The pH varies interspecifically between pH 6 and pH 7.7 and intraspecifically, during metamorphosis, up to 0.7 of a pH unit. An examination of the pH values for several species of insects compiled by Buck (1953) shows that the pH for Coleoptera ranges from 5.9 to 7.3, for Diptera from 6.3 to 7.7, for Lepidoptera from 6.2 to 7.6, and for Orthoptera from 6.0 to 7.6.

These figures show that within each order there is a broad range of blood pH; however, the pH values of the various tissue culture media do not reflect this range. The pH values of media intended for the culture of Lepidoptera tissue ranged from 6.2 to 6.7, for Diptera from 6.5 to 7.2, and for Orthoptera from 6.5 to 7.3. The media designed by Maramorosch and his co-workers for the culture of leafhopper tissue had pH values of 6.4 to 6.5. The pH values of media designed for the culture of snail tissue have been between 7.0 and 7.9, reflecting the more alkaline nature of the hemolymph of these animals.

There have been very few studies on the effect of the pH on the behavior of invertebrate cells *in vitro*. Rezzonico-Raimondi and Ghini (1963) compared the growth of *Drosophila* cells at several pH values before choosing a pH of 7.2 as optimal. A pH change from 6.5 to 6.9 in the medium for the culture of tick cells appeared to enhance the attachment of these cells to a glass surface but was not reported to increase their growth (Varma and Wallers, 1965). Burch and Cuadros (1965) used different pH values for different tissues from snails. Gonadal tissues were grown at pH 7.0 and foot muscle tissues at pH 8.5, but the authors do not report how these pH values were chosen.

These studies indicate a need for an awareness of possible pH effects when culturing tissue from various invertebrates. However, in view of the ability of many invertebrates to remain active despite rather large changes in their blood pH, a medium pH near that of the blood is probably adequate for most cultures.

Little attention has been paid to the osmotic pressure of culture media. As most media are designed from analyses of hemolymph, the osmotic pressures are usually very close to that of the hemolymph. The range of values for the freezing-point depression of insect hemolymph is −0.5 to −0.9. Where they have been determined, the values for insect tissue culture media usually fall within this range (S. S. Wyatt, 1956; Martignoni and Scallion, 1961). Trager's medium (1935) for the culture of silkworm did not (freezing-point depression was −0.29), but the cells still survived and divided. Marks and Reinecke (1965) developed a medium for cockroach tissue which had a suitable osmolarity with a freezing-point depression of —0.45°. Carlson (1961) found that the maximum mitotic activity could be obtained with grasshopper neuroblasts only when the medium was adjusted to be isotonic with the embryonic cells of each different egg pod. However, his studies required standard conditions and quantitation not needed for ordinary culture. The hemolymphs of most marine invertebrates are nearly isotonic with seawater (freezing-point depression was —1.8), and Necco and Martin (1963) found that medium TC 199 in which the freezing-point depression had been adjusted to —2.22 by the addition of NaCl was suitable for the culture of white body cells from the octopus.

As in many of the other important aspects of designing tissue culture media, the ability of invertebrate cells to regulate the intracellular environment or to function in a broad range of environments reduces the need for highly critical studies in the initial stages of media development. These critical studies are best made *in vitro* after primary cultures have been established. Osmotic pressure and pH, as well as other factors, perhaps yet unknown, will become more important as the methods for the culture of invertebrate tissues improve to the degree that it is possible to culture functioning, differentiated cells.

II. SELECTION OF TISSUE FOR CULTURE

Despite the considerable progress that has been made in developing media for the culture of invertebrate cells, the current media support growth of only a few types of tissue. Thus, the selection of the tissue for culture still remains a problem. The tissue and organs of invertebrates differ in their physiology, growth, and morphology from the tissues and organs of vertebrates. Therefore, the experience gained with the culture of vertebrate cells has been of value only as a general guide in the selection of invertebrate tissues. Although the successful culture of invertebrate cells has been, up to now, a matter of trial and error, the results have been sufficient to provide some guidelines for the preparation of primary cultures. In this section those studies pertaining to the selection of tissue and cells for culture will be reviewed and some guidelines for selecting tissue suggested.

The ovary from Lepidoptera has been the organ most used in the investigation of the *in vitro* culture of invertebrate tissue. The first successful demonstration of mitosis in invertebrate cells *in vitro* was by

Trager in 1935 using cultures of the silkworm ovary. The same tissue was used by S. S. Wyatt (1956) for the studies which led to the first major advance in the design of media for insect tissue culture. Grace (1958a,b, 1959) used ovarian tissue from several Lepidoptera in a series of studies which finally culminated in the development of the first established cell line from an invertebrate (Grace, 1962). Vago and his co-workers have also used this tissue in their studies on many aspects of insect tissue culture (e.g., Vago and Chastang, 1958a,b; Aizawa and Vago, 1959a; Vago and Chastang, 1962a).

Ovaries have been used successfully as explants from other insects besides the Lepidoptera. Hirumi and Maramorosch (1964b) and Mitsuhashi and Maramorosch (1964) obtained survival and the migration of free cells from ovaries of the leafhopper (Homoptera). Trager (1938) has obtained similar results with adult ovaries from the mosquito (Diptera). In all of these reports, mitoses were observed in the migrated cells. Only in the cells that migrated from grasshopper ovaries and their attached oviducts was mitosis not found (Ting and Brooks, 1965). These cells were probably not from the ovarian tissue since the ovaries alone did not produce migrating cells.

The culture of cells from other organs or tissues has not been as routinely successful. Martignoni and Scallion (1961) obtained monolayers with the hemocytes of *Peridroma saucia* Huber but did not observe mitosis in the cultures. Blood cells from *Drosophila* have survived in culture for 75 days and mitosis was observed in the cultures during the entire period (Horikawa and Kurada, 1959). The only long-term cultivation of blood cells was accomplished by Mitsuhashi (1966) using cells from the rice stem borer (Lepidoptera). He had maintained the culture for 12 months through eight subcultures.

Various investigators have attempted to culture cells from the wall of the gut. Hirumi and Maramorosch (1963) and Mitsuhashi and Maramorosch (1964) obtain migration of fibroblast-like cells from the gut tissue of leafhoppers, with mitotic division occurring in these cells for periods as long as eight weeks. However, only survival of the gut tissue with some migration of free cells, but not mitosis, has been reported for tissue from the tsetse-fly (Trager, 1959), the tick (Rehacek, 1963), and some Lepidoptera (Sen Gupta, 1964).

Various organs of the nervous system have also been cultured by some investigators. Rezzonico-Raimondi and Ghini (1963) obtained sufficient cell outgrowth from the brain tissue of *Drosophila* to permit successful subculture. Hirumi and Maramorosch (1964a) obtained cell migration and division in cultures of tissue from the ganglia of the monarch butterfly but not from the brain and optic lobe. Cell migration, but not division, has been obtained from the organs of the nervous system of the tsetse-fly (Trager, 1959) and the rice stem borer (Mitsuhashi, 1965b).

Various appendages have also been used in attempts to establish primary cultures of insect cells. Marks and Reinecke (1964) used regenerating nymphal legs from cockroaches for explants and obtained migration, but no mitosis; however, mitosis was observed in the cells from nymphal legs of leafhoppers by Mitsuhashi and Maramorosch (1964) and from the nymphal wing of the monarch butterfly by Hirumi and Maramorosch (1964a).

Some tissues rarely provide suitable primary cultures. Explants of fat body, testes, and integument may survive in culture, but migrating cells are rarely present and mitosis has not been reported (Mitsuhashi and Maramorosch 1964; Miciarelli et al., 1967; Rehacek, 1963; Mitsuhashi, 1965b).

Because of their small size, it has been possible to use entire mosquito larvae for explant cultures. The insects are hatched in a sterile environment, from surface-sterilized eggs, and the young larvae are aseptically cut into small pieces to provide explants. Peleg (1965) obtained cell migration and mitosis in cultures of such tissue from Aedes aegypti. The free cells first appeared after 8–10 days and mitotic figures were observed in the cells after four to five months. Subcultures were not obtained in this study; however, Grace (1966) used a similar method in establishing his cell line from Aedes aegypti. Later, improved cell migration was obtained from the minced larval explants by treating them with trypsin for a short time before placing them in culture (Schneider, 1969, and Singh, 1967).

The origin of the cells which migrate from explants of such complex organs as the ovary or from minced whole insects is nearly impossible to determine. Thus far only cultures of hemocytes can be identified in terms of the tissue of origin. But, because of the many successful attempts to culture ovarian explants (Trager, 1935; Vago and Chastang, 1958a, 1962a; and Grace, 1962) attempts have been made to identify the tissue source of the migrating cells. Trager (1935) observed that the cells which migrated from the explants appeared to come from the tissue which forms the lining of the ovarioles, and Grace (1958a) attempted to test this observation by culturing the ovariole sheaths and the ovarioles separately. He obtained cell migration in cultures of ovariole sheaths but not in those containing only the ovarioles. Thus, he too concluded that the migrating cells came from the muscular tissue lining the ovarioles. The problem was later studied in more detail by Jones and Cunningham (1961). They reported that some migrating cells did appear to come from the ovariole sheath but that the intermediate layer cells which are internal to the sheath cells and separated from them by a thin membrane could also migrate from an explant. Jones and Cunningham also found that when the membrane enclosing the follicle cells was broken, these cells, too, were capable of migrating from the explant.

The origin of these migrating cells was further studied by Stanley and Vaughn (1968a). In examining the histological changes which occurred in the cultured silkworm ovary they found that the ovariole sheath and the associated ovarian stroma normally exhibited little change or breakdown in organization during culture and therefore were not likely to contribute many free cells to the culture. However, when breaks occurred in the membranes enclosing either the intermediate cells or the follicular cells, these cells migrated from the explant. Stanley and Vaughn thus concluded that these tissues were the source of the free cells.

In a later study (Stanley and Vaughn, 1968b) it was found that in four of the five Lepidoptera species studied the ovariole stroma was absent or degenerate at the time these tissues produced the best culture and, therefore, unlikely to be a source of migrating cells. In all five species tested, the best cultures were obtained during the time between the beginning of follicular development and follicular maturation. During this time healthy intermediate layer cells were also present in all ovaries and were a likely source of cells. Thus, the property of the ovary which contributes most to its usefulness as a source of tissue for primary cultures is that it contains a large number of immature, growing cells, namely, the immature follicle cells.

Another possible source of this type of cells are the embryonic tissues. Indeed many investigators have found that embryonic tissue grows well *in vitro*. Carlson (1961) used embryonic neuroblasts from grasshopper embryos in an *in vitro* system for studies on the effects of radiation on mitosis. Hirumi and Maramorosch (1964b) published a method for the culture of embryonic leafhopper tissue which produced growth only when taken during the stage of blastokinetic movement; older embryonic tissues were not suitable. However, after some changes in the methodology, it was found that tissues from the older stages of leafhopper embryo were also suitable for primary culture (Mitsuhashi and Maramorosch, 1964). Cultures of these tissues were transferred several times, but subcultures of the free cells grew poorly and died within a week. Mitsuhashi (1965a) established primary cultures of embryonic cells from the green rice leafhopper (*Nephotettix cincticeps* Uhler), which grew for as long as four months; however, subculturing was not attempted. Seven-day-old embryos of another leafhopper, *Agallia constricta*, have been used to establish primary cultures by Chiu and Black (1967). These authors treated the minced embryonic tissue with 0.25% trypsin for 15 minutes at room temperature before culturing them. The trypsin treatment was reported to improve the cell migration but was not considered essential. The outgrowth was primarily of epithelial-type cells which formed heavy cell sheets. After several months, subcultures were made and eventually cell lines were established.

Primary cultures of cockroach cells have also been obtained using trypsinized embryonic tissues (Landureau, 1968). Outgrowths of fibroblast-like cells developed which were firmly attached to the surface. These cells could also be subcultured, and an established cell line was eventually developed.

Diptera embryonic cells have also been a fruitful source of tissue for primary cultures. Horikawa and Fox (1964) and Horikawa et al. (1966) reported the culture of embryonic cells from *Drosophila* embryos taken from the egg eight hours after their fertilization. The cultures were maintained for 110 days with 11 splits (subcultures made by dividing the culture into new cultures). Primary cultures of embryonic *Drosophila* cells have also been obtained by Echalier et al. (1965). Growth in these cultures was maintained for as long as five months. Peleg (1966) obtained primary cultures of embryonic mosquito cells, but again, although prolonged growth was achieved, no subcultures were made. However, the results showed that the methods held considerable promise, and eventually both groups of investigators were able to obtain established cell lines for *Drosophila* (Echalier and Ohanessian, 1969) and for *Aedes aegypti* (Peleg, 1969).

The culture of Lepidoptera embryonic cells is conspicuous in its absence. Although the eggs of some Lepidoptera are quite large and embryonic tissue should be abundant, there have been no reports of successful culture of embryonic tissue from these insects. Gaulden and Kokomoor (1955) found that excess yolk reduced the mitotic rate in embryonic grasshopper neuroblasts, and it has been the author's impression that the large amount of yolk present in the eggs of Lepidoptera interferes with the culture of these embryonic tissues. Perhaps, if the embryonic cells can in some way be separated from this yolk, embryonic tissue would be an excellent source of cells from Lepidoptera.

It appears that, at this period in the development of insect tissue culture, success in establishing primary cultures depends upon the use of tissue containing immature, rapidly dividing cells. In the Homoptera these cells have been obtained, for the most part, from embryonic tissue. Investigators attempting to culture cells from various Diptera have found embryonic tissues or minced whole body tissue (containing imaginal discs) suitable sources of such cells. Ovarian tissue has been by far the most fruitful source from Lepidoptera. With the present media, the culture of differentiated cells from functioning tissue has been very difficult, if not totally unsuccessful.

III. PREPARATION OF TISSUE FOR CULTURE

A. Surface Sterilization of the Animals

The external surfaces of most invertebrates are heavily contaminated with microorganisms which, if care is not used, will contaminate the resulting tissue cultures. As the interior of the body cavity of most animals is free of such organisms, the problem usually is one of sterilizing the outer surfaces before opening the animal. Because of the small size of most invertebrates, it is often most efficient to sterilize the entire outer surface by immersing the whole animal. The most commonly used disinfectants are 70% ethyl alcohol, $HgCl_2$ in alcohol, NaClO, and quaternary ammonium compounds, e.g., Hyamine. These agents have been used either alone or in various combinations. The disinfectants have been used with eggs, larvae, and pupae of insects, but the procedures vary, depending upon the stage to be treated. In all methods the disinfectant is removed from the animal by thorough rinsing with sterile water or saline to prevent it from contacting the tissue to be cultured.

Larson (1963) surface-sterilized the eggs of grasshoppers with 0.05% $HgCl_2$ in 50% ethanol. Eggs from leafhoppers have been surface-sterilized with 70% ethanol followed by treatment with 0.1% Hyamine 2389 (Hirumi and Maramorosch, 1964b) and by treatment with 70% ethanol alone (Mitsuhashi, 1965a). Mercuric chloride, either as a 0.05% solution in 70% ethanol or as a component of White's solution, was used to surface-sterilize eggs from *Aedes aegypti* (Peleg, 1965, 1966). The above solution of $HgCl_2$ in ethanol has also been used to surface-sterilize *Drosophila* eggs before they were disrupted (Horikawa and Fox, 1964). *Drosophila* eggs have also been surface-sterilized in dilute solutions of NaClO (Lesseps, 1965; Echalier *et al.*, 1965).

Lepidoptera larvae and pupae have been surface-sterilized by immersion in 70% alcohol for short periods of time (Grace, 1958a; Vaughn, 1963). Silkworm larvae have been surface-sterilized by dipping them in 1:1000 $HgCl_2$ solution (Trager, 1935). A more complex routine was used to surface-sterilize cutworm larvae (Martignoni *et al.*, 1958). The larvae were passed successively through 5% ethanol, 4% formaldehyde, and two changes of 70% ethanol.

The problem of surface sterilization can be avoided when it is possible to rear the animals aseptically. This method was used by Trager (1959) to obtain uncontaminated tissue from the tsetse-fly. Cultures of mosquito tissue from aseptically reared larvae have been obtained by Peleg and Trager (1963) and by Grace (1966). Those Lepidoptera that can be reared on synthetic diets can also be obtained contaminant free. Contaminant free *G. mellonella* larvae have been produced as sources of aseptic tissue for culture (Vago et al., 1961) as have larvae of the rice stem borer (Mitsuhashi, 1965a). Insects which feed on plants can be reared aseptically if it is possible to grow the plants aseptically. Aseptically reared leafhoppers (Vago et al., 1961; Mitsuhashi and Maramorosch, 1964) as well as several Lepidoptera and aphids (Fosset and Chastang, 1963) have been used as sources of tissue without the need for prior surface sterilization.

B. Preparation of Tissue Fragments by Dissection

Tissues of invertebrates are most commonly cultured as small fragments, and because of the small size of most invertebrate organs, tissue from several animals is required for most experiments. To prevent dehydration, the dissected tissues are held in balanced salt solutions or culture medium until a sufficient amount has been collected. Insect tissue usually contains fat body and tracheal tissue attached to the organ or tissue being collected for culture. This extraneous tissue is first removed and then the remaining tissue is washed in clean medium. Then the tissue is cut into small pieces for explantation. For culture in hanging drops or other such small systems, the tissues are usually cut into small fragments, 1–2 mm in diameter (Trager, 1935; S. S. Wyatt, 1956; Grace, 1958a; Jones and Cunningham, 1961). The pieces of tissue are then transferred by pipette in a small amount of medium to the culture vessel. In handling the tissue, care must always be taken to avoid contamination and dehydration.

C. Mechanical Dissociation of Tissue

This method has been used to prepare early embryonic tissues for culture. Suspensions of embryonic *Drosophila* cells have been prepared by the following procedure: The eggs were soaked in a dilute solution of sodium hypochlorite to surface-sterilize them and to remove the chorion. The embryos, enclosed in the vitelline membrane, are then rinsed and transferred to a glass homogenizer and the embryonic tissues disrupted by gentle grinding. This procedure yields a mixture of individual cells and aggregates of a few cells which are then transferred to media for culture (Horikawa and Fox, 1964; Echalier *et al.*, 1965). Embryonic mosquito cells were prepared by Peleg (1966) in a homogenizer fitted with a stainless steel grid. The eggs were forced through the grid, which ruptured the chorion and dispersed the cells. The cells and the broken chorions were collected in a centrifuge tube, the broken chorions allowed to settle out, and then the suspension of cells removed for culture.

D. Chemical Dissociation of Tissue

Chemical dissociation of invertebrate tissue can be accomplished by either the action of enzymes such as trypsin or by the action of calcium chelating agents such as ethylenediaminetetraacetic acid (EDTA). Both of these compounds, either alone or in combination, have been used to dissociate vertebrate tissues. However, it was found that trypsinization methods used with vertebrate tissue (0.25% trypsin at 37°) were harmful to some insect cells (Martignoni *et al.*, 1958). Martignoni and his co-workers found that an extract prepared from the hepatopancreas and crop of the snail, *Helix aspersa* Muller, would dissociate insect tissue and was not as damaging as was trypsin. Other investigators have found that they could reduce the damage to the cells by treating for only short periods of time, i.e., 5 to 10 minutes (Rehacek, 1963), or by reducing the level to 0.1% or lower (Aizawa and Vago, 1959b; Hirumi and Maramorosch, 1964b).

However, these investigators found that often the tissues were not completely dissociated and the remaining fragments became sticky and difficult to handle. Aizawa and Vago (1959b) overcame this problem by treating these tissues with hyaluronidase. This two-step treatment resulted in a high yield of individual cells that showed little damage. Trypsin has been used in combination with EDTA to dissociate *Drosophila* embryonic tissue (Lesseps, 1965).

IV. CULTURES IN FLUID MEDIUM

A. Microculture Systems

Because of the small size of most invertebrates, obtaining adequate amounts of tissue for culture has been a problem and many of the failures to culture tissues from invertebrates were undoubtedly the result of too small an inoculum. Most of the early successes in invertebrate tissue culture were in hanging or sitting drop cultures, which required only small amounts of tissue (Trager, 1935, 1938, 1959; S. S. Wyatt 1956; Grace 1958a; Vago and Chastang, 1958a). These cultures usually contained one to three pieces of tissue, 1 mm in diameter, per drop of medium, which gave a relatively high ratio of tissue to medium. Microcultures have also been obtained in droplets covered with paraffin oil (Vago and Chastang, 1962b; Echalier et al., 1965). A modified Carrel-type flask was developed by Vago and completed by Hirumi (1963) which contained a hole in one surface over which coverslips were attached with a mixture of paraffin and Vaseline. Sitting drop cultures were established on the coverslip. The medium could be easily changed through the neck of the flask, and the coverslip provided a high-quality optical surface for observing the culture.

B. Flask and Tube Cultures

When sufficient tissue is available invertebrate cells can be grown in the standard tissue culture flasks and in roller tubes. Invertebrate cells have been cultured in Pyrex glass, soft glass, and in plastic tissue culture vessels (S. S. Wyatt, 1956; Grace, 1962; Aizawa and Vago, 1959a). Investigators using standard tissue culture flasks must always be aware of the need for adequate tissue inoculum. Grace (1962) found that four ovaries from diapausing *Antheraea eucalypti* pupae with 0.9 ml of medium/flask, gave adequate growth. For cultures of mosquito larvae the tissue from three larvae, less the head and tail, in 1 ml of medium was satisfactory (Grace, 1966). To establish primary cultures of embryonic leafhopper tissue, Hirumi and Maramorosch (1964c) used the trypsinized tissue fragments from 10 embryos with 0.2 ml of medium.

In preparing flask cultures, care must be taken to obtain attachment of the explants. This can often be accomplished by adding the tissue in a small drop of medium and allowing a short time for the tissue to attach before adding the remainder of the medium. Mitsuhashi and Maramorosch (1964) found that incubating the tissue fragments for a short time in calcium-free saline caused the tissue to soften and increased the chances of its attachment to the flask surface.

C. Plasma Clot Cultures

To facilitate holding the explant in a fixed position a chick plasma clot has often been used for various vertebrate tissues. The clot is made by mixing equal parts of chick plasma with media containing chick embryo extract. Peleg (1965) was able to culture mosquito larval tissue in this type of plasma clot. However, Flandre *et al.* (1962) attempted to culture Lepidoptera tissue in this type of clot without success. They found that a 1:20 dilution of the plasma, which formed a semisolid clot, was needed for the culture of Lepidoptera cells. The system was also suitable for culture of tissues from leafhoppers and various hematophagous insects (Vago and Flandre, 1963). The foot, heart, and mantel tissue from the snail, *Helix aspersa*, have also been cultured in the diluted plasma clot by Flandre and Vago (1963).

V. VAPOR PHASE

The invertebrate media are usually buffered by phosphates, and therefore, high levels of CO_2 in the vapor phase are not required to maintain the pH of the media. Thus, most invertebrate cultures have been incubated in a normal atmosphere. Low oxygen tension has been used to reduce the melanization of the insect hemolymph used in the media (Ball and Chao, 1960; Martignoni and Scallion, 1961). Grace (1958a) tested the effects of varying the O_2 and CO_2 tensions in cultures of Lepidoptera tissues and found that this had no effect on the growth or survival of the tissues.

VI. INCUBATION TEMPERATURE

Invertebrates are poikilothermic animals and thus experience a broader range in body temperatures than do those higher vertebrates that are homoiothermic animals. Also, their body temperature is near that of their environment; thus lower than that of the higher vertebrates. These facts are reflected in the temperatures at which their tissues are cultured. Insect tissues are normally cultured at from 23° to 26°. However, they will grow at 30° (Vago and Chastang, 1958a) and will support the growth of virus, although growing little themselves, at temperatures as low as 20° (Bellett and Mercer, 1964).

Mollusk cells have grown when incubated at 15° (Burch and Cuadros, 1965), at 20° to 23° (Vago and Chastang, 1958a), and at 26° (Flandre and Vago, 1963).

REFERENCES

Aizawa, K., and Vago, C. (1959a). *Entomophaga* **4**, 251.
Aizawa, K., and Vago, C. (1959b). *C. R. Acad. Sci.* **249**, 928.

Ball, G. H., and Chao, J. (1960). *J. Exp. Parasitol.* **9**, 47.
Bellett, A. J. D., and Mercer, E. H. (1964). *Virology* **24**, 645.
Buck, J. B. (1953). *In* "Insect Physiology" (K. D. Roeder, ed.), pp. 147–190. Wiley, New York.
Burch, J. B., and Cuadros, C. (1965). *Nature (London)* **206**, 637.
Carlson, J. G. (1961). *Ann. N. Y. Acad. Sci.* **95**, 932.
Chiu, R. J., and Black, L. M. (1967). *Nature (London)* **215**, 1076.
Clements, A. N., and Grace, T. D. C. (1967). *J. Insect Physiol.* **13**, 1327.
Converse, J. L., and Nagle, S. C., Jr. (1967). *J. Virol.* **1**, 1096.
Corrigan, J. J., and Srinivasan, N. G. (1966). *Biochemistry* **5**, 1185.
Day, M. F., and Grace, T. D. C. (1959). *Annu. Rev. Entomol.* **4**, 17.
Echalier, G., and Ohanessian, A. (1969). *C. R. Acad. Sci.* **268**, 1771.
Echalier, G., Ohanessian, A., and Brun, G. (1965). *C. R. Acad. Sci.* **261**, 3211.
Flandre, O., and Vago, C. (1963). *Ann. Epiphyt.* **14**, 161.
Flandre, O., Vago, C., and Chastang, S. (1962). *C. R. Acad. Sci.* **255**, 1654.
Florkin, M., and Jeuniaux, C. (1964). *In* "The Physiology of Insecta" (M. Rockstein, ed.), Vol. 3, pp. 110–149. Academic Press, New York.
Fosset, J., and Chastang, S. (1963). *Ann. Epiphyt.* **14**, 35.
Gaulden, M. E., and Kokomoor, K. L. (1955). *Proc. Soc. Exp. Biol. Med.* **90**, 309.
Goldschmidt, R. (1915). *Proc. Nat. Acad. Sci. U. S.* **1**, 220.
Grace, T. D. C. (1958a). *Aust. J. Biol. Sci.* **11**, 407.
Grace, T. D. C. (1958b). *J. Gen. Physiol.* **41**, 1027.
Grace, T. D. C. (1959). *Ann. N. Y. Acad. Sci.* **77**, 275.
Grace, T. D. C. (1962). *Nature (London)* **195**, 788.
Grace, T. D. C. (1966). *Nature (London)* **211**, 366.
Grace, T. D. C., and Brzostowski, H. W. (1966). *J. Insect Physiol.* **12**, 625.
Hirumi, H. (1963). *Contrib. Boyce Thompson Inst.* **22**, 113.
Hirumi, H., and Maramorosch, K. (1963). *Ann. Epiphyt.* **14**, 77.
Hirumi, H., and Maramorosch, K. (1964a). *Contrib. Boyce Thompson Inst.* **22**, 259.
Hirumi, H., and Maramorosch, K. (1964b). *Science* **144**, 1465.
Hirumi, H., and Maramorosch, K. (1964c). *Exp. Cell Res.* **36**, 625.
Horikawa, M., and Fox, A. S. (1964). *Science* **145**, 1437.
Horikawa, M., and Kurada, Y. (1959). *Nature (London)* **184**, 2017.
Horikawa, M., Ling, L., and Fox, A. S. (1966). *Nature (London)* **210**, 183.
House, H. L. (1965). *In* "The Physiology of Insecta" (M. Rockstein, ed.), Vol. 2, pp. 769–813. Academic Press, New York.
Hsu, S. H., Liu, H. H., and Suitor, E. C., Jr., (1969). *Mosquito News* **29**, 439.
Hukuhara, T. (1966). *J. Sericult. Sci. Jap.* **35**, 349.
Jones, B. M. (1966). *In* "Cells and Tissues in Culture" (E. N. Willmer, ed.), Vol. 3, pp. 397–457. Academic Press, New York.
Jones, B. M., and Cunningham, I. (1961). *Exp. Cell Res.* **23**, 386.
Judy, K. J. (1969). *Science* **165**, 1374.
Landureau, J. C. (1968). *Exp. Cell Res.* **50**, 323.
Landureau, J. C. (1969). *Exp. Cell Res.* **54**, 399.
Landureau, J. C., and Jollès, P. (1969). *Exp. Cell Res.* **54**, 391.
Landureau, J. C., and Steinbuch, M. (1969). *Experientia* **25**, 1078.
Larsen, W. (1963). *Life Sci.* **8**, 606.
Lesseps, R. J. (1965). *Science* **148**, 502.
Lockwood, A. P. M. (1961). *Comp. Biochem. Physiol.* **2**, 241.
Marks, E. P., and Reinecke, J. P. (1964). *Science* **143**, 961.

Marks, E. P., and Reinecke, J. P. (1965). *J. Kan. Entomol. Soc.* **38**, 179.

Martignoni, M. E. (1960). *Experientia* **16**, 125.

Martignoni, M. E. (1962). *Proc. 23rd Biol. Colloq.*, Oreg. State Univ. pp. 89–110.

Martignoni, M. E., and Scallion, R. J. (1961). *Biol. Bull.* **121**, 507.

Martignoni, M. E., Zitcer, E. M., and Wagner, R. P. (1958). *Science* **128**, 360.

Martin, B. M., and Nishiitsutsuji-Uwo, J. (1967). *Biochem. Z.* **346**, 491.

Martin, H. M., and Vidler, B. O. (1962). *Exp. Parasitol.* **12**, 192.

Miciarelli, A., Sbrenna, G., and Colombo, G. (1967). *Experientia* **23**, 64.

Mitsuhashi, J. (1965a). *Jap. J. Appl. Entomol. Zool.* **9**, 107.

Mitsuhashi, J. (1965b). *Jap. J. Appl. Entomol. Zool.* **9**, 217.

Mitsuhashi, J. (1966). *Appl. Entomol. Zool.* **1**, 5.

Mitsuhashi, J. (1969). *Appl. Entomol. Zool.* **4**, 151.

Mitsuhashi, J., and Maramorosch, K. (1964). *Contrib. Boyce Thompson Inst.* **22**, 435.

Nagle, S. C., Jr. (1969). *Appl. Microbiol.* **17**, 318.

Necco, A., and Martin, R. (1963). *Ann. Epiphyt.* **14**, 23.

Parker, R. C. (1961). "Methods of Tissue Culture." Harper, New York.

Peleg, J. (1965). *Nature (London)* **206**, 427.

Peleg, J. (1966). *Experientia* **22**, 555.

Peleg, J. (1969). *J. Gen. Virol.* **5**, 463.

Peleg, J., and Trager, W. (1963). *Amer. J. Trop. Med. Hyg.* **12**, 820.

Prosser, C. L. (1950). *In* "Comparative Animal Physiology" (C. L. Prosser, ed.), pp. 75–102. Saunders, Philadelphia, Pa.

Rehacek, J. (1962). *Acta Virol. (Prague)* **6**, 188.

Rehacek, J. (1963). *Ann. Epiphyt.* **14**, 199.

Rezzonico-Raimondi, G., and Ghini, C. (1963). *Ann. Epiphyt.* **14**, 153.

Sanborn, R. C., and Haskell, J. A. (1961). *Proc. Int. Congr. Entomol. 11th Vol. B3,* pp. 237–243.

Schneider, I. (1969). *J. Cell Biol.* **42**, 603.

Sen Gupta, K. (1964). *Proc. Indian Acad. Sci. Sect. B* **59**, 103.

Shaw, E. I. (1956). *Exp. Cell Res.* **11**, 580.

Singh, K. R. P. (1967). *Current Sci. (India)* **36**, 506.

Sohi, S. S. (1969). *Can. J. Microbiol.* **15**, 1197.

Stanley, M. S. M., and Vaughn, J. L. (1967). *J. Insect Physiol.* **13**, 1613.

Stanley, M. S. M., and Vaughn, J. L. (1968a). *Ann. Entomol. Soc. Amer.* **61**, 1064.

Stanley, M. S. M., and Vaughn, J. L. (1968b). *Ann. Entomol. Soc. Amer.* **61**, 1067.

Thomson, J. A., and Grace, T. D. C. (1963). *Aust. J. Biol. Sci.* **16**, 869.

Ting, K. Y., and Brooks, M. A. (1965). *Ann. Entomol. Soc. Amer.* **58**, 197.

Trager, W. (1935). *J. Exp. Med.* **61**, 501.

Trager, W. (1938). *Amer. J. Trop. Med.* **18**, 387.

Trager, W. (1959). *Ann. Trop. Med. Parasitol.* **53**, 473.

Vago, C. (1959). *Entomophaga* **4**, 23.

Vago, C., and Chastang, S. (1958a). *Experientia* **14**, 110.

Vago, C., and Chastang, S. (1958b). *Experientia* **14**, 426.

Vago, C., and Chastang, S. (1960a). *C. R. Acad. Sci.* **250**, 2751.

Vago, C., and Chastang, S. (1960b). *C. R. Acad. Sci.* **251**, 903.

Vago, C., and Chastang, S. (1962a). *Entomophaga* **7**, 175.

Vago, C., and Chastang, S. (1962b). *C. R. Acad. Sci.* **255**, 3226.

Vago, C., and Flandre, O. (1963). *Ann. Epiphyt.* **14**, 127.

Vago, C., Fosset, J., and Meynadier, G. (1961). *C. R. Acad. Sci.* **252**, 2759.

Varma, M. G. R., and Wallers, W. (1965). *Nature (London)* **208**, 602.
Vaughn, J. L. (1963). *Bacteriol. Proc.* p. 131.
Wilson, H. V. (1907). *J. Exp. Zool.* **5**, 245.
Wyatt, S. S. (1956). *J. Gen. Physiol.* **39**, 841.
Wyatt, G. R., and Kalf, G. F. (1957). *J. Gen. Physiol.* **40**, 833.
Yunker, C. E., Vaughn, J. L., and Cory, J. (1967). *Science* **155**, 1565.

2

ORGAN CULTURE METHODS

N. Le Douarin

I. INTRODUCTION

From the start, two main lines of research have been followed: on one hand, the culture of isolated cells, and on the other, the culture of more or less complex cell associations, i.e., tissues, organs, fragments of organisms, complete organisms. In 1910 Carrel and Burrows devised a general method of explantation for Amniote vertebrates. Thereafter, histiotypic culture techniques developed extensively. Survival and proliferation of cells were achieved independently of the organ from which they originated. It was then possible to establish pure lines of normal and cancerous cells from various origins, and these could be maintained indefinitely. The cells of these strains arise from elements which have migrated from the initial explant building into an outgrowth generally fibroblastic in appearance.

Organ culture, more recently developed, aims at preserving the cohesion between the cells of a tissue or between the tissues of an organ, which retains its structure and integrity. It is therefore necessary to avoid favoring some elements more than others and to prevent their incoordinate proliferation. The escape of too many cells out of the explant is to be avoided since such escape empties it and disorganizes its structures. Early workers such as Thomson *et al.* (1914) and Maximow (1925) used techniques little different from those of cell culture. Strangeways and Fell (1926, 1928) started developing organotypic culture in upper vertebrates. Thereafter, Fell and her collaborators made clear the importance of organotypic culture for studying problems of differentiation and organogenesis. Since then a number of organ culture methods have been used (Gaillard, 1951; Martinovich, 1953; J. Chen, 1954; Trowel, 1954; etc.).

In France, Wolff and Haffen (1952) have devised a technique which precludes all cellular migration around the explant; this perfect organotypic culture ensures maintenance of the structure and integrity of the cultured tissue. The Wolff and Haffen technique consists of the incorporation of agar–agar in the nutritive medium; the culture substratum thus has a semisolid gel consistancy. The explant is in contact with the air and is rapidly surrounded, whatever its origin, with a layer of epithelium-like cells. The substratum plays a decisive part in the evolution of the culture towards the histiotypic or organotypic modes. Thus, Wolff and Marin (1960) were able to provoke the migration of cells around liver explants first cultivated according to the organotypic method: If a glass coverslip is placed on the cultivated organ, cells adhere to this new solid substratum and migrate onto its surface. Thus, true histiotypic culture is obtained in the nutritional conditions of organ culture.

Whether concerning cell or organ culture, the early research was done on vertebrate tissues—essentially Amniote vertebrates. The explantation of invertebrate organs and tissues has been extensively developed only in the last 10 years. The techniques are adapted from those used for vertebrates. This adaptation encounters particular difficulties due to the great diversity of the invertebrate world. We will be concerned here with the culture techniques ensuring survival, for a certain length of time, of organs, tissues, fragments of organisms, whole embryos, and finally, of organisms which normally live as parasites. We shall go into the study of cultures which last a few days at the minimum, leaving aside short-term experiments done in view of studying certain physiological phenomena. Our study will include techniques which, even if they do not totally inhibit cellular migration around the explant, preserve at least for some time its structure and eventually allow its differentiation. The plan of this chapter will lead us to study successively culture techniques in a liquid medium, some not very different from certain cell culture techniques, then techniques of explantation onto a semisolid medium where the tissues are in contact with air. Each of these parts will be dedicated to the techniques used for each group of invertebrates, the medium having to be adapted to the particular needs of each.

II. ORGAN CULTURE TECHNIQUE IN LIQUID MEDIUM

The technique most currently used is that of the hanging drops. However, certain authors also practice culture in flasks or in roller tubes. The various techniques will be explained together with the composition of the medium for each zoological group.

A. Arthropoda

1. Crustaceans

The earliest works on organ culture in these groups were done by Lewis (1916).

The medium was composed of 90% seawater and 10% crab tissue broth containing 1% NaCl, 0.02% $NaHCO_3$, and 0.25% dextrose. A few migrating cells escaped from the explanted organs (claws and fragments of *Limulus* or *Pagurus* hypoderm). The author did not specify how long the experiment lasted.

Fischer-Piette (1929, 1933) cultivated the lymphatic gland of the lobster (*Homarus vulgaris*) for several days *in vitro*. The lymphatic gland of Decapods is a very thin organ with a succession of nodules; it is located on the dorsal side of the stomach and made up of lymphocytogenous follicles. It is taken from adult lobsters, 18- to 22-cm long, and cultivated on a medium composed of clotted lobster blood. Lobster blood,

TABLE I
Culture Medium for *Carcinus maenas*[a]

Substances		Concentration (parts)
NaCl	0.6 M	100
KCl	0.6 M	2.5
CaCl$_2$	0.4 M	3.5
MgCl$_2$	0.4 M	7
NaHCO$_3$	to pH 7	

[a] From Pantin (1934).

as a rule aseptic, is drawn with a pipette at the level of the articular membrane of the legs or the abdomen, the area having previously been cleansed with alcohol and ether. The blood, which contains fibrine, coagulates spontaneously and can be used as a culture medium. The culture is done in a humid chamber at a temperature of approximately 10°–15°. The medium is renewed every three days. The gland survives perfectly well for at least 11 days and continues producing lymphocytes, which leave the explant and form around it an aureola of migrating cells. In the center of the explant, cellular density remains constant, the emission of lymphocytes being regularly compensated by the multiplication of follicular cells, whose mitotic activity remains constant during the first nine days of culture.

In view of studying various physiological properties of crustacean muscles, Pantin (1934) perfected a medium capable of ensuring survival of crab's muscles. This medium, based on the data given by Bethe (1929) on the composition of the internal environment of *Carcinus maenas,* is indicated in Table I.

2. Insects

a. Generalities. Although there have been many attempts to culture organs and tissues of insects since the beginning of the century (Goldschmidt, 1915), notable progress has only been made in this field in the last 10 years or so. Numerous difficulties are encountered in the culture of insect tissues, but most of them have been overcome now.

i. Sterilization of Organs in Culture. This difficulty results either from the imperfect disinfection of the surface of the insects because of their small size and the irregular surface of their tegument or from the presence of cryptograms and various bacteria in certain organs, e.g., the digestive tract or the trachea. Sterilization of the external surface of the insects, larvae, or eggs is realized by immersion in various disinfectants such as potassium permanganate (Maramorosch, 1956), mercury chloride (Trager, 1935; Schmidt and Williams, 1953a; Goodschild, 1954), 70% ethyl alcohol, mercury chloride diluted in 70% ethyl alcohol, hyamine (S. S. Wyatt, 1956), or hexylresorcinol (Ball, 1947). However, such treatments are insufficient and particularly inadequate at destroying the internal infectious elements, so that aseptic breeding of insects has become a necessary complement to an insect tissue or organ culture department (Vago et al., 1961; Fosset and Chastang, 1963; Horikawa and Kuroda, 1959). This breeding has been successful for numerous groups of insects such as Diptera, Lepidoptera, Orthoptera, Coleoptera, etc. For details on the methods of aseptic breeding see the above-mentioned publications and Chapter 4.

ii. COMPOSITION OF THE CULTURE MEDIA. Composing the culture media is made difficult by the variability of the internal environment of the insects, particularly as regards the ionic concentration. It has thus seemed necessary to compose a particular culture medium for each group and sometimes even for each species to be cultured.

a. *Ionic composition.* Research has mostly dealt with the value of the sodium/potassium ratio in the hemolymph. Generally, this ratio is higher than 1 in the circulating liquids of Metazoa, particularly vertebrates. Insects are an exception to this rule: Their sodium/potassium ratios vary according to different orders and even species.

The first numerical data on this point, in the group of Lepidoptera, are due to Brecher (1929) and with *Sphynx pinastri* and *Pieris brassicae*. These species have a very low sodium content (traces) and 0.035 and 0.037 meq/liter (milliequivalents per liter) respectively of potassium Babers (1938) found in another Lepidoptera (*Prodenia eridiana*) a sodium content of 0.022 meq/liter and a potassium content of 0.040 meq/liter. Many more data were later established by Drilhon (1957); Bialaszewicz and Landau (1938), and Tobias (1948). In Lepidoptera the Na/K ratio is higher than 1 and very similar among *Bombyx mori*, *Lymantria dispar*, and *Arctia caja*. In *Galleria mellonella* the sodium content is higher than in these latter species (Vago and Bergoin, 1963; Vago and Flandre, 1963).

Boné's (1944) analyses, dealing with 27 insects, show that the Na/K ratio varies widely within the various orders. Each order includes insects with a predominating sodium or potassium content in the coelom liquid. Boné could establish a correlation between the insects' diet and the Na/K ratio of its hemolymph. Insects feeding on plants generally have a high potassium concentration whereas sodium is predominant in carnivorous insects. Certain cases are particularly striking, such as in the larvae of Cyclorraph dipterans: *Pegomyia,* 0.026 meq/liter Na and 0.058 meq/liter

K; *Calliphora*, 0.148 meq/liter Na and 0.037 meq/liter K. Those species are difficult to recognize from one another and yet have a Na/K ratio related to their diet, the first being vegetarian, the second carnivorous. Duchateau *et al.* (1953) and others confirm these data. Table II (from Hoyle, 1954) indicates the numerical values of Na, K, Ca, and Mg concentration in the hemolymph of various insects.

This relationship, however, is not absolute. There are special cases, especially in insects with a mixed feeding and in aquatic insects. In these latter, according to Boné (1944), the sodium content largely exceeds the potassium, whatever their diet.

Vago and Flandre (1963) show that, among the *Cicadella* (Homoptera), *Macrosteles* and *Philaenus* belong to the category with high potassium and magnesium and low sodium contents.

As could be foreseen, the blood-sucking Heteroptera such as *Rhodnius* and *Triatoma* have a Na/K ratio higher than 1 (Boné, 1944; Clark and Craig, 1953; Ramsay, 1953).

Landureau (1966) has given data concerning the composition of the internal environment of cockroaches (Dictyoptera).

TABLE II

CATION CONCENTRATION IN THE HEMOLYMPH OF VARIOUS INSECTS[a]

Insect[b]	Stage	Diet	Na[c]	K[c]	Ca[c]	Mg[c]	Authors
(L) *Bombyx mori*	Larva	Leaves	6	33	36	1000	Bialaszewicz and Landau (1938)
(L) *Samia walkeri*	Pupa	Nil	3	42	18	64	Babers (1938)
(O) *Carausius morosus*	Adult	Leaves	9	28	16	145	Duchateau *et al.* (1953)
(O) *Schistocerca gregaria*	Fifth	Leaves	81	5	18	35	Duchateau *et al.* (1953)
(C) *Lytta molesta*	Adult	Leaves	—	—	—	186	Clark and Craig (1953)
(H) *Oncopeltus fasciatus*	Adult	Leaves	—	—	—	52	Clark and Craig (1953)
(O) *Stenobothrus stigmata*	Adult	Leaves	61	62	—	—	Boné (1944)
(C) *Cicindela maritima*	Adult	Insects	162	9	—	—	Boné (1944)
(O) *Gryllotalpa vulgaris*	Adult	Insects	174	11	—	—	Boné (1944)
(O) *Locusta migratoria*	Adult	Leaves	103	11	—	—	Hoyle (1954)
Locust saline (starved)			140	10	4	4	Hoyle (1954)

[a] From Hoyle (1954).
[b] (C), Coleoptera; (H), Hemiptera; (L), Lepidoptera; (O), Orthoptera.
[c] A dash indicates that no analysis was made.

Many authors have analyzed the internal milieu of Diptera. P. S. Chen and Hadorn (1954) should be mentioned for *Drosophila*, *Ephestia*, and *Corethra;* Croghan and Lockwood (1960), Begg and Cruickshank (1963), and Leloup (1964) for *Calliphora*. It should be noted that tissues of insects are less sensitive to ionic balance than those of vertebrates. It is indeed possible to get a long-term culture in media such as TC 199, a medium composed for the culture of vertebrate tissue by Morgan *et al.* (1950). With this medium Loeb and Schneiderman (1956) could keep the epidermis of the silkworm alive for 35 days and Beckel (1956) could cultivate the ovaries of *Aedes* for over 60 days. Lewis and Robertson (1916), later Stern (1940), also cultivated respectively grasshopper's spermatocytes and *Drosophila*'s testes in diluted seawater and observed the evolution of these tissues *in vitro*.

Day and Grace (1959) reached a similar conclusion when they emphasized that the medium composed by S. S. Wyatt (1956) is suitable for the culture of silkworm tissues although the Na/K ratio of this medium is very different from that of the insect's hemolymph. Clark and Ball (1954) considered that the saline solutions of Bradford and Ramsay (1949) and of Hayes (1953) may both be suitable for the culture of mosquitoes' tissues although they differ appreciably from one another.

b. Amino acids. The preparation of synthetic or semisynthetic media requires a knowledge of the organic compounds in the hemolymph. It has been established that the hemolymph of insects contains high concentration of free amino acids (Buck, 1953).

Important changes in amino acid concentrations in the hemolymph take place during development. As these changes are incompletely known, the incorporation of elements in the culture media is obviously empirical. It should be emphasized here that the absence of one component in the hemolymph of a species does not imply that this component is harmful to cultivated tissues of this species. Thus, the hemolymph of *Bombyx mori* contains neither tryptophan, cystine, nor cyteine, but these substances have been found suitable for the culture of Bombyx and also of other insect tissues (S. S. Wyatt, 1956).

c. Other organic acids. The high concentration of organic acids in the hemolymph of most of the insects analyzed suggests that these substances play an important role in their intermediate metabolism. S. S. Wyatt (1956) has shown that an association of malate, ketoglutarate, succinate, and fumarate stimulates the growth of cultivated tissues whereas citrate and lactate are not effective. Ball (1954), Leloup (1964), and J. Schneider (1964) also incorporated organic acids in their culture media composed for Diptera.

d. Carbohydrates. In the case of vertebrate tissues culture the main source of energy supplied by the medium is glucose. It has been shown

that in the hemolymph of insects the principal simple sugar is trehalose
(G. R. Wyatt and Kalf, 1957; Dutrieu, 1961). Since trehalose is the most
abundant simple sugar in the hemolymph of insects, it was supposed that
insect cells could use this source of energy more readily than glucose
and it was incorporated in the culture media. However, Grace (1958b)
observed no improvement in the culture of silkworm tissues when trehalose
replaced glucose. In fact, it seems that, whatever the molecular form in
which energy is supplied, the quality of the cultures is hardly modified.
Trager (1935) recommended maltose rather than saccharose for the
culture of Bombyx tissues while S. S. Wyatt (1956) preferred a mixture
of glucose, fructose, and saccharose in the respective proportions of
4:2:1.

Concerning Diptera, Table V shows that several sugars may be
incorporated into the media, i.e., glucose and trehalose (Leloup, 1964;
Schneider, 1964) or glucose, mannose, and trehalose (Gottschewski,
1960), whereas some authors use glucose alone (Kuroda and Tamura,
1956; Horikawa and Kuroda, 1959) or fructose alone (Ball, 1954).

Laverdure, cultivating the ovaries of *Tenebrio molitor* on a semisolid
medium, found that the survival rate of explants is higher if the medium
contains trehalose but that vitellus appears in oocytes only in the
presence of glucose. For the *Schistocerca gregaria* larvae hypoderma.
Miciarelli *et al.* (1967) used a half-and-half mixture of glucose and
trehalose.

The concentration in carbohydrates does not seem to be a crucial factor.
According to Gottschewski (1960), 100 to 850 mg/ml of glucose and
fructose are well tolerated by dipteran organs although such a concentration is well above the physiological one.

e. Vitamins. Vitamins are necessary in a synthetic culture medium.
The medium composed by Ball (1954) for mosquitoes' organs, although
it contains chick embryo extract, also includes various vitamins. Kuroda
and Tamura (1956), Horikawa (1958), Gottschewski (1960), Horikawa
and Kuroda (1969), and J. Schneider (1964) incorporated a mixture of
vitamins in the media they composed for dipteran organs. Grace (1958b)
added the B-vitamin group to the medium composed by S. S. Wyatt
(1956) for *Bombyx mori*. Mixture of vitamins used by the aforementioned
authors can be replaced by yeast extracts (Trager, 1959; Leloup, 1964;
Schneider, (1964).

f. Hemolymph. For a long time hemolymph, a more complex substance,
has been a widely used medium for the culture of insect organs or cells
(Table III).

Recent knowledge of the internal environment of insects has made it
possible to compose well-defined synthetic solutions. However, in many

TABLE III

USE OF HEMOLYMPH AS A CULTURE MEDIUM FOR INSECT ORGANS

Authors	Species and tissues	Medium	Results
Goldschmidt (1915)	*Cecropia* moth spermatocyte	Adult hemolymph	Mitosis and spermatogenesis
Goldschmidt (1916)	*Cecropia* moth spermatocyte	Adult hemolymph	Survival
Takakusoh (1924)	*Cecropia* moth spermatocytes	Pupal hemolymph	Survival
Palliot (1924)	Various insects	Hemolymph	Survival
Chambers (1925)	Grasshopper spermatocytes	Hemolymph	Mitosis
Lazarenko (1925)	*Oryctes* hemocytes	Larval hemolymph	Mitosis and syncitium formation
Frew (1928)	Fly larva and imaginal discs	Treated lymph	Cell migration and partial differentiation
Takeda (1937)	Light organ of *Luciola vitticolis*	Silkworm hemolymph	62–67 hour survival and light production
Millara (1946)	Various sp. hemocytes	Hemolymph	Short survival
Arvy and Gabe (1946)	*Forficula* hemocytes	Hemolymph	Mitosis and 24 hours survival
Lüscher (1947)	*Rhodnius* epithelial cells and hemocytes	Nymphal hemolymph	Migration Survival for 40 days
Ris (1949)	Grasshopper spermatocytes	Hemolymph	Mitosis and spermatogenesis
Schmidt and Williams (1949)	*Platysamia cecropia and Samia walkeri* spermatocytes	Larval, pupal, or young adult hemolymph	Spermatogenesis
Goodschild (1954)	*Rhodnius prolixus* epiderm	Hemolymph	A few days survival

cases the addition of natural compounds to these solutions improves the culture conditions. Hibbard (1935) obtained the survival of silkworm ovarian tubules and other tissues for over a month in a saline solution into which hemolymph and chick embryo extract were added. Trager (1935, 1937) and S. S. Wyatt (1956) cultivated ovaries of *Bombyx mori* in a saline solution with added silkworm hemolymph. For the culture of *Callosamia promethea* ovaries Grace (1959) incorporated 3% pupal homologous plasma or *Samia Walkeri* plasma in a saline solution, plus 22 amino acids, organic acids, sugars, 10 vitamins of group B, and cholesterol. Miciarelli *et al.* (1957) cultivated *Schistocerca gregaria* epidermis in a medium containing cricket hemolymph.

TABLE IV

CHEMICAL INHIBITION OF TYROSINASE IN SILKWORM HEMOLYMPH IN TEST TUBES AT ROOM TEMPERATURE[a]

Substances	Concentration in hemolymph	Period before development of visible darkening
Phenylthiourea	Saturated	Indefinite
p-Aminobenzoic acid	Saturated	1 week
Ascorbic acid	$0.1\ M$	4 days
Glutathione	$0.03\ M$	4 days
Disodium ethylenediaminetetracetate	$0.03\ M$	12 hours

[a] From S. S. Wyatt (1956).

The hemolymph of insects contains tyrosinase or phenoloxydase, which, when blood is extravasated, oxidizes the phenols into quinones; these are toxic for cultivated tissues. S. S. Wyatt (1956) reduced this action of tyrosinase by various inhibitors such as phenylthiourea, p-aminobenzoic acid, ascorbic acid, glutathione, and disodium ethylenediaminetetraacetate. Table IV shows the relative values of these various inhibitors. Phenylthiourea completely inhibits the tyrosinase but has also some toxic influence. Glutathion produces a shorter inhibition but is less noxious to the culture. However, the best way to inhibit tyrosinase is to destroy it by heat (Ducceschi, 1902; Levenbook, 1950). By heating at 60° for five minutes, the enzyme is precipitated but not completely inactivated. The blood is then cooled, centrifuged, and the supernatant is clear and totally free from tyrosinase (S. S. Wyatt, 1966). This method is now almost universally adopted. The treatment by heat does not alter the nutritive properties of the hemolymph. Indeed, Drilhon and Vago (1960) showed, on the serum of *Bombyx,* that lymph, heated at 60° for five minutes, gives almost the same electrophoretic bands as fresh hemolymph.

Sen Gupta (1963) investigated the influence of hemolymph in cultures. It seems that the factors supplied by hemolymph can be replaced by vertebrate serum or by various substrates such as lactalbumin hydrolysate, bactopeptone, etc. The role of the hemolymph, as that of the protein, would essentially be to improve the adhesion of the cells to the substrate.

g. Tissue extracts. Vertebrate or insect tissue extracts have very often been used and have generally been found favorable for survival and growth of the explants. Lewis (1916) was the first to cultivate grasshopper spermatocytes in diluted seawater plus 20% grasshopper extract. S. S. Wyatt (1956) and Grace (1958a) used silkworm embryo extract to cultivate the ovaries of the same species. In media prepared for Diptera crushed larvae or pupae are often added (Friedman and Burton, 1956; Demal, 1955, 1956; Trager, 1959); Demal and Leloup, 1963; Leloup and Gianfelici, 1966, etc. The medium of Miciarelli *et al.* (1967) for orthoptera contains locust embryo extract.

Chick embryo extract is frequently used in liquid and semisolid media. This does not exclude simultaneous use for insect extracts: Gavrilov and Cowez (1941) incorporated, in a saline solution, extract of mosquito larvae, chicken plasma, and chick embryo extract. Demal (1956) used pupae and chick embryo extracts to cultivate imaginal discs of *Calliphora* and *Drosophila* larvae. Ball (1954) incorporated chick embryo extract in his complex medium.

Lender and Duveau-Hagège (1962) and Lender and Laverdure (1967) cultivated *Galleria mellonella* and *Tenebrio molitor* ovaries on a medium derived from the Wolff and Haffen medium (1952) devised for bird embryonic tissues (Fig. 1).

h. Complex substances and extracts. Complex substances, other than hemolymph and tissue extracts that are added to culture media are various. For example, coagulated frog plasma was used by Takeda (1937) to cultivate the luminous organs of the glow-worm, and Ball (1954) used a vertebrate liver extract. Also, lactalbumin hydrolysate (Trager,

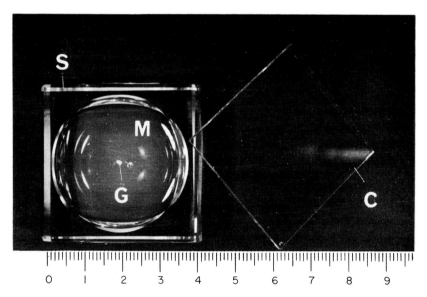

FIG. 1. Photograph of a salière(s) containing the culture medium (M) and an explanted gonad of *Galleria mellonella* (G) and glass cover (C) of the "salière." (From Lender and Duveau-Hagège, 1963a.)

1959; Leloup 1964; J. Schneider, 1964; Miciarelli *et al.*, 1967) and casein hydrolysate (Kuroda and Tamura, 1956; Horikawa, 1958; Gottschewski, 1960) have been used, as well as horse serum (Lender and Duveau-Hagège, 1962; J. Schneider, 1964; Lender and Laverdure, 1967).

These data show that complex protein substances have no toxicity on the insect tissues. Inversely, Mandin and Vago (1963) studied the effects of insect serum (*Bombyx mori*) on vertebrate cell cultures. The culture of human cells of Eagle's KB strain and those of Toolan's Hep2 strain was possible in a medium where mammalian serum was partly replaced by *Bombyx* serum (2% calf serum for 10% *Bombyx* serum). However, a small quantity of mammalian serum has appeared essential. In this connection, it should be emphasized that electrophoresis shows that several globulin fractions are common to both sera and, besides, that the quantity of albumin is too low in the insect serum for the development of human cells.

i. Hormones. Insect tissues appear to be more dependent on their hormonal environment than vertebrate tissues so that addition of hormones to the culture medium was considered necessary by many authors. The hormones can be added to the medium either by incorporation of hemolymph by simultaneous culture of the endocrine organs themselves or else by addition of organ extract or crystalline hormone. Schmidt and Williams (1953b) showed that spermatocytes can differentiate in the presence of the blood of young imagos but not of diapausing larvae. The studies of Kuroda and Yamaguchi (1956), Horikawa (1960), and Fujio (1960, 1962) show clearly the importance of the cephalic complex in *in vitro* differentiation of the *Drosophila* eye imaginal discs.

Grace (1958b) observed a considerable stimulation of mitosis in cultures of silkworm ovaries when endocrine organ extracts or ovary extracts are added to the medium.

b. Dipteran Organ Culture. i. Culture of Larval Organs. Frew (1928), dealing with *Calliphora*, was probably the first to obtain cultures of dipteran imaginal discs. The medium used was a drop of collodion-filtered hemolymph. The leg disc began differentiation, formed a segmented member up to the stage reached on the fourth or fifth day of pupation. However, in the presence of larval hemolymph, the evolution of the disc does not proceed. This result already suggested the need of hormonal factor for *in vitro* differentiation of the imaginal disc.

Demal (1955, 1956) cultivated imaginal discs of *Drosophila melanogaster* and *Calliphora erythrocephala*, the proventricle of *Drosophila*, and the brain of *Calliphora pupa*. He used a modification of the Wolff and Haffen (1952) technique devised for vertebrate embryonic organs.

After some preliminary attempts, the gel medium had to be given up, the adherence of the explants to the substrate preventing normal morphogenetic movements. The organs were then cultivated by the hanging drop technique. Demal's medium contents the following components:

Physiological solution (see Table V)	3 parts
Chick embryo extract diluted by	3 parts
half in physiological solution	
Aseptic pupa extract diluted by half	1 part
Penicillin	

The pupal extract proved necessary for differentiation, and the embryo extract for survival of the explants. The tissues were washed, placed in a fresh medium every day, and kept at 25°.

Calliphora pupa brain survives for five days, *Drosophila* proventricle spontaneously contracts during the first three days of culture and remains excitable after four days. Imaginal discs of legs and eyes of prepupae of both species survive for three or four days and differentiate, but evolution of these anlages remains limited since no cellular differentiation occurs *in vitro*.

Further, Demal (1961) reported results of the culture of testes and ovaries of *Drosophila melanogaster* and *Calliphora erythrocephala* prepupae on media with various modifications from his standard medium. In order to obtain mitosis *in vitro*, vertebrate oestrogenic hormone, known for its mitotic influence, was incorporated in the basic culture medium. One-half milligram oestradiol for 100 ml of medium slightly enhances survival but does not promote growth of cultivated organs. Demal also tried replacing the chick embryo extract by insect extracts which were prepared from eggs, larvae, prepupae, or pupae of the same species. The insects are minced; tyrosinase is inhibited by phenylthiourea or by heating. The homogenate is centrifuged and only supernatant is used. On the standard medium (physiological solution plus 15% chick embryo extract) ovaries and testes of prepupae survive for 12 days. Male germ cells differentiate if the explanted testis came from pupae. The insect extract proves harmful when prepared from larvae, prepupae, and young pupae; extract from older pupae is less toxic. The extract prepared with the anterior part of the animal (approximately 1/3) which contains the cephalic complex is less noxious than that prepared from the whole animal, but the medium thus obtained is less suitable than the standard medium. The extract can also be improved by eliminating the larvae's fat body.

Demal and Leloup (1963) cultivated fragments of aorta and imaginal discs of *Calliphora* larvae and prepupae, and salivary glands of *Drosophila*

TABLE V
Composition of Some Media of Dipteran Organ Culture[a]

Substances	Ball (1954)	Kuroda and Tamura (1956)	Horikawa (1958) K6	Gottschewski (1960)			Horikawa and Kuroda (1959)
				I	III	IV	
Inorganic salts							
NaCl	7875	7000	7000	1000	14000	5000	7000
NaH$_2$PO$_4$	—	200	200	—	400	—	200
NaHCO$_3$	—	50	50	—	100	—	50
NaCO$_2$CH$_2$	—	—	—	—	10	50	—
Na$_2$HPO$_4$	16	—	—	—	—	10000	—
KCl	596	200	200	2500	200	300	200
KH$_2$PO$_4$	712	—	—	500	—	—	—
CaCl$_2$	1540	20	20	1000	40	20	20
MgCl$_2$	—	100	100	1000	200	300	100
MgSO$_4$	—	—	—	—	—	300	—
Amino acids							
β-Alanine	100	—	—	—	—	—	160
L-Arginine	2.1	—	—	—	—	170	560
L-Aspartic acid	120	260	260	—	—	—	280
L-Cysteine	—	1000	1000	—	520	40	64
L-Cystine	20.1	100	100	—	200	3	20
L-Glutamic acid	170	—	—	—	20	—	580
L-Glutamine	103	—	—	—	—	—	480
L-Glycine	3.3	—	—	12000	—	12000	520
L-Histidine	0.9	—	—	—	—	196	2000
L-Isoleucine	3.3	—	—	—	—	—	80
L-Leucine	6.2	—	—	—	—	200	120
L-Lysine	4.4	—	—	—	—	140	1000

	1	2	3	4	5	6
L-Methionine	1.9	—	—	—	(d-)50	80
L-Proline	80	—	—	—	—	280
L-Serine	100	—	—	—	—	880
L-Threonine	1.6	1000	—	—	120	280
L-Tryptophan	0.5	1000	10	200	20	80
L-Tyrosine	—	—	—	—	—	40
L-Valine	3.9	—	—	—	—	160
L-Phenylalanine	1.9	—	—	—	200	120
DL-Alanine	—	—	—	—	—	360
Sugars						
Glucose	—	800	800	1600	1600	800
Mannose	—	—	—	—	1600	—
Fructose	2668	—	—	—	1600	—
Trehalose	—	—	—	—	—	—
Ribose	0.5	—	—	—	—	—
Fructose-2-phosphate	212	—	—	—	—	—
Organic acids						
α-Ketoglutaric	—	—	—	—	—	—
Fumaric	—	—	50	—	50	—
Acetic[b]	268	—	50	—	50	50
Succinic	296	—	—	—	—	—
Malic	—	—	—	—	—	—
α-Aminobutyric	100	—	—	10	—	—
Vitamins and enzymes						
Choline hydrochloride	0.5	2.5	2.5	50	5	2.5
Folic acid	1	0.05	0.05	10	0.5	0.05
Inositol	—	0.25	0.25	5	1	0.25
Niacinamide	1	0.125	0.125	25	5	0.125
Pantothenic acid	0.5[c]	0.05[c]	0.05[c]	10	1	0.05[c]
Aneurin	—	—	—	10	0.5	—

TABLE V (Continued)

Substances	Ball (1954)	Kuroda and Tamura (1956)	Horikawa (1958) K6	Gottschewski (1960)			Horikawa and Kuroda (1959)
				I	III	IV	
Lactoflavin	—	—	—	—	10	0.5	—
Adermin	—	—	—	—	25	1	—
Ascorbic acid	0.56	250	250	20	500	—	250
Vitamin A	—	0.5	—	—	30	—	0.5
Vitamin B$_{12}$	—	0.5	—	—	—	—	0.5
p-Aminobenzoic acid	0.1	0.25	0.25	—	5	—	0.25
DPN	—	1	1	—	100	10	1
TPN	—	—	—	—	—	5	—
Biotin	0.03	0.05	0.05	—	10	—	0.05
Riboflavin	0.5	0.05	—	—	—	—	0.05
Thiamin	1	0.05	0.05	—	—	—	0.05
Pyridoxinehydrochloride	0.5	0.125	0.125	—	—	—	0.125
Nicotinamide	1	—	—	—	—	—	—
Co carboxylase	0.5	—	—	—	—	—	—
Purine, pyrimidine, and nucleic acids							
Hypoxanthine	0.5	—	—	—	—	—	—
Xanthine	0.5	—	—	—	—	—	—
Guanine	0.5	—	—	—	—	—	—
Thymine	0.5	—	—	—	—	—	—
Adenine sulfate	0.5	—	—	—	—	—	—
Uracil	0.5	—	—	—	—	—	—
Cytosine	0.5	—	—	—	—	—	—
Adenine desoxyribose	—	—	—	—	—	0.5	—
Guanine desoxyribose	—	—	—	—	—	0.5	—
Uridine 5-triphosphate	—	—	—	—	—	0.5	—

Desoxycytidine diphosphate	—	—	—	—	0.5	—
Desoxy-5-methylcytidil acid	—	—	—	—	0.5	—
Thymidine diphosphate	—	—	—	—	0.5	—
ATP	—	—	—	—	5	—
RNA	—	—	—	—	50	—
DNA	—	—	—	—	50	—
Pentose nucleic acid	500	500	—	500	500	500
Peptides, proteins, and others substances						
Glutathione	10	10	10	1000	500	10
Peptone	—	—	2000	—	1000	—
Cholesterol	0.3	—	—	—	—	30
Glycylglycine	—	—	—	—	1000	—
Glycerol	231	—	—	—	—	—
L-Asparagine	—	—	—	—	—	280
Hydrolysates and extracts						
Lactalbumin hydrolysate	—	—	—	—	—	—
Casein hydrolysate	50,000	50,000	—	10,000	5000	—
T.C. Yeastolate	—	—	—	—	—	—
Chick embryo extract	8 ml	—	—	—	—	—
Liver extract	0.02 ml	—	1:1	—	—	—
Yeast extract	—	—	—	—	15	—
Tween 80	0.02 ml	—	—	—	—	—
pH	7.2	7.2	6–6.9	7.2	7–7.2	6.4

TABLE V (*Continued*)

Substances	Demal (1961)	Leloup (1964) M1	Leloup (1964) M2	Leloup (1964) M3	I. Schneider (1964)
		Inorganic salts			
NaCl	6500	6500	6500	3600	2100
NaH_2PO_4	—	—	—	7800	—
$NaHCO_3$	—	—	—	—	700
$NaCO_2CH_2$	—	—	—	—	—
Na_2HPO_4	—	—	—	—	—
KCl	250	250	250	500	1600
KH_2PO_4	—	—	—	—	600
$CaCl_2$	300	350	350	300	600
$MgCl_2$	—	—	—	—	600
$MgSO_4$	350	300	300	1650	3700
		Amino acids			
β-Alanine	—	—	—	—	500
L-Arginine	—	—	—	—	600
L-Aspartic acid	—	—	—	—	400
L-Cysteine	—	—	—	—	60
L-Cystine	—	—	—	—	20
L-Glutamic acid	—	—	750	—	800
L-Glutamine	—	—	—	—	1800
L-Glycine	—	—	750	—	250
L-Histidine	—	—	—	—	400
L-Isoleucine	—	—	—	—	150
L-Leucine	—	—	—	—	150
L-Lysine	—	—	—	—	1650
L-Methionine	—	—	—	—	150

L-Proline	1700	—	—	—
L-Serine	250	—	—	—
L-Threonine	350	—	—	—
L-Tryptophan	100	—	—	—
L-Tyrosine	500	—	—	—
L-Valine	300	750	—	—
L-Phenylalanine	—	—	—	—
DL-Alanine	—	(L-)750	—	—
Sugars				
Glucose	2000	700	700	—
Mannose	—	—	—	—
Fructose	—	—	—	—
Trehalose	2000	800	800	800
Organic acids				
α-Ketoglutaric	350	250	250	—
Fumaric	60	50	50	—
Acetic	600	—	—	—
Succinic	60	50	50	—
Malic	—	500	500	—
Vitamins and enzymes				
Choline hydrochloride	0.05	—	—	—
Folic acid	0.02	—	—	—
Inositol	0.02	—	—	—
Niacinamide	0.02	—	—	—
Pantothenic acid	0.02c	—	—	—
p-Aminobenzoic acid	0.01	—	—	—
Biotin	0.1	—	—	—
Riboflavin	0.02	—	—	—
Thiamin	0.02	—	—	—
Pyridoxine hydrochloride	0.02	—	—	—

TABLE V (Continued)

Substances	Demal (1961)	Leloup (1964)			I. Schneider (1964)
		M1	M2	M3	
Purine, pyrimidine, and nucleic acids			None		
Peptides, proteins, and other substances			None		
Hydrolysates and extracts					
Lactalbumin hydrolysate	—	10,000	7000	10,000	10,000
Casein hydrolysate	—	—	—	—	—
T. C. Yeastolate	—	1000	1000	—	1000
Chick embryo extract—15%	—	—	—	—	—
pH	—	7–7.1	7–7.1	7–7.2	—

[a] Concentrations are in milligrams/1000 ml of H_2O.
[b] Na salt.
[c] Ca salt.

in various media: the standard Demal medium (1961) with 20% chick embryo extract, this same medium with additional insect lymph, Trager's A_1, A_2, C_1, C_2 media (1959) (see below), the Vago and Chastang (1960) medium with *Calliphora* hemolymph and no antibiotics, and finally, the TC 199 (Difco) medium. All these trials lead to the conclusion that the appropriate medium as well for survival as for differentiation of the explants is the one which contains chick embryo extract. The salivary glands cultivated in the Vago and Chastang medium and in Trager's A_2 medium survived for four days without showing any histolysis signs which would normally have appeared by this time *in vivo*. According to the authors the low Na/K ratio of the Vago and Chastang medium devised for lepidopteran tissues would explain the particularly unfavorable influence of this medium on the fragments of aorta of *Calliphora*.

Leloup (1964), bringing some changes to the original Demal medium, made up a synthetic medium for *Calliphora* organs based on the composition of this insect's internal environment. To elaborate the culture media, Leloup measured the Na^+, K^+, Ca^{2+}, Mg^{2+}, and Cl^- ions in the plasma of *Calliphora* at the third larval stage (L3), at the pronymphal stage (L4), and in the young imago (Ij).

The results of this author and previous bibliographical data are condensed in Table VI.

For the blood-free amino acids content, Leloup uses Hackman's (1956) and Finlayson and Harmer's data (1949), and for organic acids, Levensbook's data (1950). The compositions finally adopted are given in Table V.

These media are used either without any addition or with 10% additional heated hemolymph from young imagos. The media are sterilized by filtration. The male and female gonads of pronymphs, nymphs, and young imagos are cultivated. In these media without chick embryo extract, the survival span was equivalent to that obtained in the medium with embryo extract, and differentiation of the gonads proceeded to a point. The various media differing only slightly from each other gave very similar results.

Leloup and Gianfelici (1966) cultivated the cerebral complex of *Calliphora* for three or four days in the Leloup M1 medium enriched with 10% hemolymph. Histochemical techniques showed that neurosecretory activity persisted during the whole culture period.

Other studies investigated the role of the cephalic complex and of various chemical substances in the differentiation of the antennoocular discs of *Drosophila*. Kuroda and Yamaguchi (1956) established that the cephalic complex is essential for the differentiation of the eye imaginal

TABLE VI

Calliphora PLASMA ORGANIC IONS CONTENTS

	Concentration (milliequivalents per liter)				
	Na$^+$	K$^+$	Ca^{2+}	Mg^{2+}	Cl$^-$
Calliphora hemolymph					
Larva[a]	148	37			
Pupa[b]	139.6	26.1	20.8	34.3	
Calliphora plasma[c]					
L3	152	10.6	13	30	76
L4	158	19.5	7.5	28	57
Ij-1	157	6.7	5.5	13.5	74
Ij-2	143.8	8.6	7.9	11.6	60.5
Culture media[d]					
M1 and M2	123.6	3.3	6.3	2.4	120.7
M3	157	6.7	5.5	13.5	74

[a] Boné (1944).
[b] Duchateau et al. (1953).
[c] Results of the analyses.
[d] Calculated numbers.

disc of *Drosophila*. Horikawa (1958) perfected a synthetic medium (K6) which allows differentiation *in vitro* of the ocular anlage. The composition of this medium is indicated in Table V. The explants came from third stage larvae (96 hours after hatching at 25°) and were transplanted every three days. Incorporation into the culture medium of tryptophan (5 mg/ml) or of intermediate pigmentation metabolites such as kynurenine (4 mg/ml) or DL-3-hydroxykynurenine (2 mg/ml) makes the pigment appear more quickly. These results show that as early as the third larval stage, all the enzymes necessary for synthesis of the pigment from tryptophan are present in the eye anlage. Horikawa's medium was used in a number of other cases, by Horikawa himself (1960) and by Fujio (1960, 1962), to study the influence of the cephalic complex on differentiation of the antennoocular discs. Cerebral hormone has to be added to the medium in order for *in vitro* differentiation of these discs to occur. The optimum hormonal stimulation is obtained by the association of 10 cephalic complexes to one disc. The efficiency of the hormone varies with the genome of the larvae used. The addition of hormone may also be realized by the conditioned medium technique. Fujio (1962) established that differentiation of the discs may occur in a medium which has previously contained for 24 hours cephalic complexes from larvae at the end of the third stage. Ten to 60 cephalic complexes per milliliter of K6 medium were placed in rolling tubes (8 rph). The oculoantennar discs were cultured at 25° in hanging drops in these media. When the conditioned medium had contained at least 20 cephalic complexes, the quantity of hormone present was sufficient to promote differentiation of the ocular discs within 48 hours. Horikawa and Sugahara (1960) also used the K6 medium to study the action of x rays on the development of drosophila larvae. Among other organs, Horikawa and Sugahara cultivated the salivary glands and the fat body of third stage larvae associated with 10 cephalic complexes. Within 72 hours they observed cellular growth of the cultivated salivary glands and normal histolysis of the fat body.

Gottschewski (1960), then Gottschewski and Querner (1961), cultivated the ocular discs of *Drosophila melanogaster* larvae on synthetic media. Table V indicates the composition of these media. Media I and II are equivalent for morphological differentiation of the ocular disc, but pigmentation only appears if 2 mg of tryptophan are added to medium I and 1 mg of tryptophan to medium II. This high concentration of tryptophan having its drawbacks, the author devised medium III and IV, the latter being the most appropriate.

Gottschewski's studies led him to the following conclusions concerning the composition of a synthetic medium suitable for the culture of *Drosophila* imaginal discs. The chances of survival are reduced if the following amino acids are lacking: arginine, cysteine, cystine, histidine, leucine, lysine, methionine, phenylalanine, threonine, and tryptophan. Others may be omitted, such as isoleucine, glutamine, glycocolle, serine, alanine, aspartic acid, hydroxyproline, and proline. The following substances are necessary: choline, folic acid, inositol, nicotinic amide, pantothenic acid, vitamin B_6, lactoflavine, aneurine (Vitamin B_1). Others have no appreciable effect: ascorbic acid, vitamins A, B_{12}, D, E, H (*p*-aminobenzoic acid), and K. Finally, some promote cellular division: coenzyme A, cocarboxylase, di- and triphosphonucleotide codehydrase (DPN and TPN), mononucleotide flavine, and dinucleotide adenine. According to Gottschewski the addition of organic acids and lipids is not necessary.

On the other hand, all media must contain purine and pyrimidine bases (adenine, guanine, hypoxanthine, thymine, uracil) preferably in the nucleoside form. Some peptides or protides are favorable, for example, glutathione and glycylglycine. Peptones promote cellular proliferation. Casein has also proven useful. Lastly, some complex substances such as yeast extract stimulate growth.

I. Schneider (1964) devised a medium in which he cultivated, in association, cephalic complex, antennoocular discs, ring gland, aorta, lymphatic gland, oesophagus and proventricle of *Drosophila melanogaster* and of *Drosophila virilis*. These organs were taken from third stage larvae, 95 hours after hatching for *Drosophila melanogaster* and 145 hours for *Drosophila virilis* (at 25°). The composition of the culture medium is essentially based on analyses of larvae hemolymph done by P. S. Chen and Hadorn (1954), Croghan and Lockwood (1960), and Begg and Cruickshank (1963). The medium exists in two forms as follows:

1. A saline solution containing sugars, organic acids, lactalbumin hydrolysate, and yeast extract. The last two substances provide respectively amino acids and group-B vitamins; their concentration in the media are chosen according to Jones and Cunningham (1961).

2. A well-defined synthetic medium containing a saline solution, organic acids, and sugars, vitamins, and amino acids, which replace the complex substances previously used. Table V gives the components and concentrations used.

The two media are equivalent for differentiation of the explants, but survival is better in the first. In some cultures Schneider added the following substances: extracts of *Drosophila melanogaster* third stage larvae and prepupae, extract of *Drosophila virilis* pupae, fetal bovine serum, chick embryo extract, horse serum, and heat-treated hemolymph of *Hyalophora cecropia* and *Rothschildia orizaha* pupae. Among these supplements only the first three (i.e., *D. melanogaster* and *D. virilis* extracts and bovine fetal serum) have a slight beneficial effect on the cultures: cephalic and ventral ganglia remain transparent for one or two more days, oesophagus and aorta pulsate more vigorously. However, no effect on differentiation is observed. The cultures were done in hanging drops of 0.008 ml/drop. The medium was changed every one to six days in one-third of the culture, and in the others it is not renewed. The change of the medium definitely lengthened survival of the explants, e.g., *D. melanogaster* organs survived for 8.4 days on an average in the medium not renewed and for 14.3 days if it was partially replaced once or several times For *D. virilis* the averages are 9.9 and 16.9 days, respectively. The evolution of the antennoocular discs in culture was followed and minutely described by I. Schneider day by day. The histological study of the cultivated organs, which he reported recently (1966), indicates that in *in vitro* conditions relative differentiation capacities of the cephalic organs decrease in the following order: antennar discs, ocular discs, cerebral lobes, ventral ganglion. As a rule, if a sequence of development takes place *in vivo* within 24 hours following the formation of the pupa, the same sequence will appear *in vitro* without appreciable delay. However, after this stage of development, a delay of three to nine days is observed if a similar development is to occur.

The medium composed by Schneider has been used recently by Hanly *et al.* (1967) and by Hanly and Hammert (1967) to study the pigmentation of the *Drosophila* eye. These authors used the complete Schneider medium enriched with 10% fetal bovine serum. The culture was done in hanging drops of a volume of 0.05 ml at the temperature of 25°. Their results show that the larval eye cultivated in association with the cerebral complex forms homochromic pigments as well as pterines. The eye cultivated alone, i.e., in hormone-free medium, is not apt to produce these pigments unless it comes from a 40- to 45-hour-old pupa (at 25°).

The culture of dipteran imaginal discs and larval organs has also been done by Trager (1938, 1959). In his first attempts (1938) this author cultivated imaginal discs and portions of the alimentary canal of *Aedes* larvae in a medium composed as follows: (a) 50% chicken or guinea-pig plasma, heparinized and diluted by half in distilled water. (b) 50% nutritive solution including 33 ml of glucose (0.3 M); 4.5 ml of NaCl (0.3 M); 0.4 ml of KCl (0.2 M); 0.7 ml of CaCl$_2$ (0.2 M); phosphate buffer 0.2 M for pH 7.2; 10 ml of peptic digest egg albumin; and 49 ml of distilled water.

Later, Trager (1959) composed a series of more or less complex media in which he cultivated *Glossina palpalis* pupae tissues, which can in turn bear a culture of trypanosomes.

Although considerable cellular migration occurred around the explants, the organs maintained their morphological and functional integrity long enough for the results to come under the heading of organ culture.

The cultivated organs were brain, optical lobe, eye, intestine, proventricle, posterior intestine, spermatheca, and imaginal discs of six-day-old pupae.

The composition of the culture medium, based on the work of S. S. Wyatt (1956) and Grace (1958b), is given in Table VII.

C series media are used for dissection of insect organs; they are thereafter cultivated in the corresponding D series media. Trypanosomes of the circulating blood were introduced into the hanging drops which contained the cultures. These trypanosomes are provided either by whole infected blood or by blood in which trypanosomes have been concentrated.

Trager used the hanging drop technique on square coverslips over hollow slides or on large coverslips above Maximow slides. Some cultures are done in Carrel-type bottles. In the case of hanging drop cultures, the medium is partially renewed about every five days: A drop of the old

TABLE VII
CULTURE MEDIA FOR *Glossina palpalis*

Substances	Concentration (mg/100 ml)
Solution A[a]	
Solution A₁	
NaCl	90
KCl	300
$NaH_2PO_4 \cdot H_2O$	110
$MgSO_4 \cdot 7H_2O$	370
$CaCl_2$	80
Glucose	150
Lactalbumin hydrolysate	1000
Solution A₂	
Same as A₁ plus:	
Yeast extract (Difco)	
Solution A₃	
Same as A₁ plus	50
Trehalose	50
L-Malic acid	50
α-Ketoglutaric acid	25
Succinic acid	5
Yeast extract (Difco)	200

Solution B
    Reduced glutathione 200 mg, ascorbic acid 2 mg, in 10 ml of redistilled water. Sterilized through ultrafine glass filter.
Solution C
    Solutions C₁, C₂, and C₃ are 8 ml solutions A₁, A₂, or A₃ respectively plus 2 ml of sheep serum. Solution C₄ is same as solution C₃ plus 0.5 ml of solution B.
Solution D
    Solutions D₁, D₂, D₃, and D₄ are, in 1 ml of solution C₁, C₂, C₃, or C₄ respectively, two freshly sterilized 12-day-old pupae of *G. palpalis* crushed gently with a pipette and centrifuged for 15 minutes at 2000 rpm. The supernatant, with the resuspended fatty layer at the surface, constitutes the culture medium (pH 6.7–6.9).

[a] Ingredients dissolved in water, redistilled in a Pyrex glass still, and pH adjusted to 6.8–6.9 with 10 N NaOH. Solutions sterilized through Selas 03 porcelain filters.

medium is sucked with a capillary pipette, fresh medium is immediately added and the coverslip turned over on the hollow slide. The incubation temperature is between 27° and 29°.

The C₁ medium turned out best for culture: the posterior intestine, for example, survives and keeps up its peristaltic activity for at least two weeks. The tissues placed in this medium sometimes produce a more or less sizeable aureola of migration cells. If 12- or 13-day-old pupae extract (media D_1 to D_4) is added to the C media, the migration aureola appears regularly. Enriching the culture medium thus makes it possible to pass from organ to cell culture.

If the lactalbumin hydrolysate is omitted, or replaced by an acid casein hydrolysate enriched with tryptophan, the tissues neither survive nor grow satisfactorily. Trager obtained growth and differentiation of certain organs in culture, i.e., brain, optical lobe, and ocular disc grow during the first few days of culture. Toward the 12th day the ommatidies appear; around the 18th day both eyes are brown; they are well differentiated on the 25th day. Cellular migration appears only on the 35th day. The proventricle and the intestine become contractile *in vitro*.

Spontaneous muscular contractions are usual in culture. Thus Chabaud *et al.* (1960), cultivating fragments of *Aedes aegypti* imaginal discs of the fourth larval stage, observed cellular outgrowths from cells with rhythmic contractions. These authors unfortunately do not give any precisions about the culture media they used.

Numerous publications have been dedicated to the culture of dipteran salivary glands because of their giant chromosomes. We shall not go into short-span experiments (sometimes only a few hours) in which various agents are used to induce puffing; this type of culture is often done in Ringer liquid or in Ephrussi and Beadle (1936) solution. We shall only deal with a few techniques with which the culture of salivary glands was possible for at least 24 hours.

Cannon (1964) composed a chemically defined medium for the culture of *Sciara coprophila* salivary glands. Over a 24-hour period the polytene chromosomes of the glands from six different larval stages had a normal physiological behavior in culture as far as the formation and condensation of puffs and the synthesis of DNA was concerned. The medium composed by Cannon is indicated in Table VIII.

Cannon separately prepared several solutions using tridistilled water. The inorganic salts, $CaCl_2$ excepted, are dissolved in 60 ml of water; $CaCl_2$ in 14.4 ml; the sugars in 20 ml; the organic acids in 10 ml; the amino acids in 80 ml; the vitamins, cholesterol, penicillin, trehalose, and the phenol red in 10 ml. The solutions are mixed, $CaCl_2$ being added last. The pH is adjusted to 6.35 by addition of KOH, then water is added to get a final volume of 200 ml. The solution is sterilized by filtering through a millipore filter; it can be stocked in tightly stoppered bottles at 4°.

Tulchin *et al.* (1967) cultivated *Drosophila* salivary glands at the third larval stage in various media for 24 hours. These authors compared the influence of these different media on the morphological integrity of

TABLE VIII

CULTURE MEDIUM FOR *Sciara coprophila* SALIVARY GLANDS[a]

Substances	Concentration (mg/200 ml)
(1) Inorganic salts	
NaH_2PO_4	220
$MgCl_2 \cdot 6H_2O$	608
$MgSO_4 \cdot 7H_2O$	740
KCl	596
$CaCl_2$	162
(2) Sugars	
Glucose	140
Fructose	80
Sucrose	80
Trehalose	1000
(3) Organic acids	
Malic	134
α-Ketoglutaric	74
Succinic	12
Fumaric	11
(4) Amino acids	
L-Arginine–HCl	140
DL-Lysine–HCl	250
L-Histidine	500
L-Aspartic acid	70
L-Asparagine	70
L-Glutamic acid	120
L-Glutamine	120
Glycine	130
DL-Serine	220
L-Alanine	45
L-Proline	70
L-Tyrosine	10
DL-Threonine	70
DL-Methionine	20
L-Phenylalanine	30
DL-Valine	40
DL-Isoleucine	20
DL-Leucine	30
L-Tryptophane	20
L-Cystine	5
Cysteine–HCl	16
(5) B-Vitamin group	
Thiamine–HCl	0.004
Riboflavin	0.004

TABLE VIII (*Continued*)

Substances	Concentration (mg/200 ml)
Nicotinic acid	0.004
Pantothenic acid	0.004
Biotin	0.004
Folic acid	0.004
Inositol	0.004
Choline	0.004
(6) Other	
Cholesterol	6
Penicillin	12
Phenol red	20

a From Cannon (1964).

the giant chromosomes and on synthesis of DNA during culture. The media used are those of I. Schneider (1964), Grace (1962), Cannon (1964), Horikawa and Fox (1964) (H5 medium), and that of Jones and Cunningham (1961).* In this last medium insect hemolymph is replaced by 10% newborn calf serum. It should be noted that the various media used differ by several points, i.e., ionic content, osmotic pressure, sugars, and amino acids. The most suitable media for culture of *Drosophila* salivary glands are those of Cannon, Grace, and Jones and Cunningham* (with serum). In these three media the morphological integrity of the chromosomes is well preserved after 24 hours in culture. In the H_5 media the chromosomes already become vacuolated on the first day, and in the Schneider media the differences between bands and interbands are attenuated.

Besides larval organs and imaginal discs, dipteran adult organs (genital glands, alimentary canals carrying pathogenic protozoa), blood cells, and tumoral tissue have also been cultivated.

ii. ADULT ORGAN CULTURES. Trager (1938) cultivated fragments of freshly hatched adult *Aedes* ovaries in the media described earlier and composed of a saline solution, albumin, and vertebrate plasma. The ovary showed contractility over 20 days of culture.

Ball (1947, 1948, 1954) composed a synthetic media for the culture of a mosquito's alimentary canals. During the first attempts (1947, 1948) the canal remained contractile in culture for seven days. In his later experiments Ball (1954) kept the alimentary canal contractile for

* The Jones and Cunningham media was devised for the culture of cells from *Philosamia advena* ovaries.

34 days. The culture also included *Plasmodium* oocysts fixed to the stomach surface. These developed up to a point but not mature *in vitro*. The culture medium used was either the Ball synthetic medium (see Chapter 22) or a modified Trager (1938) medium. The modifications consist in an addition of chick embryo extract and amino acids. The latter are provided by the "paranemine" mixture (Winthrop Sterans) plus alanine, aspartic acid, serine, aminobutyric acid, proline, and glycine. The amino acids are in the same concentrations as in the Ball synthetic medium (Table V). The cultures are done in hanging drops or in flask rockers. The first technique makes it possible to observe and measure frequently the cultivated organs, but it is necessary to renew the media often. The flask rocker culture technique is used by Geiman *et al.* (1946). The vessels are placed on a dialyzing cellophane membrane fixed around the end of a glass cylinder inside a flask. This flask contains the culture media. A few drops of medium are added on the inside of the membrane in order to avoid dessication of the culture before dialysis starts. The flasks are placed on a rocker so that the tissue is washed about 10 times per minute. This technique uses a relatively large quantity of medium (15–18 ml) and ensures good oxygenation of the cultures, but measuring the oocysts is possible only at the start and at the end of the experiment. The culture temperature is 25°, but Ball noticed that the results are better if the organs are explanted at a lower temperature (17°–18°) for the first 24 hours. Seemingly, the tissues adapt better to the culture conditions in that way.

Beckel (1956) cultivated adult ovaries of three species of *Aedes* on a medium devised for vertebrate tissues, the 199 modified M 150 medium of Morgan *et al.* (1950). The cultures were done in hanging drops. The muscles of *Aedes hexodontus* and *Aedes communis* ovaries keep contracting for seven days but the ovocytes do not develop. The muscular tissue of the ovary of *Aedes aegypti* shows contractions for 60 days but no development of ovocytes occurs in this case. Experiments done with Ringer and *Polyphemus* and *Cynthia* (Lepidoptera) hemolymph only showed muscular movements for two or three days, and still no ovocytes developed. No mitoses were found in the cultures.

iii. TUMORAL TISSUE CULTURE. Friedman and Burton (1956) cultivated melanotic tumors induced in the normally healthy 51–52 wild strain of *Drosophila melanogaster* by a "tumors inducing factor" extracted from spontaneous tumors. The induced tumor tissue is cultivated on a medium composed of a larvae extract and a saline solution; one lot (5 mg) of 96-hour-old larvae of the 51–52 wild strain is minced in a morter and put in suspension into 15 ml of Waddington saline solution. This mixture is centrifuged at 35,000 *g* for 30 minutes at 0°. The supernatant is sterilized by filtration on a Swinny filter. The culture is done in hanging drop at the temperature of 25°. During the first three days in culture the tissue does not grow. From the third to the seventh day *in vitro* the tumor grows slightly. After 14 days, the tumor cells have infiltrated the neighboring healthy tissues of the explant.

Kuroda and Tamura (1956) devised a synthetic medium which allows considerable growth of these melanotic tumors in culture (Table V).

The medium is sterilized by filtration through a Seitz filter and the cultures are done in hanging drops at 25°. The components of the Kuroda and Tamura synthetic medium are indicated in Table V. The substances are dissolved separately in 10 stock solutions kept at 0°. The purines (adenine, guanine, xanthine, and hypoxanthine) and the pyrimidines (thymine and uracile) are absent from the medium, Healey *et al.* (1954) having demonstrated the toxic effect of these substances.

iv. CULTURE OF DROSOPHILA BLOOD. Horikawa and Kuroda (1959) composed a synthetic medium indicated in Table V. The pH of the solution is 6.4 (with sodium hydroxide) and the medium is sterilized by filtration through Seitz filters. The blood is taken from larvae dilacerated in sterile medium. The blood cells obtained from 10 larvae are scattered in 10 ml of synthetic solution. The concentration varies from 500 to 1000 cells per mm^3. The cellular suspension is placed in roller tubes turning at 1 revolution/5 minutes. Each tube contains 1 ml of medium. The temperature of the culture is 25°.

In this medium, the cells show normal movements and mitosis for at least two weeks if the medium is not changed. The culture can also be done in hanging drops. In this case, when the medium is renewed twice a week, survival and mitosis of the blood cells are observed for 75 days. Also, however, the cells degenerate less rapidly than in the K6 medium used earlier by Horikawa (1958).

It is worth mentioning in this connection the cultures of Drosophila blood done by Fischer and Gottschewski (1939) with a technique based on vertebrate tissue culture methods. In this case the cells in culture formed "pseudoepithelia" and showed mitosis.

c. Lepidopteran Organ Cultures. The first successful attempts are due to Trager (1935) who cultivated fragments of *Bombyx mori* larvae ovaries in a physiological solution to which 10% silkworm hemolymph was added. The composition of the physiological solution is indicated in Table IX. This medium allows a survival of two weeks for the ovaries.

S. S. Wyatt (1956) based his work on the composition of *Bombyx* hemolymph as determined by Sarlet *et al.* (1952) and by G. R. Wyatt *et al.* (1956). The composition of Wyatt's medium is given in Chapter 6.

TABLE IX
PHYSIOLOGICAL SOLUTION[a]

Substances	Concentration (gm/liter)
NaCl	15
$MgCl_2 \cdot 6H_2O$	1
$CaCl_2$	1
$NaH_2PO_4 \cdot H_2O$	1.5
KH_2PO_4	1.5
Maltose	60
Total	80
pH	6.7

[a] From Trager (1935).

It should be noted that the medium thus composed differs from the hemolymph in the ratios of aspartic acid and glutamic acid to their amides. This change was introduced because these acids may become useful by combining with the ammonium formed in the medium. Hemolymph is added to the medium, its tyrosinase being inhibited by glutathion. The suitable proportions of hemolymph may vary from 5 to 50%. In most of his experiments Wyatt used a proportion of 10%. The synthetic solution without hemolymph is much less favorable for the growth of the culture; it allows the cells to retain a normal appearance.

In roller tubes, when the medium is changed twice a week, cellular migration appears within four or five days; mitosis are observed for two weeks.

The Wyatt medium was later used by Grace (1958b) who added vitamins of the B group and cholesterol to it. With this medium Grace could establish new cell lines from *Callosamia promethea* and *Samia walkeri* larval ovaries (1958b, 1959). The composition of this culture medium can be found in Chapter 1.

Successful attempts were also made by using hemolymph as a culture medium (Table II). Thus, Goldschmidt (1915) observed mitosis and spermatogenesis by cultivating spermatocytes of *Cecropia* in homologous hemolymph.

Schmidt and Williams (1953a,b) also obtained the evolution of spermatocytes of *Platysamia cecropia* and *Samia walkeri* pupae, when cultured with blood from larvae in the course of pupation or from young imagos. Similar development does not occur when the culture is done in the blood of diapausing pupae or of larvae before prepupa stage.

d. Orthoptera Organ Culture. The various media used are hemolymph (see Table II) as well as different saline solutions.

Lewis (1916) cultivated grasshoppers' testes in diluted seawater plus insect extracts. His medium is as follows:

90% seawater or Locke's solution (isotonic to the plasma of the insect of which the organs are cultivated)

10% minced insect muscles

0.02 gm NaHCO₃ (which neutralizes the acidity of the culture)

0.02 gm dextrose (energy-providing substance necessary for the growth of the tissues)

Others should be mentioned briefly: Lewis and Robertson (1916) obtained mitosis and gametogenesis of grasshopper spermatocytes cultivated in Locke's solution enriched in peptone and sugar. Murray (1926) obtained survival of cricket ovaries in diluted seawater with additional dextrose. Bělǎr (1929) observed mitosis and gametogenesis of grasshopper spermatocytes, using a saline solution also with additional dextrose. Baumgartner and Payne (1930) obtained the partial development of grasshopper spermatocytes in saline solutions. Carlson (1946) cultivated grasshopper neuroblasts and observed mitosis in a saline solution with glucose and vitellus added. Gametogenesis *in vitro* was obtained by Duryee (1948) from grasshopper spermatocytes in a saline solution.

Recently, Miciarelli *et al.* (1967) cultured the larval epidermis of *Schistocerca gregaria*. The medium used is Hoyle's (1955) solution (0.075 gm KCl; 0.75 gm NaCl₂; 0.041 gm MgCl₂; 0.034 gm NaHCO₃; 0.083 gm NaH₂PO₄; and 100 ml distilled water), enriched with organic substances (0.1 gm glucose; 0.1 gm trehalose; 1 gm lactalbumin hydrolysate; 10 ml cricket hemolymph; and 10 ml cricket embryo extract). The hemolymph is treated by heat (60° for five minutes). The embryo extract is prepared from eggs incubated for eight days. The eggs are minced, centrifuged at 20,000 g for 30 minutes, and only the supernatant is used. Antibiotics are added and the medium is sterilized by filtration before use. The explants are made up of fragments of abdominal sternites of 1 to 2 segments from fourth or fifth instar larvae. They are placed in 0.5 ml of medium; the temperature of the culture is 30°. The results vary according whether the medium contains embryo extract or not. The life span is 12 days in the medium with extract, only four days if the extract is absent. On the other hand, the medium proves suitable for survival of the epidermis but does not allow cellular multiplication, and the synthesis of the cuticle can occur to some extent *in vitro*.

B. Martin and Nishiitsutsuji-Uwo (1967) cultivated trachea of the cricket *Locusta migratoria*. The trachea coming from locusts 1 or 2 days before the last molt are dissected, rid of their fat bodies, and cut into 1-mm pieces. The explants are washed three times in a saline solution

TABLE X
KIRSTEN'S PHYSIOLOGICAL SOLUTION

Substances	Concentration (gm/liter)
CaCl$_2$	0.302
NaCl	5.22
KCl	0.968
MgSO$_4$·7H$_2$O	2.500
Na$_2$HPO$_4$	0.105
KH$_2$PO$_4$	0.060
Sodium acetate	0.050
Dextrose	1.00
Antibiotics	
Neomycin	12 mg
Streptomycin	12 mg
Penicillin	6 mg/100 ml

composed by Kirsten. The composition of Kirsten's physiological solution is given in Table X.

The culture technique used is the hanging drop. Each explant is placed in 0.005 ml of medium spread on a coverslip; the coverslip is then turned over on to a hollow slide 5 mm deep containing 0.03 ml of medium. The culture medium is composed of the medium 199 to which various substances are added as indicated in Table XI. The temperature adopted for the cultures is 29° to 36°. This temperature, relatively high, is suitable for locust tissues.

TABLE XI
CULTURE MEDIUM FOR ORTHOPTERA ORGANS[a]

Substances	Concentration	
	(mg)	(ml)
TC 199 (9)		100
Trehalose	500	
Glucose	70	
Fructose	40	
Sucrose	40	
Phenylthiourea	40	
Coenzyme A	0.3	
Diphosphopyridine nucleotide	1.5	
Triphosphopyridine nucleotide	0.2	
10% Calliphora eggs extract or 5 to 10% young Philosamia cynthia imago hemolymph; both are treated at 60° for 5 minutes. pH is adjusted to 6-7 by adding KOH.		

[a] From Martin and Nishiitsutsuji-Uwo (1967).

e. **Homopteran Organ Culture.** Hirumi and Maramorosch (1963) cultivated gonads, Malpighi tubes, salivary glands, intestine, and brain of two *Cicadella* species in several culture media. These organs, especially nymph and adult testes, can survive over three months. Although the organs retain their structure, cellular migration occurs around the explant. The authors used nine different media as indicated in Table XII.

TABLE XII
CULTURE MEDIA FOR CICADELLA[a]

Substances	Concentration (ml)
Medium 1	
Medium 199 of Morgan *et al.* (1950)	10
Distilled water	85.6
$NaHCO_3$ (7.5%)	2.4
Antibiotics	2.0
Medium 2	
Medium 1	90
Newborn calf serum	10
Medium 3	
Medium 1	80
Newborn calf serum	20
Medium 4	
Medium 1	60
Newborn calf serum	40
Medium 5	
Medium 1	70
Newborn calf serum	10
Lactalbumin hydrolysate at 5%	20
Medium 6	
Eagle's MEM medium	90
Newborn calf serum	10
Medium 7	
Vago's 22 medium	85
Newborn calf serum	15
Medium 8	
Vago's 22 medium	85
Cicadella nymph extract	2
Newborn calf serum	13
Medium 9[b]	
Vago's 22 medium	83
Cicadella nymph extract (1/1)	2
Army worm serum (1/1)	2
Newborn calf serum	13

[a] From Hirumi and Maramorosch (1963).

[b] Medium 9 is used which one drop of coagulated chicken plasma [one drop of plasma plus one drop of the mixture containing 0.9 ml of medium and 0.1 of chick embryo extract (1/1)].

TABLE XIII

SIMPLE MEDIA USED TO CULTIVATE THE DORSAL VESSEL OF VARIOUS INSECTS

Authors	Material	Concentration (gm/liter)						
		NaCl	KCl	$CaCl_2 \cdot 2H_2O$	PO_4NaH_2	CO_3HNa	Glucose	$MgCl_2 \cdot 12H_2O$
Levy (1928)	Calliphora	9.00	0.7	0.46	0.01	0.16	0	
Ludwig et al. (1957)	Periplaneta	9.00	0.7	0.50				
Bělâr (1929)	Melanoplus differentialis	9.00	0.2	0.2		0.2		
Jahn et al. (1936)								
Jahn and Koel (1948)								
Yeager and Hager (1934)	Periplaneta	9.82	0.77	0.50	0.01	0.18	1	
Agrawal and Srivastava (1962)	Mylabris	9.82	0.77	0.50				
Yeager (1939)	Periplaneta	10.93	1.57	0.85			0	0.17
Richards (1963)	Periplaneta	10.93	1.57	0.85			0	0.17
Bergerard et al. (1950)	Gryllus Galleria	10.8	0.85	0.55	0.01	0.2	1	
Gaulden and Carlson (1951)	Popilius	6.8	0.2	0.2	0.2	0.12	7.7	0.1
Wilbur and MacMahan (1958)								
Davenport (1949)	Stenopelmatus	6.7	0.15	0.12		0.15		
Dreux and Grapin-Poupeau (1963)	Galleria	8.5	3.40	1.07	0.01	0.20	1	
Butz (1957)	Tenebrio	16.0	1.4	1.0				
Ludwig et al. (1957)	Periplaneta	11.0	1.4	1.1				
David and Rougier (1965)	Cybister	9.82	0.77	0.50	variable	variable	1.5	

The cicadella nymph extract used in two of the media is prepared from 100 individuals of the *Agallia constricta* species at the fifth stage. The outside of the insects is sterilized by immersion in a solution of hyamine at 0.1% for three minutes. They are then washed in sterile distilled water and in Earle's solution. The nymphs are crushed in 2 ml of Vago's 22 medium, and the homogenate is then heated at 60° for five minutes. Two milliliters of fresh 22 medium are added, and the solution is centrifuged at 6000 rpm for 10 minutes three times. The nymph extract is kept at 20°.

Vago's 22 medium consists of 99 ml of distilled water, 1 ml of phenol red at 0.2%, 0.120 mg $NaHPO_4 \cdot H_2O$, 0.300 mg $MgCl_2 \cdot 6H_2O$, 0.400 mg $MgSO_4 \cdot 7H_2O$, 0.300 mg KCl, 0.100 mg $CaCl_2 \cdot 2H_2O$, 0.150 mg glucose, 1000 mg lactalbumin hydrolysate, KOH (5%) added to get a pH of 6.4, 20,000 units of specillin, and 2 mg of streptomycin.

f. **Culture of the Dorsal Vessel of Insects.** To experiment on the heart physiology of insects, some authors have cultivated this organ, usually for a short time. The media used can be classified into simple or complex.

i. SIMPLE MEDIA. The most frequently used media are those of Levy (1928), Yeager (1939), and Yeager and Hager (1934). Levy devised the composition of the physiological solution used for *Calliphora* larvae hearts from cinder analyses of the blood of this insect. Yeager modified Levy's solution by adding glucose.

David and Rougier (1965) used a saline solution enriched with glucose to cultivate the dorsal vessel of *Cybister lateralimarginalis* and studied the influence of the pH on the length of survival *in vitro*. Variations of the pH between 6.45 and 7.7 are obtained by adding Na_2HPO_4, KH_2PO_4, and $NaHCO_3$ in suitable quantities.

Table XIII indicates the compositions of media used for the dorsal vessel of various insects.

ii. COMPLEX MEDIA. These media contain mineral salts and a large number of organic substances (glucose, bactopeptone, lactalbumin hydrolysate, calf serum, antibiotics, etc.). Mitsuhashi (1965) observed that explanted heart tissues of the lepidopter *Chilo suppressalis* stayed contractile for about 10 days. Larsen (1963) succeeded in maintaining the activity of fragments of the dorsal vessel of the *Blaberus* embryo for several weeks.

g. **Insect Embryo Culture.** Slifer (1934) devised the first technique for the *in vitro* culture of insect embryos. The species cultivated was *Melanopus differentialis*. The medium used by Slifer is a Ringer solution with the following salt concentrations [first proclaimed by Bĕlăr (1929)] for the culture of grasshopper germinal cells: 0.9% NaCl, 0.02% KCl,

0.02% $CaCl_2$, and 0.02% $NaHCO_3$. This basic solution is variously diluted according to the culture series, in order to study the effect of anisotonic media on embryos.

Later, Bucklin (1953, 1959), N. A. Schneider and Bucklin (1958), and Mueller (1963) cultivated embryos of *Melanopus differentialis* with their vitellus, in hanging drops of a physiological solution. Grellet (1965a,b) cultivated the embryo of *Scapsipedus marginatus* partially deprived of its vitellus. He used, as did Müeller (1963) for Acridians, a Ringer solution with a pH of 6.8. The embryos taken at four days survived for six days without amnion and for eight days with it. It was also possible to culture some embryos totally deprived of their vitellus; such was the case for *Locusta pardalina* and *Locusta migratoria* (Jones, 1956), *Bombyx mori* (Takami, 1958, 1959, 1961, 1963; Krause and Krause, 1963, 1964, 1965), and *Carausius morosus* (Koch, 1962, 1964; Seidel and Koch, 1964).

Bergerard and Morio (1963) cultivated seven-day-old *Locusta migra-*

TABLE XIV

SHAW MEDIUM FOR INSECT EMBRYOS[a]

Substances	Concentration (gm)
Solution A[b]	
Potassium glutamate	7.36
Glycocolle	3.75
Solution B[c]	
Sodium glutamate	7.36
Glycocolle	3.75
Solution C	
$CaCl_2 \cdot 3H_2O$	0.2 $\}$ [d]
$MgCl_2 \cdot 6H_2O$	0.1
Solution D	
PO_4H_2Na	0.8 $\}$ [d]
CO_3HNa	0.5
Solution E	
Anhydrous glucose	7.0[d]

0.75 ml of solution A, 1.25 ml of solution B, and 1 ml each of solutions C, D, and E are mixed. 5.5 ml of distilled water are added to adjust the tonicity to the material considered. In some cases egg extracts embryos and vitellus are also added to the medium.

[a] From Shaw (1956).
[b] The solution is adjusted to pH 7.3 by adding concentrated bicarbonate-free KOH diluted with water distilled on Pyrex so as to attain 100 ml of solution.
[c] Prepared like solution A, NaOH replacing KOH.
[d] For 100 cm³ of solution.

toria embryos to study the action of colchicine on mitosis. The Shaw medium (1956) turned out suitable to ensure stability of the mitotic index of embryonic cells. It is prepared as indicated in Table XIV.

The cultures are done in plastic salt cellars and not in hanging drops as in the technique used by many authors such as Gaulden and Carlson (1951) and Shaw (1956). The embryos, rid of their vitellus in the medium, are suspended in paraffin oil with a small drop of medium. In these conditions the mitotic index remains normal for 17 hours if the medium does not contain egg extract and for 24 hours if it does.

3. Arachnidae (Acaridae and Opilionidae)

A. M. Martin and Vidler (1962) composed a medium enabling the nymphal and adult tissue of the tick (*Rhipicephalus appendiculatus*) to survive. The culture is done in Leighton tubes and some cellular migration occurs around the explant which, however, retains its structure and survives for over 60 days. The surrounding cells keep up their movements and continue multiplying for 173 to 175 days. Some of the tissues cultivated are explanted from unfed adults, others from nymphs in the process of metamorphosis. The whole group of viscera is explanted (esophagus, salivary glands, intestine, rectal bag, Malpighi tubes, gonads, and genital tract as well as some muscles, trachea, the brain, and some nerves.

The culture media used are composed as follows: (a) Medium A is made up of the mineral salts of the S. S. Wyatt solution (1956), of glucose, Eagle's vitamin mixture, and lamb serum (5 to 20%). (b) Medium B consist of Hank's saline solution, the amino acids and vitamins of Eagle's basic medium (1955), and 20% bovine serum. (c) Medium C is prepared by adding lactalbumin hydrolysate (0.5%) and folic acid (0.00882 mg/liter) to medium B.

Penicillin and streptomycin are added to all media with a concentration of 100 units/ml, and Mycostatine was also incorporated into some media. The pH is adjusted to 6.8–7, and the media are sterilized by filtration. Among the three media used, B gave the most satisfying results for survival and growth of the explants. The authors noted that the addition of fresh medium to the culture almost always results in degeneration of the cells surrounding the explant and by a temporary interruption in cellular proliferation.

Fowler and Goodnight (1966) undertook the culture of neurosecretory tissues of an Opilionida, *Leiobunum longipes*, by the A. M. Martin and Vidler (1962) technique. Immobilization and external sterilization of the animals are obtained by immersion in 70% alcohol. The cultivated organs are brain, associated nerve structures, and intestine.

The medium is the A. M. Martin and Vidler (1962) medium B. The initial pH is 7, but it becomes acid after a few hours or days of culture (with no adverse effect on the tissues). The cultures are kept in a moist atmosphere, rich in carbon dioxide, at the temperature and the photoperiodic cycle suitable for Opilionidae bred in the laboratory.

The tissues of adult Opilionidae easily adapt to these conditions of culture. They keep healthy and maintain their structure for several weeks up to a year or more. There is no cellular migration or very little around the explant, and the neurosecretory tissues remain active *in vitro*.

B. Other Invertebrates

1. Molluscs

The first successful organ culture of mollusc tissues in a liquid medium is due to Zweibaum (1925a,b) who explanted small fragments of anodonte gills. The epithelium kept vibratile for 63 days, and small epithelial spheres full of lymphocytes formed. Zweibaum's technique is very simple: In Ringer solution diluted by half, the culture is done in the dark at a temperature of 12° to 15°.

Bevelander and Martin (1949) cultivated, in mollusc plasma, fragments of the mantle of *Pinata radiata*. The mantle functioned normally *in vitro*, secreting fibrous conchine and producing crystals characteristic of shell formation.

In a series of studies Benex (1961, 1964) cultivated tentacles of *Planorbis* using a technique derived from Thomas's (1941a). The culture medium is made up of a buffered synthetic physiological solution at pH 7.6, bactericides, and a nutritive solution.

The physiological solution is close to the internal environment of *Australorbis*, based on the data given by Florkin (1943) and Deschiens (1954) on the internal environment and needs of this animal. The bactericides are colimycine and tetracycline, because antibiotics and antimycosics usually used in tissue culture turned out toxic for *Planorbis* explants.

Besides glucose, the nutritive solution contains amino acids provided by a casein hydrolysate with additional glycocolle, cystine, yeast extract, and ascorbic acid. The final composition is indicated in Table XV.

The addition of ATP or of total *Planorbis* extracts in various concentrations has only resulted in rapid differention or in death of the explants. On the contrary, the addition of 10% planorb muscle extracts

TABLE XV

MEDIUM FOR THE CULTURE OF *Australorbis glabratus* TENTACLES[a]

Substances	Concentrations	
	(gm %)	(parts)
Physiological solution		3
Solution A[b]		
NaCl	3.25	
KCl	0.25	
MgSO$_4$	0.08	
HNa$_2$PO$_4$[c]	0.10	
H$_2$KPO$_4$[c]	0.02	
Solution B		
Calcium gluconate	2.4	
Prepared in sterile vials		
of final medium		
Solution C		
Na bicarbonate	0.2	
with additional phenol red and		
Prepared in sterile vials dosed for		
250 ml of final medium		
Nutritive solutions		4
Solution D		
Glucose	1	
Prepared in sterile vials		
Solution E		
Casein	0.5	
Cystine	0.2	
Glycocolle	0.2	
Ascorbic acid	0.02	
Prepared as stock solution		
concentrated 25 times sterilized by		
filtration and neutralized by 1/10 N NaOH		
Solution F		
Yeast extract	1	
Prepared in sterile vials		
Solution G		
Planorb muscle extract		
Whole blood prepared aseptically 10%		
of final medium		
Solutions are kept cold		
Antibiotics prepared extemporaneously:		
mixture of { colimycin 80 ml		
tetracycline 50 ml		

TABLE XV (*Continued*)

Substances		Concentrations	
		(gm %)	(parts)
250 cm³ of final medium:			
Sol A	125 ml		
Sterile water	106 ml		
Sol B and C	1 phial		
Sol D	1 ml		
Sol E	10 ml		
Sol F	0.25 ml		
Antibiotics	1 ml		
Adjust pH to 7.6 by			
1/10 *N* NaOH			
Sol G—in each tube	0.5 ml/5 ml		

[a] From Benex (1961).
[b] Prepared as stock solution in double concentration and sterilized by filtration.
[c] Dissolved separately.

plus whole blood yields interesting results. The culture is done on slides in 5 ml of medium. The medium is renewed every day. To ensure asepsis at the time of explantation the whole animal is dipped into a saturated solution of furadoine, *Australorbis* being particularly sensitive to bactericides and antibiotics (Seneca and Bergendahl, 1955) (which rules out usual antiseptics). After a rinse in sterile water, the explant is placed in a culture medium where it will survive for at least three weeks.

Isolated tentacles are actively and spontaneously motile during the first week *in vitro*. Afterwards, contractions persist in response to stimulation, but disappear progressively while structural dedifferentiation occurs towards the 15th day. Death happens during the fourth week. Benex (1964) indicates that the presence of some nerve tissue (ganglionic mass and eye) definitely increases survival of a differentiated tissue.

More recently Benex (1967a,b) assayed substances liable to lengthen survival of *Mytilus edulis* explanted organs. Cultivated organs are the edge of the mantle and the gills. Criteria of survival in the explants are movements of the cilia and muscular contractions. The composition of the nutritive medium used for these tissues, indicated in Table XVI, is based on analyses of their constitutive elements.

The culture is done in Petri dishes in 10 ml of medium renewed every two days. The addition of various substances to this basic medium makes it possible to study their influence on the survival of organs in culture. Vitamin C, paraminobenzoic acid, and sulfanilamide are active, whereas vitamins B_1, B_6, and B_{12}, and calcium pantothenate and procaine have no effect on muscle organs.

TABLE XVI
MEDIUM FOR THE CULTURE OF *Mytilus edulis* ORGANS[a]

Substances	Concentrations (gm %)
NaCl	10
KCl	1
$MgCl_2$	0.15
$CaCl_2$	0.20
CO_3HNa_2	0.70
Na_2HPO_4	0.30
KH_2PO_4	0.12
Glucose	2
Vitamin C	0.10
Phosphate and bicarbonate buffers	
Antibiotics	(IU/ml)
Penicillin	100
Colimycin	500

[a] From Benez (1967).

2. Parasitic Helminths

Bazin and Lancastre (1967) cultivated, in anaerobiosis in a liquid medium, *Schistosoma mansoni* (Trematode) adults or schistosomula. The following technique is used. The worms are washed in a warm physiological solution containing penicillin. Then they are placed in a liquid medium warmed to 37°; this medium is the modified Morgan, Morton, and Parker 199 solution, diluted by half or third with Hanks buffer solution. Glucose is added to get a final concentration of 2 to 3%, and 10 to 20% calf or horse serum is also added after making sure, by the Vogel-Minning test, that this serum has no immunologic reactivity towards *Schistosoma mansoni*. Washed rabbit red blood cells complete the mixture in the proportion of about 5%. The basic solutions (199 and Hanks) contain penicillin (200 IU/ml), streptomycin (0.05 mg/ml), and B amphotericine (0.005 mg/ml). Finally, the medium is covered with 1-cm-thick film of sterile paraffin oil to ensure anaerobiosis. The medium is renewed every week by siphoning about a third of the volume, then adding an equivalent quantity of fresh medium plus washed rabbit red blood cells. The oil film is unmoved during these manipulations. In these conditions, at 37°, survival of three weeks and more has been obtained. The worms keep normal motility and feed satisfactorily, and blood is present in their alimentary canal, which shows powerful peristaltic movements.

Hirumi *et al.* (1967) cultivated the female reproduction organs of plant parasitic nematodes. They could follow the development of the embryos in the cultivated uterus. During 14 days in culture the embryos grew to the stage of hatching which occurs within the uterus. The species used was a parasite of tomato roots: *Meloidogyna incognita acrita*.

The medium devised by these authors is composed of

Morgan's medium TV 199	20 ml
Saline solution	20 ml
Foetal calf serum	6 ml
Penicillin	100 IU/ml
Streptomycin	

The pH is adjusted to 6.4.

The saline solution contains the following substances per 100 ml: 120 mg of $NaH_2PO_4 \cdot H_2O$, 300 mg of $MgCl_2 \cdot 6H_2O$, 40 mg of fructose, 1000 mg of lactalbumin hydrolysate, and 0.5 ml of 0.5% phenol red solution. The organs are placed on Maximov slides in drops of the culture medium. These slides are put in T-type culture plastic vessels.

3. Other Groups

Thomas (1932) obtained excellent survival (three to six months), intensive multiplication, and activity *in vitro* of *Sipunculus* "enigmatic vesicles." Homologous plasma was used as a medium. Blood is drawn from 30 animals and centrifuged for 10 minutes. The supernatant is kept cold and centrifuged again on the second and fourth day. It is left to decant and then filtered.

Thomas (1941a,b) also showed that some organs of Asteroidea can survive and even retain functional activity in a most simple medium: filtered seawater. The culture is done in Petri dishes at the temperature of 20° to 22°, and the medium is renewed daily. The species used by Thomas are *Astropecten aurentiacus* (L), *Echinaster sepositus* (Gray), and *Marthasterias glacialis* (L). The ambulacral tubes survive for 5 to 20 days and the pedicellarias for three months (*Marthasterias glacialis*). The latter show great muscular activity in culture. An amputated pedicellary was able to regenerate an extremity with its calcareous parts. Thus, this organ is capable of metabolizing calcium *in vitro*.

Seawater has been used to cultivate a number of marine invertebrates. Thus, many studies on morphogenesis in sponges have been performed. The technique is very simple: The cells of sponges are dissociated through a gauze and sedimented on glass slides where they move freely and form small aggregates which gradually organize; from that point true organotypic culture is obtained. Wilson (1907) did this type of experiment for the first time, after him many authors pursued these studies: Müller (1911), Huxley (1921a,b,c), Galtsoff (1925a,b), Fauré-Frémiet (1925, 1932a,b), Curtis (1962), and Humphrey (1963). Wilson (1911), also studied the reconstitution of coelenterates with this technique.

III. ORGAN CULTURE METHODS ON A GEL MEDIUM

A. General Techniques

The Wolff and Haffen (1952) technique, which was devised for embryonic tissues of birds and mammals, has been adapted to the culture of invertebrate organs with great success. Since the early work of P. Sengel (1961), several French laboratories using it have put out a whole array of highly interesting results. Being simple and easily adapted to a wide range of animals, this technique, of ever widening use, has made it possible to study hormonal or neuroendocrine connections, particularly sexual differentiation in numerous groups of invertebrates.

An outline of the Wolff and Haffen technique should be given here. The "standard medium" used by these authors for the culture of bird or mammal embryonic tissues is composed of Gey physiological solution with agar to obtain semisolid state and Tyrode solution and chick embryo extract in the following proportions:

1% agar in Gey solution	7 parts
Tyrode solution	3 parts
Chick embryo extract diluted by half in Tyrode solution. Penicillin G in Specia "Subtosan" at the dose of 10 Oxford units per each medium is added to the Tyrode solution	3 parts

The medium is poured into neutral glass flat-bottomed vessels with hemispherical cavities called "salières." Agar, dissolved in the Gey solution, heated to 70°–80° in a water bath is first poured into the vessel, and 3 parts of Tyrode solution, then 3 parts of nutritive liquids, are added. The components are thoroughly mixed with a glass rod. The medium, left to cool and solidify, becomes an elastic homogeneous gel, and the explant is laid on its surface. Each medium has an approximate volume of 1 ml. The upper surface of the gel medium is 0.5 cm below the top of the salière, and a glass lid is sealed with paraffin. The explant, being in contact with a large volume of air and medium, needs no subculturing in most cases. The cut surfaces of the cultivated tissues heal rapidly, and in most cases no cells migrate around the explant, which retains its integrity and structure.

This culture technique is particularly convenient for the study of endocrine relationships between organs. Organs placed side by side on the medium stay in close contact and even merge together into a parabiosis. Such parabiosis, easier to realize than in liquid media, have been widely used in the culture of invertebrates organs.

The essential modifications of the Wolff and Haffen medium for the culture of invertebrate tissues bear on the nature of the physiological solutions and must be adapted to the cultivated species. The nutritive liquids must also satisfy the needs of the organs. It should be noted, however, that 7- to 9-day-old chick embryo extract is suitable for the culture of tissues of very wide origins. The composition of the media, as well as the details of the techniques used by the various authors, will be exposed along which each zoological group studied.

B. Techniques and Media Used in Various Invertebrate Groups

1. Annelida

Durchon and co-workers have studied the endocrinology of Polychete annelidae. Durchon and Schaller (1963, 1964) have devised the medium given in Table XVII.

The explanted organs are the parapods, the prostomium, fragments of intestine, and muscles of four species of Nereidians, i.e., *Nereis pelagica* (L), *Platymerius dumerilii* (And. and M. Edw.), *Perinereis cultrifera*

TABLE XVII
CULTURE MEDIUM FOR ANNELIDA[a]

Substances	Concentration		
	(drops)	(mg)	(IU)
1% agar in sterile seawater with 1‰ glucose	7		
Sterile seawater with 1% glucose	3		
50% egg albumin in seawater with 1‰ glucose	3		
Horse serum (Difco)	1		
50% chick embryo extract in seawater with 1‰ glucose	1		
Specillin G			100
Streptomycin		0.009	

[a] From Durchon and Schaller (1963, 1964).

(Grube) and *Nereis diversicolor* (O. F. Muller). Before explantation of the organs the animals are sterilized by isolation for two or three days in sterile seawater containing penicillin and streptomycin (50,000 IU and 2.5 mg/100 ml) and exposed to ultraviolet rays for about 15 minutes. The culture are kept at a temperature of 20° and retransplanted every three days.

a. Survival and Behavior of the Explants. Survival of the explants may last one month. At the beginning of the culture a little cellular migration occurs, especially of muscular elements. This migration stops within two to three days when the explant heals. During the whole period of culture the organs contract spontaneously and blood circulates in the vessels. The histological structures are preserved and numerous mitoses occur, especially in the epithelium.

b. Differentiation. Isolated parapods go through the transformations linked with sexual maturation, such as formation of heteronereidian bristles in *Perinereis cultrifera* and *Nereis pelagica* (an epitoquial species) and spermatogenesis in all four species studied. The technique being particularly adequate for organ parabiosis, it has been possible to associate the prostomium with the parapods of immature worms. In these conditions spermatogenesis is inhibited. It is known that a hormonal substance from the brain of Nereidians has an inhibiting effect on the evolution of the genital products (Durchon, 1952). This substance, extracted from brains of *Nereis diversicolor*, incorporated in the culture medium, delays the appearance of spermatogenesis in explanted immature parapods (Durchon *et al.*, 1963). With the same method, Durchon and Dhainaut (1964) and Durchon and Boilly (1964) studied ovocyte evolution in explanted parapods of *Nereis diversicolor*. The Durchon and Schaller medium allows considerable growth of the ovocytes; their initial diameter of 60 μ may increase by 40 μ in 10 days and 100 μ in 20 days. However normal vitellogenesis cannot proceed *in vitro* and the ovocytes show signs of degeneration after 20 days in culture. Brain hormone, administered by means of parabiosis between parapods and prostomium, inhibits the evolution of ovocytes in culture.

Recently, Malecha (1967a) obtained development of heteronereidian, and even lamellae and gametogenesis of the parapods, of *Nereis succinea* cultivated on the Durchon and Schaller medium. The same author (Malecha, 1965, 1967b) cultivated the testes and the peripharyngian nerve complex of *Hirudo medicinalis* (L) on a medium derived from the Durchon and Schaller medium. Seawater is replaced by Ringer solution for leeches (Nicholis and Kuffler, 1965). The composition of the medium for Hirudinae is given in Table XVIII.

TABLE XVIII
CULTURE MEDIUM FOR HIRUDINAE[a]

Substances	Concentration		
	(parts)	(mg)	(IU)
Leech Ringer solution with 2‰ glucose	3		
50% egg albumin in Ringer solution with glucose	3		
Horse serum (Difco)	1		
50% chick embryo (Difco) in Ringer solution with glucose	1		
1% agar in Ringer solution with glucose	7		
Specillin G			100
Streptomycin		0.009	
pH 7.5 (A 0.05% phenol red solution is added to the physiological solution in proportion of 1‰.)			

[a] From Nicholis and Kuffler (1965).

The leeches come from a commercial source; collected in February, they are bred in the darkness at a constant temperature of 6°. These conditions stop their sexual maturation. Before culture, the donors are isolated in dechlorated sterile water containing specillin G (500 IU/ml) and streptomycin (0.05 mg/ml). A small fragment of the body wall is taken along with the organs, which ensures rapid healing, the epidermis enveloping the explant. The culture are kept in darkness at a constant temperature of 20°. Retransplantation is done immediately when any variation in the pH of the medium occurs. In these conditions, after three weeks in culture, complete spermatogenesis occurs in the testis, particularly when this organ is cultivated in association with the peripharyngian nerve complex.

Gay (1963) cultivated fragments of Lumbricidae on a synthetic gel medium. The worms are sterilized with either 6% iodine (eliminated by rinsing with sterile Ringer solution) or antibiotics. A week before culture the worms are made to ingest filter paper saturated with antibiotics. Thus, the alimentary canal is rid of its bacterian and fungal flora. The culture medium is composed of an amino acid saline solution and of earthworm extract. Just before use, worm extract is added in various concentrations according to experimental series. The extract is obtained by mincing whole sterile worms in some culture medium (10 worms/100 ml of medium). The minced worms are centrifuged for 15 minutes at 4000 rpm, the supernatant is filtered through an LS filter. The solid medium is obtained by mixing this nutrient solution to an equal volume of 1% agar in Tyrode solution. The pH of the medium is close to 7. This technique is suitable for long-term experiments, of over one month. *In vitro* survival goes along with important histological transformations such as involution of the clitellum, dedifferentiation of muscular fibers, thickening of the collagenic lamellae, and disappearance of the endodermis. Healing seems to proceed normally in culture.

2. Culture of Planarian Regeneration Blastemas

The culture of young regeneration blastemas on a semisolid medium was undertaken by C. Sengel in order to study the state of determination and the capacity of autodifferentiation of regenerates precociously separated from their bases. When this research was started (C. Sengel, 1959, 1960), very few studies concerning the culture of cells or tissues of Planarian had been published. Murray (1927, 1928, 1931), Seilern-Aspang (1958, 1960), and Freisling and Reisinger (1958) had tried to keep alive Planarian cells in culture, either isolated or grouped. These experiments concerned adult cells and were not true organotypical cultures.

Sengel's experiments were done on the freshwater species, *Dugesia lugubris* and *Dugesia tigrina,* Planarians with a high regeneration ability (C. Sengel, 1959, 1960, 1963; Ziller-Sengel, 1964, 1967).

a. **Culture Medium.** Theoretically, any fragment, even minute, of the Planarians used for these experiments can survive in plain water, heal, and regenerate a whole organism. Sengel tried to cultivate 2- or 3-day-old regeneration blastemas cut off from the fragment which produced them. Blastemas of *Dugesia lugubris* (about 0.1 mm in diameter) are placed in salières containing the solution to be assayed. The physiological solutions contain pure or diluted Holtfreter's solution for amphibian embryos (Holtfreter, 1931).

The following solutions were assayed:

Plain water
Holtfreter solution (H1) (see Table XIX)
Holfreter solution diluted by half (H½)
Holtfreter solution diluted by quarter (H¼)

The results of these attempts are represented on the diagram of Fig. 2. Plain water and the solution H¼ do not allow more than 24- to 48-hour survival. On the other hand, H½ and H1 solutions allow over 25% of the blastemas to survive over five days. For *Dugesia tigrina* Holtfreter solution must be diluted by 8 to 10. In these liquid media the blastemas heal rapidly but never differentiate any further. They become spherical and finally burst. Sengel adopted a gelified medium derived from the Wolff and Haffen medium, in which Gey and Tyrode solutions are re-

TABLE XIX
HOLTFRETER'S SOLUTION FOR AMPHIBIAN EMBRYOS[a]

Substances	Concentration (gm)
Distilled water	1000
ClNa	3.50
Cl₂Ca	0.20
ClK	0.10
CO₃NaH	0.20

[a] From Holtfreter (1931).

placed by Holtfreter solution. The Sengel medium is composed as indicated in Table XX.

The addition of chick embryo extract has been found particularly favorable for survival of the explants. The culture of blastemas on a medium solely composed of agar and Holtfreter solution (6 parts of 1% agar in Holtfreter solution plus 6 parts of Holtfreter solution) only allows a maximum five-day survival whereas on the medium containing embryo extract the blastemas remain healthy for over 20 days (Fig. 3) (Ziller-Sengel, 1967). Two and one-half to three days after their formation the blastema are already capable of autodifferentiation. Thus, a cephalic blastema differentiates into a normal head with brain and eyes whereas a caudal blastema forms a tail [Fig. 4 (A–C)].

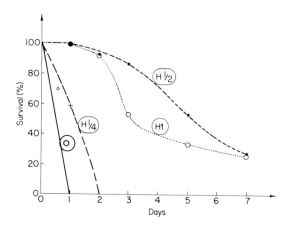

FIG. 2. Survival of fragments of *Dugesia lugubris* regeneration blastemas in various physiological solutions. O: pure water; H¼: 75% water, 25% Holtfreter solution; H½: 50% water, 50% Holtfreter solution; H1: pure Holtfreter solution. (From Ziller-Gengel, 1967.)

TABLE XX
SENGEL'S MEDIUM FOR AMPHIBIAN EMBRYOS[a]

Substances	Concentration (parts)
1% agar in Holtfreter solution	5
Holtfreter solution	4
9-day-old chick embryo extract diluted by half in Holtfreter solution	3
Penicillin: 1000 IU/medium (each medium represents approximately 1 ml)	
Glucose in the concentration of 1‰ is added to the Holtfreter solution	

[a] From C. Sengel (1963).

b. Asepsis of the Cultures. Like Murray (1927), C. Sengel treated the Planarians with uv for a few minutes under a thin film of water. The animal were then rinsed for one or two hours in two successive baths of sterile water containing penicillin. The cultures are sterile in 8 to 9% of cases.

3. Echinoderms

Delavault and Bruslé (1965) and Bruslé (1966, 1967) cultivated *Asterina gibbosa* gonads. In preliminary experiments these authors used a simple medium only composed of 1% agar in sterile seawater added with specillin G. The cultures are kept at 18°. On this medium the organs

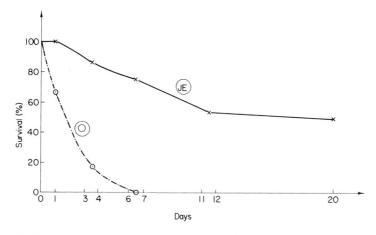

FIG. 3. Influence of chick embryo extract on the survival of *Dugesia lugubris* regeneration blastemas in culture. O: medium without extract; JE: medium with embryo extract. (From Ziller-Sengel, 1967.)

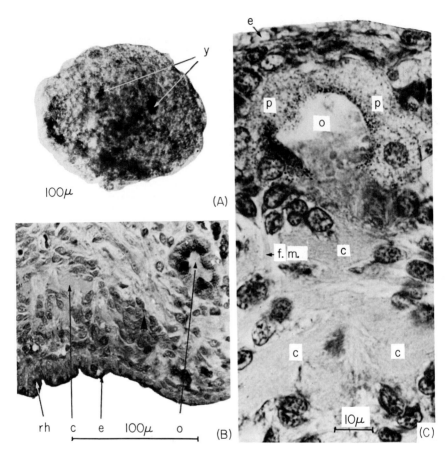

Fig. 4. (A) Macroscopic view of a *Dugesia lugubris* cephalic blastema in which
the eyes (y) are differentiated (12 days in culture). (B) Differentiated brain and
eye in a *Dugesia lugubris* cephalic blastema (eight days in culture) c: brain; e:
epidermis; o: eye; ch: rhabdites. (C) Differentiated brain and eye in a *Dugesia
tigrina* cephalic blastema (four days in culture). f.m.: muscle fibers; p: pigmentary
cupule of the eye. (From Ziller–Sengel, 1967.)

are still healthy 18 days after their explantation; spermatogenesis and
ovogenesis are not disturbed, and normal mitosis and meiosis are present.
Later on, Delavault and Bruslé (1965) elaborated a medium enriched
with nutritive organic substances, on which the gonads can survive 60
days. This medium contains the components indicated in Table XXI.

4. Molluscs

P. Sengel (1961) explanted fragments of gills and intestine of the
Bivalve *Barnea candida* on the media given in Table XXII.

TABLE XXI
CULTURE MEDIUM FOR ECHINODERMS[a]

Substances	Concentration (parts)
1% agar in filtered seawater	16
1‰ Glucose in filtered seawater	2
50% egg albumin in filtered seawater	1
0.5% yeast extract (Yeastolate Difco)	1
Specillin G (25,000 IU/100 ml)	

[a] From Delavault and Bruslé (1965).

All the organs survive for seven days without subculture on any of the two media. On the "St M" medium containing chick embryo extract, considerable outgrowth of cells occurs around the explant. On the "M" medium the outgrowth is not so important, so the integrity of the organ is better preserved. The activity of the cilia of the gills and of the intestinal epithelium continues in culture.

Streiff and Peyre (1963) cultivated various organs of *Calyptraea sinensis* (L) on the Sengel "M" medium, and later on, various media derived from the Vakaët and Pintelon "K" medium (1959). These authors finally adopted the media indicated in Table XXIII.

The Sengel "M" medium has been found convenient for culture of intestine or penis. However, even for these organs, the A6 and A7 media give better results. The organs cultivated are the tentacles, the penis, the ovaries, the testes, the seminal vesicle, and the intestine, which survive during 8 to 17 days on the A6 medium. The hepatopancreas can survive only on the A7 medium during 8 to 12 days. The tentacles remain healthy longest (17 days) and the contraction response to stimu-

TABLE XXII
CULTURE MEDIA FOR MOLLUSCS[a]

Substances	Concentration (parts)
Medium M	
1% agar in Gey solution	7
Sterile filtered seawater with 50 IU penicillin/ml	6
Medium St M	
1% agar in Gey solution	7
Sterile filtered seawater with 50 IU penicillin/ml	4
9-day-old chick embryo extract	2

[a] From P. Sengel (1961).

TABLE XXIII
CULTURE MEDIA FOR MOLLUSCS[a]

Substances	Concentration (drops)
Medium A6	
1% agar in Gey solution	7
Sterile filtered seawater	6
50% egg albumin in Tyrode solution	3
Medium A7	
A6 medium plus albumin solution	4

[a] From Streiff and Peyre (1963).

lation is maintained up to the end of the culture. The penis survives
eight days and keeps the "elongation response" to mechanical or thermic
stimulation. Retransplanting may lengthen survival; this is the case for
the ovary, which remains healthy for eight days without retransplanting
and for 12 days after retransplantation on the fifth day.

After these first results, Streiff (1963, 1964, 1966a,b) modified the
culture medium and obtained longer survivals. He perfected the media
given in Table XXIV.

In these series of culture, Streiff succeeded in maintaining the penis
alive for 93 days and preserving the elongation reflex. These constant
results enabled Streiff to study the hormonal determinism of the variations in size and shape of the penis during the various sexual phases of
Calyptraea sinensis (Streiff, 1966a).

Immature gonads of *Calyptraea sinensis* in the male phase were cultivated for 20 days. In these conditions all the male germinal elements
disappear while active ovogenesis is observed. The previtellogenesis
ovocytes are numerous.

A7 and B2 media are suitable for the culture of more demanding organs such as the alimentary canal, the mantles, the seminal vesicles, and
the nervous ganglia, which can survive for five weeks *in vitro*. A7 C and
A8 C media, characterized by the presence of cysteine, are particularly

TABLE XXIV
CULTURE MEDIA FOR MOLLUSCS[a]

Medium A7 C: medium A7 added with 3 drops of cysteine
Medium B2: medium A7 in which the egg albumin is
  replaced by bovine serum
Medium A8 C: medium A7 containing 5 drops of albumin
  solution and 3 drops of cysteine

[a] From Streiff (1963, 1964, 1966a,b).

adequate for the culture of the hepatopancreas, which can survive three weeks and in which the ferment cells retain their polyedric inclusions up to the 20th day. The temperature of the culture is 20° to 23°.

The Durchon and Schaller medium for Polychaeta Annelid organs is also suitable for mollusc tissues. Thus, Choquet (1964, 1965) could keep gonads of *Patella vulgata* (L) alive on this medium for over three months. The gonads contract spontaneously at the beginning of the culture and may even move on the surface of the medium. After 100 days spontaneous movements disappear but the gonads still remain very sensitive to thermic and mechanic stimulations. The Durchon and Schaller medium allows spermatogenesis in culture, as well as maturation of the ovocytes which undergo previtellogenesis and the first stages of vitellogenesis.

The culture of terrestrial gasteropod organs was attempted successfully by Guyard and Gomot (1964), who could study with this technique some aspects of sexual differentiation in *Helix aspersa* (Müller). The authors cultivated young gonads from approximately two-month-old animals with an average shell diameter of 10 mm. They showed that the evolution of these gonads is strongly influenced by trophic factors supplied by the medium. Moreover, parabiosis experiments between young gonads and nerve ganglia from adult snails or paludins show that neuroendocrine factors may influence the male or female cell line evolution (Gomot and Guyard, 1967).

To achieve asepsis of the explants, young snails are washed in sterile water, deprived of their shell, and immersed in three successive baths of a physiological solution with specillin G added in decreasing concentrations (1000, 700, and 500 IU/ml). The gonad made up of tubules interplaced with hepatopancreatic tissue is again washed in three baths of physiological solution containing respectively 500, 200, and 100 IU of specillin G/ml.

Guyard and Gomot used two sorts of media: one without any organic compounds, the other containing various organic compounds (Table XXV).

At the stage of explantation the gonads contain spermatogonia, nurse cells, and ovocytes. On R and T media, free of organic substances, survival of the germ cells is 10 to 15 days. During the first days *in vitro* spermatogonia develop into spermatocyte I, but thereafter, the male elements rapidly degenerate. From the 10th to the 15th day, the gonads contain only oocytes and nurse cells. Later on, around the 18th day, germ cells are no longer observed.

On the complex G1 and G2 media, containing Morgan's 199 solution and yeast extract, survival is considerably increased. Both male and female gonocytes undergo differentiation *in vitro* equally well.

TABLE XXV
Culture Media for Terrestrial Gasteropods[a]

Substances	Concentration		
	(parts)	(drops)	(IU)
Media without organic compounds			
Medium R			
1% agar in Ringer[a] solution	7		
Ringer[b] solution added with 0.5 gm of glucose and			
0.5 gm of sodium bicarbonate/ml	6		
Medium T[c]			
1% agar in Gey solution	7		
Tyrode solution	6		
Media with organic compounds			
"Standard" medium[d]			
1% agar in Gey solution		7	
Tyrode solution		3	
8-day-old chick embryo extract		3	
"Complex" media G1 and G2[e]			
Medium G1			
Gel medium		7	
Gey solution	98		
Agar	1		
Peptone	1		
Nutrient solution		6	
Medium 199	49		
55% sodium bicarbonate	20		
Tyrode solution	430		
Yeast extract	2		
Penicillin (Specia)			100
Medium G2			
Gel medium		7	
Gey solution	98		
Agar	1		
Peptone	1		
Nutrient solution		6	
Medium 199	63		
Yeast extract	2		
3% sodium bicarbonate	85		
Hanks solution[f]	830		
Penicillin (Specia)			100

[a] From Guyard and Gomot (1964).
[b] Snail hemolymph type Ringer solution (Ripplinger and Joly, 1961).
[c] From Et. Wolff *et al.* (1953).
[d] From Et. Wolff and Haffen (1952).
[e] Guyard (1968).
[f] 475 ml of Hanks solution plus 7 ml of 3% sodium bicarbonate.

On the H medium, which contains adult snail hemolymph, ovogenesis, as well as spermatogenesis, is definitely stimulated. Twenty-four hours after the beginning of the culture, the tubes are full of spermatids differentiating into spermatozoa.

On the standard Wolff and Haffen medium, with chick embryo extract, spermatogonia multiply actively during the first 15 days, but the female line is more favored. The oocytes grow considerably and the follicles build up. Survival overlasts the 50th day of culture without retransplantation.

T, R, G1, and G2 media which do not favor either male or female cell lines were used by Guyard (1967) and Gomot and Guyard (1967) for the culture of nerve ganglia of the snail and of the paludine. These organs are cultivated in association with young gonads of the snail, which makes it possible to study their influence on sexual differentiation. Figure 5 A–D illustrates these data.

The Durchon and Schaller medium (1963) for Polychaeta Annelids is also suitable for the culture of Cephalopod organs. Durchon and Richard (1967) cultivated on this medium the optical gland and immature ovaries from 4- to 6-month-old *Sepia officinalis*. The duration of culture is over one month for the optical gland, and this organ retains its secretory activity in culture. The survival of explanted fragments of ovaries is excellent; after 15 days of culture these organs still show spontaneous contractions. The organs in culture are kept in the dark at a constant temperature of 21°.

5. Arthropoda

a. **Xiphosura.** The culture of limula organs was successfully carried out by Em. Wolff (1962, 1963) on various media derived from the Wolff and Haffen standard medium.

They all include seven volumes of Gey solution containing 1% agar and five volumes of sterile seawater to which are added, according to each case, various organic or synthetic solutions (Table XXVI). The cultures are kept at 20° during 4 to 14 days. The explanted organs are the dorsal vessel, the intestine, the nervous system, and the liver. They keep their characteristic structure *in vitro* for 7–12 days. The media containing nutritive solutions are more suitable for culture than medium M.

b. **Acarians.** In a preliminary note Streiff and Taberly (1964) reported attempts to cultivate organs of *Xenillus tegeocranus* and *Platynothrus peltifer* (Oribate acarians) on Ag medium. Ag medium is not very differ-

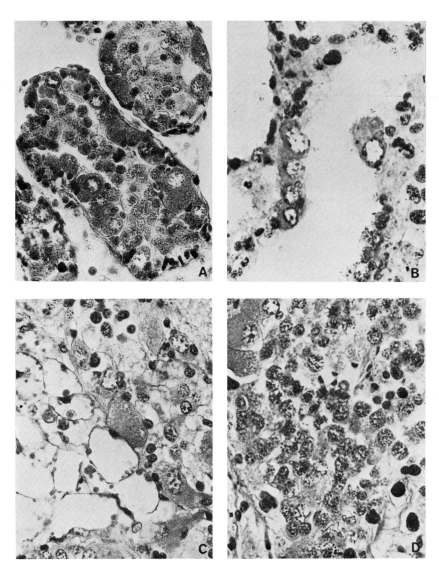

Fig. 5. A. Histological aspect of a *Helix aspersa* gonad at the moment of explantation. While the spermatogonia invade the light of the tubules, the germinative epithelium secondarily evolves into oocytes in the wall. B. Histological aspect of ovotestis after seven days in culture on medium R. The germinative epithelium as well as the oocytes still survive while the male germ cells have nearly all disappeared. C. Gonad after six days in culture on standard medium. A few spermatogonial cysts are still visible, but the young oocytes (very numerous low on the right) are continuing their differentiation. D. Aspect of the gonad after 24 days of culture on medium H. The oocytes are present, but the light is invaded by spermatocytes in the prophase of meiosis. Spermatogenesis is nearing its end: One distinguishes spermatides evolving into spermatozoa. (Transmitted by Gomot and Guyard.)

TABLE XXVI
CULTURE MEDIA FOR *Xiphosura*[a]

Substances[b]	Concentration (volumes)
Medium M	
1% agar in Gey solution	7
Filtered sterile seawater	6
Medium L	
1% agar in Gey solution	7
Filtered sterile seawater	5
Adult limula hemolymph	2
Medium LS	
1% agar in Gey solution	7
Filtered sterile seawater	5
Limula hemolymph serum	1
Medium EE	
1% agar in Gey solution	7
Filtered sterile seawater	5
Chick embryo extract (Difco)	1
Medium HS	
1% agar in Gey solution	7
Filtered sterile seawater	5
Horse serum (Difco)	1
Medium ChP	
1% agar in Gey solution	7
Filtered sterile seawater	5
Chicken plasma (Difco)	1
Medium P	
(a) 1% agar in Gey solution	7
Filtered sterile seawater	5
Parker's solution 199 (concentration 1/1)	1
(b) 1% agar in Gey solution	8
Filtered sterile seawater	5
Parker's solution 199 (1/1)	2

[a] From Em. Wolff (1962, 1963).
[b] In all the medium 150 IU of Penicillin G/ml are added.

ent from the Streiff and Peyre medium for molluscs (1963) (Table XXVII).

The alimentary canal, the genital apparatus, the central nervous system, and the whole embryo have been cultivated in each species. The culture was continued for seven days without retransplanting, and the explants remained healthy.

c. Chilopod Myriapods. Fragments of young *Lithobius fortificatus* have been cultivated by Zerbib (1967). The medium is very similar to the Berreur-Bonnenfant medium for crustacean organs (Table XXVIII).

TABLE XXVII
CULTURE MEDIUM FOR ACARIANS[a]

Substances	Concentration (parts)
1% agar in Gey solution	7
6% Filtered sterile seawater plus bidistilled water plus 1‰ glucose	6
50% Egg albumin in Gey solution	3

[a] From Streiff and Taberly (1964).

After 6 to 12 days of culture the tissue remains healthy, without migration of cells out of the explant.

d. Crustaceans. Berreur-Bonnenfant (1962) cultivated crustacean organs on a medium derived from the Wolff and Haffen. It was first tried on the adult gonads of the crustacean amphipod *Orchestia gammarella*. Later, the author extended the culture to other organs such as the androgen gland (1963), the molt gland (1964), the cerebroid ganglia (1967), and to other species of crustaceans, *Talitrus saltator, Anilocra physodes, Carcinus maenas*.

The composition of the media for *Orchestia gammarella* is indicated by Berreur-Bonnenfant (1962) in Table XXIX.

The physiological solution is modified in relationship to the composition of the internal environment of the species cultivated. Thus, for *Carcinus maenas*, the physiological solution is undiluted seawater (Berreur-Bonnenfant, 1968). The pH of the culture medium used for *Orchestia gammarella* varies between 6.4 and 6.7, the pH of the internal environment of this species being from 6.5 to 6.9.

In these conditions of culture, survival of the gonads of *O. gammarella* is four days on the C medium and 30 to 45 days on the "standard C" medium. The androgen glands survive for 8 to 15 days in culture. In

TABLE XXVIII
CULTURE MEDIUM FOR CHILOPOD MYRIAPODS[a]

Substances	Concentration (parts)
1‰ agar in physiological solution plus 1% glucose plus specillin	6
Physiological solution: 20% sterile seawater in bidistilled water plus 1‰ glucose plus specillin	3
7-day-old chick embryo juice diluted	3

[a] From Zerbib (1967). The author indicates neither the dilution of embryo extract nor the dose of specillin added.

TABLE XXIX
CULTURE MEDIA FOR *Orchestia gammarella*[a]

Substances	Concentration (parts)
Medium C	
1% agar in a physiological solution made up of 2/3 sterile seawater, 1/3 bidistilled water, glucose in 1‰ concentration	6
Physiological solution plus specillin	6
"Standard C" medium	
1% agar in physiological solution with glucose	6
Physiological solution with glucose plus specillin	3
9-day-old chicken embryo juice diluted by half in the physiological solution with glucose	3
pH varies between 6.4 and 6.7 for the culture of *O. gammarella*	

[a] From Berreur-Bonnenfant (1962).

TABLE XXX
CULTURE MEDIUM FOR GONADS[a]

Substances	Concentration (volumes)	(IU)	(mg/25 ml culture medium)
Saline solution plus agar plus Trehalose	2[b]		
9-day-old chicken embryo extract, diluted by half with the saline solution containing 2% meat peptone (Merck)	2		
Horse serum (Institut Pasteur, Paris)	1		
Antibiotics			
Penicillin		5000	
Streptomycin			0.5
The pH of the medium varies between 6.5 and 6.9.			

[a] From Lender and Duveau-Hagège (1962).

[b] The composition of saline solution with agar and containing trehalose was established by Lender and Duveau-Hagège according to data given verbally by Vago. The solution is sterilized after addition of agar:

Bidistilled water	1000 ml
KCl	5.5 gm
$CaCl_2$	0.6 gm
$MgCl_2$	1 gm
$MgSO_4 \cdot 7H_2O$	5.5 gm
NaH_2PO_4	1 gm
Trehalose	1.6 gm
Agar	1.5%

the testis the number of spermatogonia increases and spermatozoa differentiate. When the testis is cultivated with the androgen gland, the latter must be renewed frequently. Survival of the testis is bettered and the germinative zone remains healthier than in the testis cultivated alone. The standard C medium allows the culture of nerve tissue of *Orchestia gammarella* (Berreur-Bonnenfant, 1967). The cerebroid ganglia of this species are cultivated in association with gonads. It is necessary to renew the brains every two days.

e. **Insects.** i. CULTURE OF GONADS. The culture of insect gonads on a semisolid medium was performed by Lender and his collaborators (1962–1967): larval gonads of *Galleria melonella* (Lepidoptera) (Lender and Duveau-Hagège, 1962, 1963a,b), adult and larval gonads of *Periplaneta americana* (Dictyoptera) (Duveau-Hagège, 1963, 1964), and ovaries of *Tenebrio molitor* (Coleoptera) (Lender and Laverdure, 1967).

The medium of Lender and Duveau-Hagège (1962) is composed as indicated in Table XXX.

The explants survive well during 14 days or more. Inside the ovaries of last instar larvae of *Galleria mellonella* the oocytes increase in size. The spermatogonia multiply and the spermatocytes differentiate into spermatozoa inside the testes of both *G. melonella* and *P. americana*.

The medium of Lender and Laverdure for the culture of *T. molitor* is composed of

1 volume of chick embryo extract (Difco) in saline solution
2 volumes of saline solution with 10% agar
1 volume horse serum diluted in bidistilled water
20,000 IU of penicillin and 0.5 mg of streptomycin for 20 ml of medium

The pH of the medium is between 6.84 and 7.1. The saline solution is the same as before.

The ovaries of the *Tenebrio molitor* are taken, 0 to 48 hours after metamorphosis, from young imagos bred at 26°.

This basic medium allows the nurse cells and the medium oocytes to survive 4 to 6½ days, but growth of the oocytes is stopped. The oocytes in the germarium, as well as in the vitellarium, degenerate. Lender and Laverdure tried to improve the conditions of culture by various means:

1. Fat body extract is added. The ether-insoluble fraction of fat body enables the young oocyte to survive in culture. In another experiment, Laverdure (1967) added a total fat body extract to the basic medium

then, the young oocytes degenerate the nurse cells of the germarium survive, so do the medium oocytes which begin vitellogenesis.

2. Hormones are added. Cephalic complexes (renewed daily) cultivated in association with the ovary allow growth of the oocytes.

3. If trehalose is replaced by glucose, not only do nurse cells and medium oocytes survive, but vitellogenesis is promoted.

ii. CULTURE OF NERVOUS ORGANS. The culture of the brain and of the suboesophagian ganglion of *Aeschna cyanea* (orthoptera) was done by Schaller and Meunier (1967). The organs come from larvae at the last larval stages.

The larvae were sterilized by washing in water with methylene blue and antibiotics, then by a 15 minute exposition to uv rays and a rapid immersion in alcohol. In spite of these precautions the percentage of contaminated cultures remains very high, particularly when the connections between the brain and the suboesophagian ganglion are maintained, which means that the alimentary canal has to be sectioned.

The medium contains the following components given in Table XXXI.

Though the cerebral mass flattens out on the gel surface, the architecture of the various nervous centers is preserved so that the various groups of neurosecretory cells may be localized with precision.

iii. CULTURE OF DIPTERAN LARVAL ORGANS. Demaure (1968) cultivated various larval organs of *Lucilia sericata* (Diptera) on a semisolid

TABLE XXXI

CULTURE MEDIUM FOR NERVOUS ORGANS OF *Aeschna cyanea*[a]

Substances	Concentration				
	(mg)	(gm)	(ml)	(IU)	(volumes)
(1) Saline physiological solution containing trehalose					
Bidistilled water			1000		
NaCl	7				
KCl	0.2				
MgCl$_2$	0.4				
CaCl$_2$	0.75				4
NaH$_2$PO$_4$	0.4				
NaHCO$_3$	1				
Trehalose	3.5				
1% agar added					
(2) 50% chick embryo extract (Difco) in physiological solution					2
(3) 2% meat peptone (Difco) in physiological solution					1
(4) Antibiotics					
Specillin G				200	
Streptomycin	0.02				

[a] From Schaller and Meunier (1967).

TABLE XXXII
CULTURE MEDIUM FOR DIPTERAN LARVAL ORGANS[a]

Substances	Concentration		
	(parts)	(mg)	(IU)
1% agar in Gey solution	7		
Demal physiological solution[b] (with glucose instead of tre-halose)	3		
50% 9-day-old chick embryo extract in			
Demal solution	3		
Horse serum	2		
Antibiotics			
Specillin G			2000
Streptomycin		0.02	
Mycostatine			5000
The pH of the medium is 6.9 to 7.			

[a] From Demaure (1968).
[b] See Table V.

medium, derived from the Wolff and Haffen medium, composed as indicated in Table XXXII.

The organs are taken from third instar larvae, which have stopped growing and feeding (group II and III of the Possompès tables, 1953). The cultivated organs are the proventricles, the salivary glands, and the cephalic complex. In vitro, the proventricles contract with decreasing strength for the first six days. After 12 days, the cylindrical epithelium of the oesophagus valvule is healthy and the imaginal ring undergoes considerable growth in culture whereas the other regions enter necrosis.

The salivary glands do not undergo histolysis for about 15 days in culture though this phenomenon happens in vivo within the first three days of metamorphosis. Beyond this period they may still retain for a week some healthy cells in the proximal region neighboring the imaginal ring; however, the other parts of the glands become necrotic. In culture the cephalic complex remains healthy for about a week.

iv. EMBRYO CULTURE. Lender et al. (1965) obtained survival of cockroach (Periplaneta americana) (Dictyoptera) embryos in vitro. The cultures are done in salières on a gel medium which contains the following components given in Table XXXIII.

At a temperature of 26° the cockroach embryo development lasts an average of 32 days.

The ootheca generally contain 15 to 16 eggs synchronized in development. After 13 days of development, eggs are taken from the ootheca and immersed in sodium hypochlorite according to the Slifer technique (1945). This treatment removes the chorionic membrane while sterilizing the

TABLE XXXIII
CULTURE MEDIUM FOR COCKROACH EMBRYOS[a]

	Concentration		
Substances	(volumes)	(gm)	(ml)
Standard solution plus 5% agar	2		
Standard solution plus 2% peptone	1		
Horse serum (Difco)	1		
11-day-old chick embryo extract (Difco)	1		
25,000 IU of penicillin/20 ml of medium			
The standard solution is composed as follows:			
Bidistilled water			1000
Merck KCl		5.5	
Merck CaCl₂		0.6	
Merck MgCl₂·6H₂O		1	
Merck MgSO₄·7H₂O		5.5	
Merck NaH₂PO₄		1	
Difco trehalose		1.6	
pH of the medium: 6.85			

[a] From Lender et al. (1965).

eggs. After several baths in bidistilled water the eggs are dissected in the sterile standard solution with penicillin. The embryos are placed on the culture medium (2 ml) and kept at 30°. The embryos, 13-days old at the moment of explantation, survive for 12 to 18 days and undergo differentiation.

6. Ascidia

P. Sengel (1961) cultivated the ovary and the cardiopericardic organ of *Ciona intestinalis* on the media M and St M (see Table XXII). After seven days of culture the ovary was perfectly healthy and contained oocytes at all stages of development. P. Sengel and Kieny (1962a,b, 1963) further assayed the action of various nutritive media on the ovary of *Molgula manhattensis;* they also studied the influence on this organ of the complex neural gland, nervous ganglion, vibratile organ. The organs come either from young animals before sexual maturity or from adult animals with mature germ cells. The animals are washed in filtered sterile seawater plus penicillin G. Before explantation, the organs are washed in two successive baths of sterile seawater containing penicillin. The culture media are derived from the M medium enriched with various nutritive solutions (Table XXXIV).

In all cases, the explants are cultivated at room temperature for seven days without any retransplantation. The somatic structures of the ovary

TABLE XXXIV
CULTURE MEDIA FOR *Molgula manhattensis*[a]

Substances	Concentration (drops)
Medium CP	
1% agar in Gey solution	7
Filtered sterile seawater with penicillin	5
Chicken plasma (Difco)	1
Medium HS	
1% agar in Gey solution	7
Filtered sterile seawater with penicillin	5
Horse serum	1
Medium P	
1% agar in Gey solution	7
Filtered sterile seawater with penicillin	5
Parker's solution 199, concentration 1/1	1
Medium LS1	
1% agar in Gey solution	7
Limulus polyphemus serum	6
Medium LS2	
1% agar in Gey solution	7
Filtered sterile seawater with penicillin	5,2
Limulus polyphemus serum	3
Medium EJ	
1% agar in Gey solution	7
Filtered sterile seawater with penicillin	5
Chick embryo extract (Difco)	1

[a] From P. Sengel and Kieny (1962a,b, 1963).

and the testis retain their characteristic appearance *in vitro*, and whatever medium they are explanted on, they never show any sign of physiological suffering or cellular degeneration. On the contrary, germ cells are very sensitive to the composition of the medium. The oocytes survive better than the spermatocytes, as well on the M medium as on the nutritive media. On the M medium, survival is short. The most suitable media, both for testis and ovary, are the CP and HS media. P and EJ media have a beneficial effect only on the oocytes, whereas LS medium favors only the spermatocytes. However, the authors specify that none of these solutions gave perfectly satisfactory results, i.e., on all media a certain proportion of gonads after seven days of culture show necrotic germinal elements. The "neural gland–nervous ganglion–vibratile organ" complex, cultivated in association with the gonads, survives well enough in culture and promotes differentiation of the female elements.

Ghiani *et al.* (1964) cultivated the endostyle of *Ciona* on media also

TABLE XXXV
CULTURE MEDIA FOR *Ciona*[a]

Substances	Concentration (drops)
Medium SM	
1% agar in filtered sterile seawater	7
Filtered sterile seawater plus penicillin (dose of 20 IU/medium) plus streptomycin (dose of 6 mg/medium)	6
Medium SE	
1% agar in filtered sterile seawater	7
Chick embryo extract diluted by half in the Hanks physiological solution	2
Seawater plus antibiotics (cf., medium SM)	4
Medium SO	
1% agar in filtered sterile seawater	7
Ciona egg extract diluted in ratio 1/4 in filtered sterile seawater	2
Seawater plus antibiotics (cf., medium SM)	4

[a] From Ghiani *et al.* (1964).

derived from the Wolff and Haffen medium. These media are given in Table XXXV.

In order to study affinities between the endostyle of prochordates and the thyroid gland of vertebrates, the authors incorporate propylthiouracil and thyreostimuline in the culture medium.

IV. CONCLUSIONS

The number and the variety of culture media presented in this chapter show the considerable development of invertebrate organ culture over the last few years. Contrary to what happens in upper vertebrates, organ culture seems more successful than tissue culture. It is only recently with the work of Vago and Chastang (1958) and of Grace (1962) that cell lines have been established from invertebrate tissues by successive subcultures while certain organs had already been successfully cultivated for long periods. In most cases, explanted organs in liquid media become surrounded with an outgrowth of migrating cells, however this outgrowth remains limited enough for the organ to keep its structure and functional characteristics. The techniques of culture on semisolid media derived from the Wolff and Haffen method (1952) for bird embryonic organs ensure, on the contrary, perfect preservation of the integrity of the explants for the whole culture period. This advantage, as well as the simplicity of the technique and its adaptation to various purposes, explains its considerable success for the culture of a large variety of invertebrate organs. It should be emphasized that chick embryo extract is the main nutritive element of the culture media and is suitable for organs originating from a wide zoological range. The variations in composition of the media for different species mainly concern the physiological solutions, the ionic balance and the tonicity of the medium being the most important factors.

Synthetic media, with a defined composition, provide important data about the nutritional needs of the organs, particularly in certain insects such as Diptera and Lepidoptera.

However it is possible to cultivate numerous invertebrate tissues on media devised for vertebrate tissues, such as medium TC 199 (Morgan et al., 1950), which demonstrates the important capacities of adaptation of invertebrate tissues. In this connection it is interesting to notice that the culture of adult organs entails no particular difficulties for marine invertebrates or certain insects whereas the culture of vertebrate adult organs still encounters some technical problems.

Invertebrate organ culture has progressed considerably in the last fifteen years, making it possible to attack, and in some case solve, many problems of organogenesis, endocrinology, and neuroendocrinology.

REFERENCES

Agrawal, N. S., and Srivastava, S. P. (1962). *Agra Univ. J. Res., Sci.* **2**, 23.
Arvy, L., and Gabe, M. (1946). *C. R. Soc. Biol.* **140**, 787.
Babers, F. M. (1938). *J. Agr. Res.* **57**, 697.
Ball, G. H. (1947). *Amer. J. Trop. Med.* **27**, 301.
Ball, G. H. (1948). *Amer. J. Trop. Med.* **28**, 533.
Ball, G. H. (1954). *Exp. Parasitol.* **3**, 358.
Baumgartner, W. J., and Payne, M. A. (1930). *Science* **72**, 199.
Bazin, J. C., and Lancastre, F. (1967). *C. R. Acad. Sci.* **264**, 2907.
Beckel, W. E. (1956). *Nature (London)* **177**, 534.
Begg, M., and Cruickshank, W. J. (1963). *Proc. Roy. Soc. Edinburgh, Sect. B* **58**, 215.
Bělař, K. (1929). *Wilhelm Roux, Arch. Entwicklungsmech. Organismen* **118**, 359.
Benex, J. (1961). *C. R. Acad. Sci.* **253**, 734.
Benex, J. (1964). *C. R. Acad. Sci.* **258**, 2193.
Benex, J. (1967a). *C. R. Acad. Sci.* **265**, 571.
Benex, J. (1967b). *C. R. Acad. Sci.* **265**, 631.
Bergerard, J., and Morio, H. (1963). *Ann. Epiphyt.* **14**, 55.
Bergerard, J., Dreux, P., and Fisher, J. (1950). *Arch. Sci. Physiol.* **4**, 225.
Berreur-Bonnenfant, J. (1962). *Bull. Soc. Zool. Fr.* **87**, 377.
Berreur-Bonnenfant, J. (1963). *C. R. Acad. Sci.* **256**, 2244.
Berreur-Bonnenfant, J. (1968). Personal communication.

Berreur-Bonnenfant, J. (1964). *Bull. Soc. Zool. Fr. Belg.* **89,** 59.
Berreur-Bonnenfant, J. (1967). *C. R. Soc. Biol.* **161,** 9.
Bethe, A. (1929). *Pfluegers Arch. Gesamte Physiol. Menschen Tiere* **221,** 344.
Bevelander, G., and Martin, J. (1949). *Anat. Rec.* **105,** 604.
Bialaszewicz, K., and Landau, C. (1938). *Acta Biol. Exp. (Warsaw)* **11,** 307.
Boné, G. J. (1944). *Ann. Soc. Roy. Zool. Belg.* **75,** 123.
Bradford, S., and Ramsay, R. W. (1949). *Fed. Fed. Amer. Soc. Exp. Biol. Proc.,* **8,** 15.
Brecher, L. (1929). *Biochem. Z.* **211,** 40.
Bruslé, J. (1966). *C. R. Acad. Sci.* **263,** 1514.
Bruslé, J. (1967). *C. R. Acad. Sci.* **264,** 963.
Buck, J. B. (1953). *In* "Insect Physiology" (K. D. Roeder, ed.), Vol. 6, pp. 147–190. Wiley, New York.
Bucklin, D. H. (1953). *Anat. Rec.* **117,** 539.
Bucklin, D. H. (1959). *In* "Physiology of Insect Development," p. 35. Univ. of Chicago Press, Chicago, Illinois.
Butz, A. (1957). *Ann. Entomol. Soc. Amer.* **55,** 480.
Cannon, G. B. (1964). *Science* **146,** 1063.
Carlson, J. B. (1946). *Biol. Bull.* **90,** 109.
Chabaud, M. A., Ghelelovitch, S., and de Lalun, E. (1960). *Bull. Soc. Pathol. Exot.* **53,** 170.
Chambers, R. (1925). *Cellule* **35,** 107.
Chen, J. (1954). *Exp. Cell Res.* **7,** 518.
Chen, P. S., and Hadorn, E. (1954). *Rev. Suisse Zool.* **61,** 437.
Choquet, M. (1964). *C. R. Acad. Sci.* **258,** 1089.
Choquet, M. (1965). *C. R. Acad. Sci.* **261,** 4521.
Clark, E. W., and Ball, G. H. (1954). *Physiol. Zool.* **27,** 334.
Clark, E. W., and Craig, R. (1953). *Physiol. Zool.* **26,** 101.
Croghan, P. C., and Lockwood, A. P. M. (1960). *J. Exp. Biol.* **37,** 339.
Curtis, A. S. G. (1962). *Nature (London)* **196,** 245.
Davenport, D. (1949). *Physiol. Zool.* **22,** 35.
David, J., and Rougier, M. (1965). *C. R. Acad. Sci.* **261,** 1394.
Day, M. F., and Grace, T. D. C. (1959). *Annu. Rev. Entomol.* **4,** 17.
Delavault, R., and Bruslé, J. (1965). *Bull. Soc. Zool. Fr.* **40,** 361.
Demal, J. (1955). *Bull. Cl. Sci., Acad. Roy. Belg.* **5,** 41.
Demal, J. (1956). *Ann. Sci. Nat. Zool. Biol. Anim.* [11] **18,** 155.
Demal, J. (1961). *Bull. Soc. Zool. Fr.* **86,** 522.
Demal, J., and Leloup, A. M. (1963). *Ann. Epiphyt.* **14,** 91.
Demaure, J. C. (1968). *C. R. Soc. Biol.* **162,** 224.
Deschiens, R. (1954). *Bull. Soc. Pathol. Exot.* **47,** 915.
Dreux, P., and Grapin-Poupeau, D. (1963). *C. R. Soc. Biol.* **157,** 1000.
Drilhon, A. (1957). Colloque sur les metamorphoses. Périgueux.
Drilhon, A., and Vago, C. (1960). *Antonie van Leeuwenhoek; J. Microbiol. Serol.* **26,** 407.
Ducceschi, V. (1902). *Atti Reale Accad. Georgofili* **80,** 365.
Duchateau, G., Florkin, M., and Leclercq, J. (1953). *Arch. Int. Physiol.* **61,** 518.
Durchon, M. (1952). *Ann. Sci. Nat. Zool.* [10] **14,** 119.
Durchon, M., and Boilly, B. (1964). *C. R. Acad. Sci.* **259,** 1245.
Durchon, M., and Dhainaut, A. (1964). *C. R. Acad. Sci.* **258,** 917.
Durchon, M.. and Richard, A. (1967). *C. R. Acad. Sci.* **264,** 1497.

Durchon, M., and Schaller, F. (1963). *C. R. Acad. Sci.* **256**, 5615.
Durchon, M., and Schaller, F. (1964). *Gen. Comp. Endocrinol.* **4**, 427.
Durchon, M., Montreuil, J., and Boilly-Marer, Y. (1963). *C. R. Acad. Sci.* **257**, 1807.
Duryee, W. R. (1948). *J. Wash. Acad. Sci.* **28**, 31.
Dutrieu, J. (1961). *C. R. Acad. Sci.* **252**, 347.
Duveau-Hagège, J. (1963). *C. R. Acad. Sci.* **256**, 5429.
Duveau-Hagège, J. (1964). *Bull. Soc. Zool. Fr. Belg.* **89**, 66.
Eagle, H. (1955). *J. Exp. Med.* **102**, 37.
Ephrussi, B., and Beadle, B. W. (1936). *Amer. Natur.* **70**, 218.
Fauré-Fremiet, E. (1925). *C. R. Soc. Biol.* **93**, 618.
Fauré-Fremiet, E. (1932a). *Arch. Anat. Microsc.* **28**, 1.
Fauré-Fremiet, E. (1932b). *Arch. Anat. Microsc.* **28**, 121.
Finlayson, L. H., and Harmer, D. (1949). *Nature (London)* **163**, 843.
Fischer, I., and Gottschewski, G. (1939). *Naturwissenschaften* **27**, 391.
Fischer-Piette, E. (1929). *Arch. Zool. Exp. Gen.* **102**, 764.
Fischer-Piette, E. (1933). *Arch. Zool. Exp. Gen.* **74**, 33.
Florkin, M. (1943). *Bull. Soc. Roy. Sci. Liege* **5**, 301.
Fosset, J., and Chastang, S. (1963). *Ann. Epiphyt.* **14**, 35.
Fowler, D., and Goodnight, C. J. (1966). *Trans. Amer. Microsc. Soc.* **85**, 378.
Freisling, M., and Reisinger, E. (1958). *Wilhelm Roux' Arch. Entwicklungs mech. Organismen* **150**, 581.
Frew, J. C. H. (1928). *J. Exp. Biol.* **6**, 1.
Friedman. F., and Burton, L. (1956). *Cancer Res.* **16**, 1059.
Fujio, Y. (1960). *Jap. J. Genet.* **35**, 367.
Fujio, Y. (1962). *Jap. J. Genet.* **37**, 110.
Gaillard, P. (1951). *Methods Med. Res.* **4**, 241.
Galtsoff, P. S. (1925a). *J. Exp. Zool.* **42**, 183.
Galtsoff, P. S. (1925b). *J. Exp. Zool.* **42**, 223.
Gaulden, M. E., and Carlson, J. G. (1951). *Exp. Cell Res.* **2**, 416.
Gavrilov, W., and Cowez, S. (1941). *Ann. Parasitol. Hum. Comp.* **18**, 180.
Gay, R. (1963). *Ann. Epiphyt.* **3**, 61.
Geiman, Q. M., and Anfinsen, C. B., (1946). *J. Exp. Med.* **84**, 583.
Ghiani, P., Orsi, L., and Relini, G. (1964). *Atti Accad. Ligure Sci. Lett., Aenoa* **20**, 93.
Goldschmidt, R. (1915). *Proc. Nat. Acad. Sci. U. S.* **1**, 220.
Goldschmidt, R. (1916). *Biol. Zentr.* **36**, 161.
Gomot, L., and Guyard, A. (1964). *C. R. Acad. Sci.* **258**, 2902.
Gomot, L., and Guyard, A. (1967). *Proc. Colloq. Invert. Tissue Cult., 2nd 1967 (London)* p. 22.
Goodchild, A. J. P. (1954). *Nature (London)* **173**, 504.
Gottschewski, G. H. M. (1960). *Wilhelm Roux' Arch. Entwicklungsmech. Organismen.* **152**, 204.
Gottschewski, G. H. M., and Querner, W. (1961). *Wilhelm Roux' Arch. Entwicklungsmech. Organismen* **153**, 168.
Grace, T. D. C. (1959). *Ann. N. Y. Acad. Sci.* **77**, 275.
Grace, T. D. C. (1958a). *J. Gen. Physiol.* **41**, 1027.
Grace, T. D. C. (1958b). *Aust. J. Biol. Sci.* **11**, 401.
Grace, T. D. C. (1962). *Nature (London)* **195**, 788.
Grellet, P. (1965a). *C. R. Acad. Sci.* **260**, 5100.
Grellet, P. (1965b). *C. R. Acad. Sci.* **260**, 5881.

Guyard, A. (1967). *C. R. Acad. Sci.* **265**, 147.
Guyard, A. (1968). Personal communication.
Guyard, A., and Gomot, L. (1964). *Bull. Soc. Zool. Fr.* **89**, 48.
Hackman, R. H. (1956). *Aust. J. Biol. Sci.* **9**, 400.
Healy, G. M., Fischer, D. C., and Parker, R. C. (1954). *Can. J. Biochem. Phys.* **32**, 327.
Hanly, E. W., and Hemmert, W. H. (1967). *J. Embryol. Exp. Morphol.* **17**, 501.
Hanly, E. W., Fuller, C. W., and Stanley, M. S. M. (1967). *J. Embryol. Exp. Morphol.* **17**, 491.
Hayes, R. O. (1953). *J. Econ. Entomol.* **46**, 624.
Hibbard, H. (1935). *Mt Desert Isl. Biol. Lat. Bull.* **37**, 16.
Hirumi, H., and Maramorosch, K. (1963). *Ann. Epiphyt.* **14**, 77.
Hirumi, H., Chen, T., and Maramorosch, K. (1967). *Proc. Int. Colloq. Invert. Tissue Cult., 2nd 1967,* p. 147.
Holtfreter, J. (1931). *Wilhelm Roux' Arch. Entwicklungsmech. Organismen* **124**, 404.
Horikawa, M. (1958). *Cytologia* **23**, 468.
Horikawa, M. (1960). *Jap. J. Genet.* **35**, 76.
Horikawa, M., and Fox, A. (1964). *Science* **145**, 3639.
Horikawa, M., and Kuroda, Y. (1959). *Nature (London)* **184**, 2017.
Horikawa, M., and Sugahara, T. (1960). *Radiat. Res.* **12**, 266.
Hoyle, G. (1954). *J. Exp. Biol.* **31**, 260.
Hoyle, G. (1955). *J. Physiol. (London)* **127**, 90.
Humphreys, T. (1963). *Develop. Biol.* **8**, 27.
Huxley, J. S. (1921a). *Quart. J. Microsc. Sci.* **65**, 293.
Huxley, J. S. (1921b). *Biol. Bull.* **40**, 127.
Huxley, J. S. (1921c). *Phil. Trans. Roy. Soc. Belg.* **202**, 165.
Jahn, T. S., and Koel, B. S. (1948). *Ann. Entomol. Soc. Amer.* **41**, 258.
Jahn, T. S., Crescitelli, F., and Taylor, A. S. (1936). *J. Cell. Comp. Physiol.* **10**, 439.
Jones, B. W. (1956). *J. Exp. Biol* **33**, 174.
Jones, B. M., and Cunningham, J. (1961). *Exp. Cell Res.* **23**, 386.
Kirsten, J. Unpublished data. [See Martin, B., and Nishiitsutsuji-Uwo (1967).]
Koch, P. (1962). *Zool. Anz.* **25**, 123.
Koch, P. (1964). *Wilhelm Roux' Arch. Entwicklungsmech. Organismen.* **155**, 549.
Krause, G., and Krause, J. (1963). *Zool. Anz.* **26**, 190.
Krause, G., and Krause, J. (1964). *Wilhelm Roux' Arch. Anat. Entwicklungsmech. Organismen.* **155**, 451.
Krause, G., and Krause, J. (1965). *Z. Naturforsch.* **20**, 332.
Kuroda, Y., and Tamura, S. (1956). *Med. J. Osaka Univ.* **7**, 137.
Kuroda, Y., and Yamaguchi, K. (1956). *Jap. J. Genet.* **31**, 97.
Landureau, J. C. (1966). *Exp. Cell Res.* **41**, 545.
Larsen, W. (1963). *Ann. Entomol. Soc. Amer.* **56**, 720.
Laverdure, A. M. (1967). *C. R. Acad. Sci.* **265**, 505.
Lazarenko, T. Z. (1925). *Z. Mikrosk.-Anat. Forsch.* **3**, 409.
Leloup, A. M. (1964). *Bull. Soc. Zool. Fr.* **89**, 70.
Leloup, A. M., and Gianfelici, E. (1966). *Ann. Endocrinol.* **27**, 506.
Lender, T., and Duveau-Hagège, J. (1962). *C. R. Acad. Sci.* **254**, 2825.
Lender, T., and Duveau-Hagège, J. (1963a). *Ann. Epiphyt.* **14**, 81.
Lender, T., and Duveau-Hagège, J. (1963b). *Develop. Biol.* **6**, 1.
Lender, T., and Laverdure, A. M. (1967). *C. R. Acad. Sci.* **265**, 451.
Lender, T., Kenneth, R., and Fisher, K.R. S. (1965). *Bull. Soc. Zool. Fr.* **5**, 591.

Levenbook, L. (1950). *Biochem. J.* **47**, 336.
Levy, R. (1928). *C. R. Soc. Biol.* **159**, 104.
Lewis, M. R. (1916). *Anat. Rec.* **9**, 287.
Lewis, M. R., and Robertson, W. R. B. (1916). *Biol. Bull.* **30**, 99.
Loeb, M. J., and Schneiderman, H. A. (1956). *Ann. Entomol. Soc. Amer.* **49**, 493.
Ludwig, D., Tefft, R., and Suchtta, M. D. (1957). *Ann. Entomol. Soc. Amer.* **50**, 244.
Lüscher, M. (1947). *Nature (London)* **160**, 873.
Malecha, J. (1965). *C. R. Soc. Biol.* **159**, 1674.
Malecha, J. (1967a). *C. R. Acad. Sci.* **265**, 613.
Malecha, J. (1967b). *C. R. Acad. Sci.* **265**, 1806.
Mandin, J., and Vago, C. (1963). *Ann. Epiphyt.* **14**, 29.
Maramorosch, K. (1956). *Virology* **2**, 369.
Martin, H. M., and Vidler, B. O. (1962). *Exp. Parasitol.* **12**, 192.
Martin, B.M., and Nishiitsuisuji-Uwo, J. (1967). *Biochem. Zentr.* **346**, 491.
Martinovitch, P. (1953). *Exp. Cell Res.* **4**, 490.
Maximow, A. (1925). *Contrib. Carneg. Inst. Wash.* **16**, 49.
Miciarelli, A., Sbrenna, G., and Colombo, G. (1967). *Experientia* **23**, 64.
Millara, P. (1946). *C. R. Soc. Biol.* **140**, 1006.
Mitsuhashi, J. (1965). *Jap. J. Appl. Entomol. Zool.* **9**, 217.
Morgan, J. F., Morton, H. J., and Parker, R. C. (1950). *Proc. Soc. Exp. Biol. Med.* **73**, 1.
Mueller, N. S. (1963). *Develop. Biol.* **8**, 222.
Müller, K. (1911). *Wilhelm Roux' Arch. Entwicklungmech. Organismen* **32**, 397.
Murray, M. R. (1926). *Biol. Bull.* **50**, 210.
Murray, M. R. (1927). *J. Exp. Zool.* **47**, 467.
Murray, M. R. (1928). *Physiol. Zool.* **1**, 137.
Murray, M. R. (1931). *Arch. Exp. Zellforsch. Besonders Gewebezuecht.* **11**, 656.
Nicholis, J. G., and Kuffler, S. W. (1965). *J. Neurophysiol.* **28**, 519.
Paillot, A. (1924). *Bull. Histol. Appl. Tech. Microsc.* **1**, 216.
Pantin, C. A. F. (1934). *J. Exp. Biol.* **11**, 11.
Possompès, B. (1953). *Arch. Zool. Exp. Gen.* **89**, 203.
Ragab, H. A. (1949). *Trans. Roy. Soc. Trop. Med. Hyg.* **43**, 225.
Ramsay, J. A. (1953). *J. Exp. Biol.* **30**, 358.
Richards, A. S. (1963). *J. Insect Physiol.* **9**, 597.
Ripplinger, J., and Joly, M. (1961). *C. R. Soc. Biol.* **155**, 825.
Ris, H. (1949). *Biol. Bull.* **96**, 90.
Sarlet, H., Duchateau, G., and Florkin, M. (1952). *Arch. Int. Physiol.* **60**, 103.
Schaller, F., and Meunier, J. (1967). *C. R. Acad. Sci.* **264**, 1441.
Schmidt, E. L., and Williams, C. M. (1953a). *Anat. Rec.* **105**, 487.
Schmidt, E. L., and Williams, C. M. (1953b). *Biol. Bull.* **105**, 174.
Schneider, I. (1964). *J. Exp. Zool.* **156**, 91.
Schneider, I. (1966). *J. Embryol. Exp. Morphol.* **15**, 271.
Schneider, N. A., and Bucklin, D. H. (1958). *Anat. Rec.* **131**, 597.
Seidel, F., and Koch, P. (1964). *Embryologia* **8**, 200.
Seilern-Aspang, F. (1958). *Zool. Anz.* **160**, 1.
Seilern-Aspang, F. (1960). *Wilhelm Roux' Arch. Entwicklungsmech. Organismen* **152**, 35.
Seneca, H., and Bergendahl, E. (1955). *Antibiot. Chemother. (Basel)* **5**, 737.
Sengel, C. (1959). *C. R. Acad. Sci.* **249**, 2854.
Sengel, C. (1960). *J. Embryol. Exp. Morphol.* **8**, 468.

Sengel, C. (1963). *Ann. Epiphyt.* **14**, 173.
Sengel, P. (1961). *C. R. Acad. Sci.* **251**, 3666.
Sengel, P., and Kieny, M. (1962a). *Bull. Soc. Zool. Fr.* **87**, 615.
Sengel, P., and Kieny, M. (1962b). *C. R. Acad. Sci.* **254**, 1682.
Sengel, P., and Kieny, M. (1963). *Ann. Epiphyt.* **14**, 95.
Sen Gupta, K. (1963). *Ann. Epiphyt.* **14**, 39.
Shaw, E. I. (1956). *Exp. Cell Res.* **11**, 580.
Slifer, E. H. (1934). *J. Exp. Zool.* **67**, 137.
Slifer, E. H. (1945). *Science* **102**, 282.
Stern, C. (1940). *Growth* **4**, 377.
Strangeways, T. S. P., and Fell, H. B. (1926). *Proc. Roy. Soc. Belg.* **99**, 340.
Strangeways, T. S. P., and Fell, H. B. (1928). *Proc. Roy. Soc. Belg.* **100**, 273.
Streiff, W. (1963). *Gen. Comp. Endocrinol.* **3**, 733.
Streiff, W. (1964). *Bull. Soc. Zool. Fr.* **89**, 56.
Streiff, W. (1966a). *Ann. Endocrinol.* **27**, 385.
Streiff, W. (1966b). *C. R. Acad. Sci.* **263**, 539.
Streiff, W., and Peyre, A. (1963). *C. R. Acad. Sci.* **124**, 337.
Streiff, W., and Taberly, G. (1964). *Bull. Soc. Zool. Fr.* **89**, 65.
Takakusoh, S. (1924). *Z. Zellforsch. Mikrosk. Anat.* **1**, 22.
Takami, T. (1958). *J. Exp. Biol.* **35**, 286.
Takami, T. (1959). *Science* **130**, 98.
Takami, T. (1961). *Rev. Ver Soie* **12**, 315.
Takami, T. (1963). *J. Exp. Biol.* **40**, 735.
Takeda, K. (1937). *Kyoto-Izadaigaku-Zasshi* **21**, 905.
Thomas, J. A. (1932). *C. R. Soc. Biol.* **110**, 451.
Thomas, J. A. (1941a). *C. R. Acad. Sci.* **213**, 85.
Thomas, J. A. (1941b). *C. R. Acad. Sci.* **213**, 252.
Thomson, D. (1914). *Proc. Roy. Soc. Med.* **7**, 21.
Tobias, J. M. (1948). *J. Cell. Comp. Physiol.* **31**, 143.
Trager, W. (1935). *J. Exp. Med.* **61**, 501.
Trager, W. (1937). *J. Parasitol.* **23**, 226.
Trager, W. (1938). *Amer. J. Trop. Med.* **18**, 387.
Trager, W. (1959). *Ann. Trop. Med.* **53**, 473.
Trowel, O. (1954). *Exp. Cell. Res.* **6**, 246.
Tulchin, N., Mateyko, G. M., and Kopac, M. J. (1967). *J. Cell Biol.* **34**, 891.
Vago, C., and Bergoin, M. (1963). *Entomophaga* **8**, N° 4.
Vago, C., and Chastang, S. (1958). *Experientia* **14**, 110.
Vago, C., and Chastang, S. (1960). *C. R. Acad. Sci.* **241**, 903.
Vago, C., and Flandre, O. (1963). *Ann. Epiphyt.* **14**, 127.
Vago, C., Fosset, J., and Meynadier, G. (1961). *C. R. Acad. Sci.* **252**, 2759.
Vakaët, L., and Pintelon, L. (1959). *C. R. Soc. Biol.* **153**, 174.
Wilbur, K. M., and MacMahan, E. A. (1958). *Ann. Entomol. Soc. Amer.* **51**, 27.
Wilson, H. V. (1907). *J. Exp. Zool.* **5**, 245.
Wilson, H. V. (1911). *J. Exp. Zool.* **11**, 281.
Wolff, Em. (1962). *Bull. Soc. Zool. Fr. Belg.* **87**, 120.
Wolff, Em. (1963). *Ann. Epiphyt.* **14**, 113.
Wolff, Et., and Haffen, K. (1952). *Tex. Rep. Biol. Med.* **10**, 463.
Wolff, Et., and Marin, L. (1960). *C. R. Acad. Sci.* **244**, 2745.
Wolff, Et., Haffen, K., Kieny, M., and Wolff, Em. (1953). *J. Embryol. Exp. Morphol.* **1**, 55.

Wyatt, G. R., and Kalf, G. F. (1957). *J. Gen. Physiol.* **50**, 833.
Wyatt, G. R., Loughheed, T. C., and Wyatt, S. (1956). *J. Gen. Physiol.* **39**, 853.
Wyatt, S. S. (1956). *J. Gen. Physiol.* **39**, 841
Yeager, J. F. (1939). *J. Agr. Res.* **59**, 121.
Yeager, J. F., and Hager, A. (1934). *Ann. Entomol. Soc. Amer.* **15**, 252.
Zerbib, C. (1967). *Bull. Soc. Zool. Fr.* **91**, 344.
Ziller-Sengel, C. (1964). *In* "Les cultures organotypiques" (J. A. Thomas, ed.), pp. 225–253. Masson, Paris.
Ziller-Sengel, C. (1967). D. Sc. Thesis, Paris.
Zweibaum, J. (1925a). *C. R. Soc. Biol.* **93**, 783.
Zweibaum, J. (1925b). *C. R. Soc. Biol.* **93**, 785.

3

ELECTRON MICROSCOPY OF CELL AND ORGAN CULTURES OF INVERTEBRATES

G. Devauchelle

I. INTRODUCTION

The techniques used in the preparation of cell or organ cultures for ultrastructural investigations do not show much difference as compared to those devised for the study of samples of animal tissue. The investigators who have used these methods for cytological, pathological, or endocrinological problems have insisted on the interest of performing cellular cultures and of studying these cultures with the electron microscope.

We shall examine here the main techniques already tested and perfectly efficient in the study of vertebrates, stressing particularly the special considerations involved in obtaining similar results in the study of invertebrates. Then we shall describe some of the research results realized in cytopathological and endocrinological studies using these methods.

II. GENERAL TECHNIQUES AND THE ADAPTATION OF THESE TECHNIQUES TO INVERTEBRATE TISSUE CULTURE

The techniques used in electron microscopy are based on a fundamental principle: The structures must be observed in a state as close as possible to the living state. In the case of cellular or organ cultures, this aspect can be checked macroscopically by comparing embedded and living objects. At the ultrastructural level, this principle is more difficult to check, and for that reason we shall define clearly those conditions and criteria of fixation used by cytologists. First of all, we shall examine the methods which allow a purely morphological observation, specifying the modifications recommended in the culture techniques and in the handling of the objects for ultrastructural observations. Then we shall indicate briefly the characteristics of the cytochemical methods, referring the reader especially interested in these techniques to specialized books (Pease, 1964; Kay, 1965).

A. Modifications in Culture Methods

These modifications concern essentially the support used for culture. In all cases it will be better to choose a small support which can be, at the beginning of the experiment, introduced into the flasks used for the culture. Glass or plastic flasks can be used (Nishiura and Ragan, 1960; Rosen, 1962; N. Anderson and Doane, 1967).

1. Culture Performed on Special Support

The use of bare glass laminas, i.e., microscope slides used in photonic microscopy, proves to be particularly convenient. They do not need extra handlings in the course of the sterilization, and the cells adhere perfectly to their surface (Laschi and Rizzoli, 1968).

a. Cover Films. These microscope slides may be covered with a film making further handlings easier. In this case different substances are available.

A collodion and collagen film (Heyner, 1963; Descarries, 1967) can be prepared by first mixing one part ether, one part 95% ethanol, and three parts collodion (U.S.P. Fisher). Two or three drops of this solution are then placed on the coverslips so that they cover the whole surface. The collagen is then placed upon this surface (Bornstein, 1958).

A Formvar film (Breton-Gorius, 1968) can be prepared by immersing the coverslips briefly in a solution of 0.5% Formvar in chloroform and then removed and dried.

A carbon film (Robbins and Gonatas, 1964) is a carbon coating applied in a vacuum evaporator. The thickness of the layer is not critical; vaporization is stopped as soon as the coat is visible. In order to sterilize and fix the coat, the coverslips are then heated for 24 hours at 180°.

Other substances, e.g., agar and Melinex 0 (Firket, 1966), have also been suggested, but they present few advantages.

b. Mica Coverslips. The use of mica coverslips has been advised by some authors (Persijn and Scherft, 1965; Laschi and Rizzoli, 1968). Mica is not toxic for cultures and is easily separated from embedding resins.

c. Polymerized Epon. Polymerized Epon, in some circumstances, seems to represent a nontoxic support (Zagury et al., 1966a,b). The resin coverslips must be sufficiently thin and prepared under conditions correct for electron microscopy.

d. Millipore Filters. Some authors recommend the use of millipore filters as well (McCombs et al., 1968). Millipore filters with a diameter of 25 mm and with pores of 0.45 μ can be used (Millipore No. HAWP 02500). Sterilization is performed with ultraviolet light for 30 to 60 minutes. The filters are placed in the culture flasks. The suspended cells become adsorbed, and the cells that have been spread out adhere perfectly.

2. Culture in Plastic Flasks

The plastic containers present a number of advantages for an ultra-structural study. Their use does not necessitate any special handling since all the processes can be made in the container. Some precautions should be taken in the course of dehydration.

3. Culture in Glass Flasks

The use of glass containers used for the culture of cells or organs presents some disadvantages. In order to obtain suitable embeddings, the flask will have to be broken at the end of the experiment if one wants to observe the cells in the monocellular layers; if not, the cells will have to be separated from their support at the time of fixation. In the latter case the methods used, i.e., mechanical processes (scraping and centrifugation) or chemical processes (trypsin, etc.), might sometimes be harmful to the integrity of the cells. Moreover, the inclusion must be done on a cellular pellet, in which the cohesion is not always perfect.

In order to remedy this drawback, there is the possibility of using the technique of preinclusion in an effort to lose as little material as possible (Aziz and Davies, 1968). Among the many methods that have been suggested, we shall present two of them.

a. Embedding in Agar (Kellenberger *et al.*, 1962). A 2% agar solution is prepared and kept at 45°. After fixation the material is centrifuged and the supernatant is removed. Then a drop of the solution of agar is put on the pellet. After homogenization the whole solution is cooled down and the resulting mass is taken out, cut into small pieces, and treated just as an ordinary tissue.

b. Embedding in Fibrin (Charret and Fauré-Fremiet, 1966). A mixture is prepared with 0.5% fibrinogen (Mann Assayed) in a buffer used for the fixation; the dissolution is made at 37°, but it takes a long time. If a cacodylate buffer is used, a precipitate is formed and the buffer must then be changed to allow preinclusion. After fixation, the cells are centrifuged and the supernatant is discarded. Then some drops of the fibrinogen solution, to which 1% $CaCl_2$ (one drop/5 ml of fibrinogen solution) has been added, are poured on the pellet. Then thrombase (Mann Assayed) is added, and after a few seconds, the cells with the clot in formation are resuspended with a needle. The clot is then removed, put into 70% alcohol, and handled like an ordinary tissue.

B. Fixation

This first phase in the preparation of objects for electron microscopy is the most important one, and in the case of cultures of cells or organs, it is also the most critical phase (Gordon *et al.*, 1963).

1. Criteria of Fixation

Though the criteria of a successful fixation are subjective, an appreciation of the importance of the quality of the fixation is in order. Observation of the size and general aspect of the treated cells as compared to those of cells *in vitro* furthers such an appreciation of the quality of the fixation.

Among the cellular organites of the cells, the mitochondria, as well as the endoplasmic reticulum, are particularly sensitive to the conditions of fixations (Fahimi and Drochmans, 1965). In the case of a very hypertonic fixation, the sections examined under the electron microscope show a compact appearance in the cells and an irregular preservation of the cellular organites; the mitochondria have a very dense matrix. If the fixative is hypotonic, many structures have a washed aspect, the mitochondria are swelled, and the matrix is emptied. In a correct, slightly hypertonic fixation, the membranous systems of the agranular reticulum are well preserved. They have a vesicular or tubular form. The mitochondria look rounded. They may sometimes be slightly vacuolized (Schultz and Karlson, 1965).

2. Conditions of the Fixation

In routine work, the pieces are first treated with an aldehyde solution in a suitable buffer. The most used so far is the glutaraldehyde proposed by Sabatini *et al.* (1963). When it is correctly prepared it fixes, in a stationary way, all the tissues though it may sometimes cause artifacts (Curgy, 1968). For the cultures of cells and organs some modifications must be introduced in order to obtain an optimal result.

The osmolality of the fixative solution, the pH, and the concentration of aldehyde will have to be checked particularly. According to the concentrations that are used, the results may vary considerably (Fahimi and Drochmans, 1965). A concentration of 37% purified aldehyde in the fixative solution is too hypertonic (4000 mOsM), and a retractation of the tissues can be observed. A 0.5% aldehyde concentration with an osmotic pressure of 290 mOsM for the fixation solution is not sufficient.

The optimal concentrations of glutaraldehyde are found between 1.5% and 3.5% of purified aldehyde.

The conditions of pH are equally important when aldehydes are used; pH values between 6.5 and 7.5 seem to be suitable for many tissues.

3. The Choice of the Buffer

The glutaraldehyde is never used alone but only in buffered solutions. As we have already pointed out, the choice of buffer must be made according to the osmolality and the pH required.

In their work on the relationships between pH, osmolality, and concentration of aldehyde in the fixative solutions, Maser et al. (1967) show the relations which exist between these factors for five different buffers: cacodylate–HCl (Gomori, 1955), s-Collidine–HCl (Gomori, 1946), Millonig's phosphate (Millonig, 1961), Sörensen's phosphate (Gomori, 1955), and veronal acetate–HCl (Palade, 1952) (see Table I). In the same manner they indicate the osmotic pressures of the fixatives (glutaraldehyde and osmium tetroxide) and of certain components that can be added (glucose, sucrose, NaCl, $CaCl_2$) (see Table II).

It will be noted that, for all the substances, the osmolality varies

TABLE I

OSMOTIC PRESSURES FOR FIVE BUFFERS FOR A pH OF 7^a

Cacodylate–HCl		s-Collidine–HCl	
Molarity (M)	Osmolarity (mOsM)	Molarity (M)	Osmolarity (mOsM)
0.2	420	0.2	300
0.1	210	0.1	140
0.05	100	0.05	70
		0.025	30
Phosphate (Millonig)		Phosphate (Sörensen)	
Molarity	Osmolarity	Molarity	Osmolarity
0.2	390	0.2	390
0.1	210	0.1	210
0.05	120	0.05	120
Veronal acetate–HCl		Phosphate (Sörensen)^b	
Molarity	Osmolarity	Molarity	Osmolarity
0.1	230	0.05	118
0.05	120	0.075	180
0.025	65	0.10	226

^{a} These data taken from the abaci of Maser et al. (1967) have only an approximate value.

^{b} From Fahimi and Drochmans (1965).

TABLE II

OSMOTIC PRESSURES OF GLUTARALDEHYDE, OSMIUM TETROXIDE, AND
ADDITIONAL SUBSTANCES[a]

Glutaraldehyde (Biological Grade)		Osmium tetroxide	
Molarity	Osmolarity	Molarity	Osmolarity
0.05	55	0.02	17
0.10	100	0.04	35
0.15	145	0.08	70
0.20	190	0.10	87
0.25	235	0.16	140
0.30	280		

Molarity	Glucose (mOsM)	Sucrose (mOsM)	NaCl (mOsM)	CaCl₂	
				Molarity	Osmolarity
0.1	90	90	190		
0.2	200	210	380	0.001	1
0.3	310	330	570	0.005	11
0.4	420	450	760	0.010	25
0.5	530	580	—		

[a] From Maser et al. (1967). The calculation of the osmolality of the fixative solution can be made simply by making the sum of the osmolality of each component part (fixative, buffer, etc.). The results in a first approximation are acceptable.

proportionally to the molarity of the solution. These values, especially those concerning glutaraldehyde are valid only for pure solutions. The commercial glutaraldehyde shows great differences from one sample to another. In this case it will be better to treat the solution with charcoal or $CaCO_3$.

4. The Choice of the Fixative

Though the glutaraldehyde seems to be the fixative of choice for routine work, some other substances have been proposed; the majority refer to particular problems.

a. Other Aldehydes. Formaldehyde, acrolein, etc., will be reserved for more specific studies.

b. Osmium Tetroxide. Osmium tetroxide used alone proves to be less successful than the aldehydes. When it is used alone, a 1 or 2% solution in a buffer is used. Problems with pH and osmolality are less important than for the glutaraldehyde.

c. Dalton's Fixative (1955). An aqueous solution of 5% potassium dichromate is neutralized with 2.5 N KOH up to pH 7.2. The solution is then diluted with water to obtain a final concentration of 4% potassium dichromate. The fixative solution is prepared by mixing 5 ml of the potassium dichromate solution with 3% NaCl (5 ml) and 10 ml of a 2% OsO_4 aqueous solution.

d. Kellenberger et al. Fixative (1958). This fixative solution is used especially for the microorganisms. It consists of a veronal-acetate buffer (Michaelis) with 2.94 gm of sodium veronal and 1.94 gm of sodium acetate made up to 100 ml with distilled water. The Kellenberger buffer is prepared by mixing 5 ml of veronal acetate, 13 ml of distilled water, 7 ml of 0.1 N HCl, and 0.25 ml of $CaCl_2$ (1.0 M) and then adjusting the pH to 6.0 with HCl. The fixative solution is prepared by making a solution of 1% osmium tetroxide in the Kellenberger buffer. The washing fluid is obtained by dissolving 0.5 gm of uranyl acetate in 100 ml of the buffer. Fixation is made in the solution of osmium tetroxide for 16 hours. Then it is washed in uranyl acetate for two hours at room temperature.

e. Terzakis Fixative (1968). This fixation is accomplished first by immersing the material in a solution of 2.5% glutaraldehyde in 0.1 M sodium citrate for 15 to 60 minutes. Then, after washing, the material is placed in a solution of 1% osmium tetroxide in sodium citrate for 15 to 60 minutes. Then one can wash the material for one to two minutes in a solution of 0.1 M sodium acetate and put it in a 0.5% uranyl acetate aqueous solution for 20 minutes. Last, it is washed in 0.1 M sodium acetate for two minutes and dehydrated.

5. Technique of Fixation

This can be done in different ways according to the technique used in the culture. Taking into account the precautions already described, two processes are possible. Either remove the coverslips from the culture flasks and immerse them immediately in the fixative solution, or immediately pour the fixative solution into the flasks containing the tissues (after having removed the culture medium). The specimens are fixed at 2° to 4°. The times of fixation vary widely according to the material: For cells that have been placed upon their support, times of 5 to 15 minutes seem to be sufficient. For cells in suspension or organ cultures the time will be more like 1 to 18 hours. (One hour usually seems to be satisfactory.)

C. Washing

After fixation with the aldehydes, a careful washing of the preparations is recommended. The washing fluid must have a correctly chosen osmolality. In fact (Fahimi and Drochmans, 1965), it may cause the same artifacts as the fixative. Therefore, the use of a slightly hypertonic washing fluid is recommended. One can use the buffer used for the fixation, readjusting its osmolality with sucrose for instance. For organs three changes of 10 minutes each represent the minimum washing.

D. Postfixation

After using aldehydes, a second fixation is absolutely necessary to avoid the extraction of certain components (lipids). The solutions can have a pH and osmolality different from those of the aldehyde, but a light hypertonicity gives the best results.

The substance which is the most used is osmium tetroxide, alone or in solution (Dalton fixative). It can be used alone at a concentration of 1 or 2% or in the same buffer as for the fixation with the glutaraldehyde. The duration of this fixation is not critical: 15 minutes is sufficient for spreading cells, 30 minutes to two hours for suspended cells or organs. This fixation preferably should be cold. A subsequent washing is not necessary.

E. Dehydration

Different techniques can be used for dehydration. Some precautions are necessary, especially for cellular cultures. This dehydration must be as thorough as possible and very quick. The problem remains the same whatever the method chosen; it consists of embedding the hydrated objects in a resin mixture only partially or not at all miscible in water. In the general case of embeddings in pellets or on glass supports, one of the following methods can be used:

1. Dehydration in a gradient of alcohol, passing it through propylene oxide, and then embedding it in resin

2. Dehydration in a gradient of acetone followed immediately by embedding in resin

Many authors have indicated the way to obtain a good dehydration. Varied times for each change have been proposed. In the ordinary case of embedding with Epon or Araldite, one could work in the following manner:

70% ethanol	twice 2 minutes	or twice 5 minutes
95% ethanol	twice 2 minutes	or twice 10 minutes

Absolute ethanol   twice 2 minutes   or twice 15 minutes
Propylene oxide   twice 4 minutes   or twice 15 minutes
Propylene oxide and resin, 3 : 1   3 minutes
Propylene oxide and resin, 1 : 1   3 minutes   or 3 to 6 hours
Propylene oxide and resin, 1 : 3   15 minutes
Resin   twice 2 hours at 35°   or overnight
                                                      pure resin 1 hour
                                                      at 35°
Final resin   Final resin

All the experiments are made at room temperature. In an acetone gradient the following average times are used:

30% acetone	5 minutes
50% acetone	5 minutes
70% acetone	5 minutes
95% acetone	twice 10 minutes
Absolute acetone	three times 15 minutes
Acetone and resin	overnight (open flask)
Pure resin	1 hour at 35°
Final resin	

If the culture is being made on a particular support (Formvar, carbon coat, millipore filters, mica, etc.), dehydration can be made in the same manner. On the contrary, for supports such as collodion or Epon slides, some precautions must be taken. With Epon slides, ethanol and propylene oxide would be preferred. With the collodion film, after absolute ethanol, the support detaches itself from the coverslips and floats on the propylene oxide. The process is then the same as for tissue fragments. These methods

TABLE III

SCHEDULE FOR DEHYDRATION WITH ETHANOL AND HPMA[a]

Ethanol, 35%	for 10 minutes
Ethanol, 50%	for 10 minutes
Ethanol, 75%	for 10 minutes
Ethanol, 90%	for 10 minutes
HPMA, 90%	three changes, 15 minutes each
HPMA, 95%	for 15 minutes
HPMA, 97%	for 15 minutes
HPMA/Epon 2/1	for 15 minutes
HPMA/Epon 1/1	for 15 minutes
HPMA/Epon 1/2	for 30 minutes
Pure Epon mixture	three changes, 10 minutes each
Pure Epon mixture and polymerization	

[a] From Brinkley et al. (1967).

TABLE IV
SCHEDULE FOR DEHYDRATION WITH ETHANOL[a]

Ethanol, 30%	for 15 minutes
Ethanol, 70%	two changes, 30 minutes each
Ethanol, 70%, and Epon mixture	for 1 hour at room temperature
Ethanol, 70%, and Epon mixture	for 1 hour at 37°
Epon mixture	overnight at room temperature
Pure Epon mixture and polymerization	

[a] From Idelman (1964).

cannot be used for cultures in plastic flasks. Indeed, plastic flasks are usually attacked by propylene oxide or acetone. Two solutions are therefore recommended:

1. A dehydration with ethanol and hydroxypropylmethacrylate (HPMA) according to Brinkley et al. (1967). (See Table III.)

2. A dehydration with 70% ethanol or absolute ethanol and embedding in Epon mixture (Idelman, 1964). (See Table IV.)

This second solution is simple and gives complete satisfaction. It is, above all, convenient for the preservation of lipids.

F. Embedding

This step is usually performed in epoxy resins. Araldite or Epon. Different mixtures have been proposed (Moppert and Hamann, 1967), but the original schedules of Glauert et al. (1956) and Luft (1961) seem to be excellent. The preparation of these resin mixtures does not present any difficulty (Table V). In some cases an Epon–Araldite mixture can be used (Voelz and Dworkin, 1962) (Table VI).

The polymerization of these mixtures is done at 60° for 24 to 72 hours. In the case of organs, the embedding is performed very simply: The objects are placed in a gelatin capsule where a drop of the whole mixture has been put. In the case of thin layers of cultured cells, some modifications can be made.

1. Flask Cultures

Cellular embeddings that have been treated in a culture flask can be treated in two manners:

1. The definitive embedding is made in the flask itself by replacing the different solutions with the final mixture in a sufficient quantity to cover the cellular layer on a low thickness (1 to 2 mm). The polymeriza-

TABLE V
Epon and Araldite Mixtures

Epon[a]

Mixture A	{ Epikote 812	62 ml
	{ Dodecenyl succinic anhydride (DDSA)	100 ml
Mixture B	{ Epikote 812	100 ml
	{ Methyl nadic anhydride (MNA)	89 ml
Accelerator	Dimethyl aminomethyl phenol (DMP 30)	1.5 to 2%

Araldite[b]		Araldite[c]	
Araldite 502	27 ml	Araldite MCY 212	10 ml
DDSA	23 ml	Hardener HY 964	10 ml
DMP 30	1.5 to 2%	Accelerator DY 064	0.3 to 0.5 ml

[a] From Luft (1961). The proportions of the mixture A and mixture B are proportional to the length of time wanted and to the quality of the different products. For instance, one can mix mixture A (15 ml), mixture B (15 ml), and accelerator (0.6 ml). If the proportion of mixture A is increased, the embeddings are softer. If the mixture B is increased, they are harder.

[b] From Luft (1961).

[c] From Glauert et al. (1956) modified.

tion presents no difficulty. One has simply to break the flask in order to take out the polymerized resin slides, on which the cellular layer is embedded.

2. The other embedding is also made in the flask. The top can be broken or pierced (plastic flasks). Gelatin capsules filled with resin are then turned over selected areas of the cellular layer. The whole system is then left, as it is, for polymerization.

2. Embedding of Cells Previously Cultivated on Support

In a first phase, one selects a group of cells or one cell. In most cases, the rigid support on which the culture was made can be easily removed. Nevertheless, this stage sometimes presents certain difficulties. This is

TABLE VI
Epon–Araldite Mixture[a]

Substances	Concentration (ml)
Epikote 812	25
Araldite MCY 212	20
DDSA	60
DMP 30	1.5 to 2%

[a] From Voelz and Dworkin (1962).

why it is necessary to proceed according to the method recommended by Breton-Gorius (1968): The polymerization must begin at 60°, for a period of 3–6 hours, and the degree of polymerization is often controlled. When the hardness is sufficient, the coverslip is detached. One can also detach the coverslip by thermic shock or liquid nitrogen.

a. **Carbon.** In the case of a carbon support, after examination, one can mark the area with a diamond tip (Robbins and Gonatas, 1964). A gelatin capsule filled with resin is then turned over the selected area, and the whole system is submitted to polymerization (Howatson and Almeida, 1958).

b. **Glass or Mica.** With a glass or mica support, the process is identical. The capsule is turned over on the chosen spot, and the coverslip works itself loose easily (Gorycki, 1966).

c. **Formvar or Collodion.** In the case of a Formvar or collodion support, the coverslip detaches easily after polymerization and sometimes before. It is therefore possible to embed it easily.

d. **Epon.** For cultures performed on an Epon support, the slide is cut into fragments, and these are embedded in the gelatin capsules.

e. **Millipore Filters.** For millipore filters, the support being rigid and able to be completely embedded, embedding takes place according to the type of result required, e.g., a simple fragment of tissue, or according to a particular plan (Dalen and Nevalainen, 1968). It is necessary to point out that the filter becomes transparent in acetone.

G. Marking of Objects

In most cases the problem is to observe cells or organs situated in a defined portion of the embedding. It is therefore indispensible to be able to mark the important areas.

For monolayers, the examination of the embedding on the coverslip under phase contrast microscope allows a marking of the cells (Sutton, 1965). It is equally possible to stain the objects, during dehydration, with a basic stain (Gorycki, 1966). This staining has no effect on the quality of the sections nor on the preservation of the cells. It is equally possible to select a particularly interesting field by first making thick sections (0.5–1.0 μ), which are examined under the photonic microscope after staining (Bloom, 1960). One can use Azur Blue B in an aqueous solution of 0.1% with 0.1 N NaOH added, just before use, in a quantity sufficient to obtain a pH of 10. The staining process is performed in a few seconds.

H. Sections

In the case of embeddings in gelatin capsules, the pyramids are cut in the ordinary way and the sections collected on empty grids or covered with a membrane (Formvar, collodion, etc.) with or without carbon. For embeddings of cells cultivated on a support, it is sometimes interesting to remove the sections in a particular way. Several methods can be used. If the supports have been stuck on gelatin capsules before polymerization, one can obtain sections in a plane parallel or perpendicular to the surface of the cell layer by adopting the technique of Breton-Gorius (1968).

If the embeddings are made in an Epon layer, after having selected the convenient area, a small disk including this area is punched out or cut with a knife. The piece obtained is stuck, according to the preferred direction, on an Epon capsule previously polymerized with the embedding mixture itself (Brinkley et al., 1967) or, more simply, with sealing wax. These pieces can be used equally well in a holder with nippers.

I. Staining of Sections

Sections are, in general, contrasted by salts of heavy metals (uranium or lead) before examination under the electron microscope (Karnovsky, 1961; Reynolds, 1963; Venable and Coggeshall, 1965). Nevertheless, in the case of cell cultures, certain authors recommend a staining en masse.

These contrast stainings are used after fixation (Kellenberger et al., 1958) or equally well during dehydration. In this case weak solutions, 0.2 to 5%, of uranyl acetate in water or in ethanol are used.

Certain authors also recommend the use of phosphotungstic acid (a 1% solution in water).

J. Special Techniques

Apart from the techniques used for the ultrastructural examination of cell cultures and organ cultures, the cytologists now use some particular methods, already used for other materials, which allow a more precise study of cellular components and their physiology.

Without going into the details of these techniques, we shall indicate simply the few precautions which must be taken in the case of cellular or invertebrate organ cultures.

1. Cytochemical Techniques

It is now possible to realize specific contrasts for cellular components such as the polysaccharides (Thiery, 1967) and lipids (Seligman *et al.*, 1966) or preferential contrast such as for nucleoproteins (Yotsuyanagi, 1960; Bernhard, 1969).

In the same way, one can use some specific enzymes, e.g., pepsin, trypsin, pronase, on ultrafine sections (Monneron, 1966; Monneron and Bernhard, 1966; W. Anderson and André, 1968).

For all these investigations, the tissues embedded in epoxy resin after aldehyde fixation (nucleoproteins) or double fixation can be used and give valuable results. No change is to be added to the general schedule which we have described for the embedding of cells and organs in culture. Likewise, for the demonstration of intracellular enzymatic activities (Ahrens and Weissenfels, 1969), the incubation of tissues can be made in culture flasks.

For enzymatic digestions with RNase or DNase, another embedding mixture is required, i.e., the glycol methacrylate (Leduc and Bernhard, 1967). In this case, it is necessary to work on a cellular pellet or, after preinclusion, in fibrinogen or agar since the capsules have to be closed for the uv polymerization. It is not possible to turn them over the supports used to make the culture. The plastic flasks cannot be used since the glycol methacrylate attacks them.

2. Autoradiography and Immunochemistry at a High Resolution

These techniques, which have now been developed to a great extent, can easily be applied to the culture of cells and invertebrate organs.

For autoradiography, the radioactive components are directly introduced into the culture medium (Bergeron and Droz, 1968).

For the detection of immunological complexes in the cell, substances visible under the electron microscope (Sternberger, 1967) or enzymes (Avrameas and Bouteille, 1968) are used. All the reactions can be made in culture flasks.

No particular change must be made to the general process of preparation of objects for ultrastructural study.

III. RESULTS

The joint use of cellular or organic cultures and of the electron microscope proves very promising. Nevertheless, the number of works based on these methods is still limited, and it is restricted, above all, in the section of cytopathological or endocrinological studies.

We shall examine here some of the results obtained so far in both cellular culture and organotypical culture.

A. Cytological Study of the Culture of Cells or Organs

A small number of works concern the cytology of the culture of healthy cells, and they have been concerned chiefly with comparing the results to those obtained for unhealthy tissues.

In this way Vago (1959) and, later, Vago and Croissant (1963) examined, for the first time under the electron microscope, cultures of fibroblasts from the ovaric case of the Lepidoptera *Bombyx mori.* Some of the healthy fibroblasts are very vacuolized and appear to undergo a degenerating process. The others, similar to those of the vertebrates, show mitochondria, ergastoplasm, storage materials, and a round homogeneous nucleus.

In organotypical cultures of the dorsal vessel of the Coleoptera *Melolontha melolontha,* Devauchelle *et al.* (1969) have rediscovered pericardial cells (Hoffman, 1966) with a very developed vacuolized system. On the other hand, the examination of connective cells and fatty tissue cells reveals a structure that is analogous to those of cells taken directly from the insect (Figs. 1–3).

After observing cellular lines in the culture of the haemocytes of the Lepidoptera *Chilo suppressalis,* Mitsuhashi (1967) noticed that, after an accidental infection by an iridescent virus [*Chilo* iridescent virus (CIV)], some cells could multiply themselves without apparently forming viral particles. By contrast, when the culture medium tended to become exhausted, the CIV reappeared: The virus would appear when the conditions of culture become unfavorable.

In the same way, Filshie *et al.* (1967), while examining three different cellular lines (one line originating from *Antheraea eucalypti,* one from *Aedes aegypti,* and the last from *Drosophila melanogaster*), found particles of about 450-Å diameter. In *D. melanogaster* they invade the nuclei of most of the cells. With the two other cultures these particles are found when the cells are exposed to *Bacillus thuringiensis* crystals (with *A. eucalypti*) or Murray Encephalitis Virus or Japanese B Encephalitis Virus (with *A. aegypti*).

Thus, under the influence of external agents, virus, or bacterial crystals, or simply when the culture substance is nearly exhausted, the ultra-

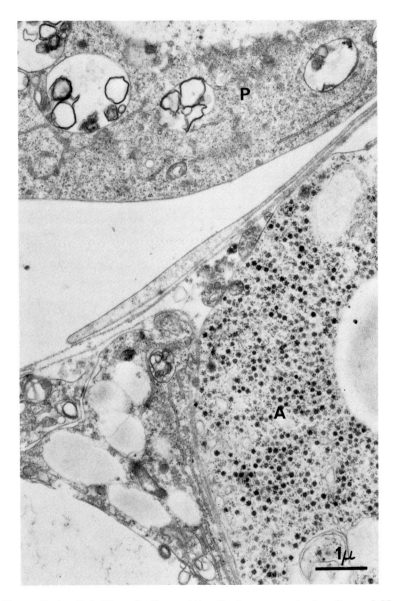

FIG. 1. Pericardial (P) and adipose (A) cells from organotypic culture of *Melolontha melolontha*.

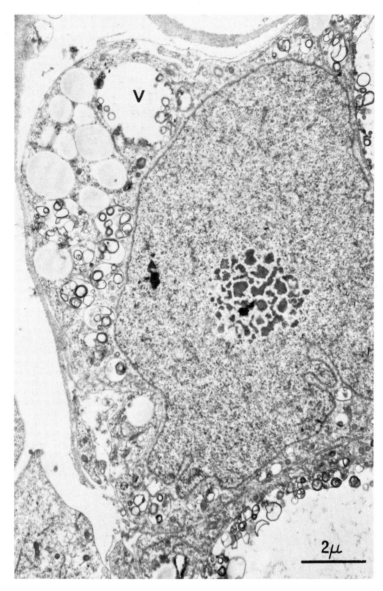

FIG. 2. Pericardial cell from organotypic culture of the dorsal vessel of *Melolontha melolontha*. Note large cytoplasmic vacuoles (V) containing membranous structures.

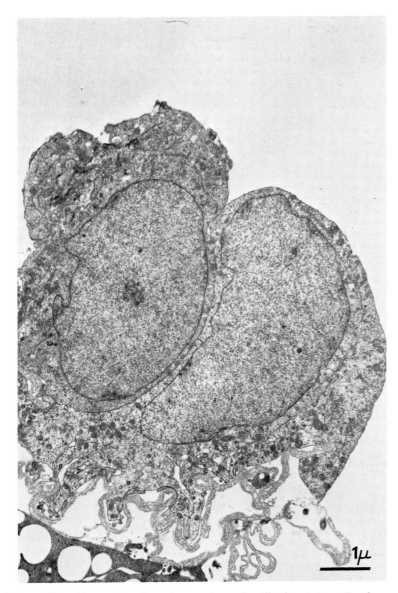

FIG. 3. Ultrathin section through a nucleus of a fibroblast from *Bombyx mori* ovarian tissue culture infected with nuclear polyhedrosis virus.

structural examination of cellular lines of apparently healthy invertebrates, or of the same lines infected on purpose, reveals the existence of
viral particles which exist in a latent state.

B. Cytopathological Study of Cells in Culture

It is chiefly in the cytopathological field that the cellular cultures have
been examined under the electron microscope. The investigations concern cellular cultures of invertebrates infected by invertebrate virus, by
vertebrate virus, or by plant virus.

1. Culture of Invertebrate Cells Infected by the Invertebrate Viruses

The examination of fibroblasts of *Bombyx mori* infected by Nuclear
Polyhedrosis (Vago and Croissant, 1963) has permitted the study of the
cycle of replication of the virus *in vitro*. In the presence of the virus, the
cells undergo a series of changes. First, a nuclear hypertrophy appears
without any marked alteration of the cytoplasmical organites. In the
nucleus, faint electron opaque zones are formed which increase progressively. In the interior of these zones, more or less elongated rod-shaped
elements are formed. Groups of rods appear in the nucleoplasma and the
polyhedra (Fig. 4). The latter, in cultured cells, are always large in size,
and some of them are even gigantic. This phenomenon is probably related to a certain deviation of the metabolism of cells cultivated *in vitro*.

The ultrastructural study of a line of haemocytar cells of the Lepidoptera *Chilo suppressalis* allowed Mitsuhashi (1966) to follow the development of an iridescent virus (CIV) which multiplies itself actively in
the cytoplasm of cells. Bellet and Mercer (1964) were also able to follow
in vitro the development of the *Sericesthis* iridescent virus (SIV) on
cells of *Antheraea eucalypti*. The infected cells appear to be large with
a dense nucleus. In the cytoplasm, viral particles are found in a dispersed state or linked to an amorphous zone. At this place some capsides
are found, some of which contain an electron opaque material. The virions
should form at this place. The "release" of the virus has been followed.
The virus acquires a supplementary covering, which comes from the
plasmic membrane of the host cell.

These different aspects of the replication cycle of the virus are difficult
to follow in the tissues of the insect. So, the examination of cellular cultures appears particularly interesting (Grace, 1962); some stages of the
cycle are very apparent in these cultures.

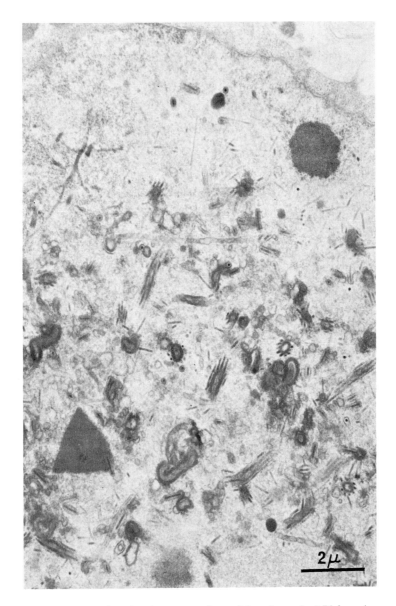

Fig. 4. Two cells migrating from an explant of dorsal vessel of *Blabera fusca*.

2. Culture of Cells of Invertebrates Infected by the Vertebrate Viruses

The cells of the mosquito *Aedes aegypti* were used by Filshie and Rehacek (1968) to study the morphology of the viruses of vertebrates, i.e., Murray Valley Encephalitis (M.V.E.) Virus and Japanese Encephalitis (J.E.) Virus. The examination of the cells under the electron microscope proved to be interesting in many ways. In the case of an infection with the M.V.E., the cells present hardly any cytological alterations. On the contrary, the cells infected with the J.E. present aspects of autolysis. Some stages of the cycle of the virus were specified: The infection results from the injection of particles which form clusters by phagocytosis. The assemblage of the viruses results from the endoplasmic reticulum (Arbovirus, Group B).

The comparison with the results obtained on the cultures of vertebrate cells shows that invertebrate cells represent a complementary material which is very interesting in this field of the virology.

3. Culture of Cells of Invertebrates Infected by the Plant Viruses

Several works have shown the interest of the culture of cells of insect embryos in the study of plant viruses transmitted by arthropods.

In the primary cultures of the leafhopper embryo (*Nephotettix cincticeps*), Mitsuhashi (1965) studied the development of the Rice Dwarf Virus (R.D.V.). In its natural state this insect transmits the disease and the leafhoppers are contaminated by the transovarial transmission of the virus. The examination of the contaminated cells shows deep changes: appearance of intracytoplasmic granules and presence of small particles 30 mμ in diameter. These granules, which are observed in other cases, appear in the case of cellular degeneration. The virus particles appear in long spirals in contrast to what is observed in insects. Nevertheless, these particles are smaller than the virus, i.e., 30 mμ against 70 mμ.

Another virus responsible for a plant disease, the Wound Tumor Virus (W.T.V.) has been studied in the same way in cultures of the embryonic cells of an insect, *Macrosteles falscifrons*, which, of course, is not a vector of this disease (Hirumi and Maramorosch, 1968). Seven days after the inoculation of the cultures, the building areas of the virus become visible in a moderately electron opaque viroplasm or in the rest of the cytoplasm, but never in the nucleus.

These works show the interest presented by the cultures of arthropod vector cells, carriers of disease in the study of the plant viruses. In fact, while it is often difficult to see the infecting agent in the insect, the whole

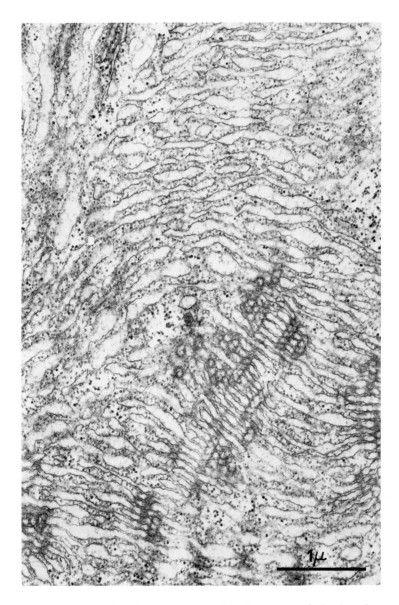

FIG. 5. Annulate lamellae observed after 20 days in organotypical cultured oocytes of *Nereis diversicolor*. From Durchon *et al.* (1965); courtesy of A. Dhainaut.

cycle can be studied in the culture. In this case, the specificity host virus is nevertheless no longer respected.

C. Endocrinological Study on Organotypical Cultures

Organotypical cultures and the electron microscope have been used by Durchon *et al.* (1964, 1965) for endocrinological problems. In their works, the authors have studied the influence of the cerebral hormone of the *Nereis* on the development of oocytes *in vitro*.

Organotypical cultures alone permit experimental variations in the hormonal conditions which act on the sexual activity of these worms, and the study with the electron microscope allows one to follow the ultrastructural changes which appear in the germinal cells.

If the oocytes of *Nereis diversicolor* are cultivated in the presence of cerebral hormones, they do not undergo any change. If the hormone is absent, deep changes are observed, i.e., the disappearance of subcortical granules and, above all, the appearance of annulate lamellae (Fig. 5). These changes are identical to those observed during natural maturation.

Only the combined use of these methods is likely to lead to the solution of some of the problems which arise in endocrinology.

IV. CONCLUSION

The techniques which we have described allow us to resolve the majority of problems which arise when one wants to observe cellular or organ cultures of invertebrates under the electron microscope. The few results which we have shown are particularly promising, and it is hoped that in other fields some problems can be resolved by using these methods.

REFERENCES

Ahrens, R., and Weissenfels, N. (1969). *Histochemie* **19**, 248.
Anderson, N., and Doane, F. W. (1967). *Stain Technol.* **42**, 169.
Anderson, W., and Andre, J. (1968). *J. Microsc. (Paris)* **7**, 343.
Avrameas, S., and Bouteille, M. (1968). *Exp. Cell Res.* **53**, 166.
Aziz, P., and Davies, M. E. (1968). *Stain Technol.* **43**, 237.
Bellett A. J. D., and Mercer, E. M. (1964). *Virology* **24**, 645.
Bergeron, M., and Droz, B. (1968). *J. Microsc. (Paris)* **7**, 51.
Bernhard, W. (1969). *J. Ultrastruct. Res.* **27**, 250.
Bloom, W. (1960). *J. Biophys. Biochem. Cytol.* **7**, 191.
Bornstein, M. B. (1958). *Lab. Invest.* **7**, 134.

Breton-Gorius, J. (1968). *J. Microsc. (Paris)* **7**, 95.

Brinkley, B. R., Murphy, P., and Richardson, L. C. (1967). *J. Cell Biol.* **35**, 279.

Charret, R., and Fauré-Fremiet, E. (1967). *J. Microsc. (Paris)* **6**, 1063.

Curgy, J. J. (1968). *J. Microsc. (Paris)* **7**, 63.

Dalen, H., and Nevalainen, T. J. (1968). *Stain Technol.* **43**, 217.

Dalton, A. J. (1955). *Anat. Rec.* **121**, 281.

Descarries, L. (1967). *J. Microsc. (Paris)* **6**, 313.

Devauchelle, G., Vago, C., Giannotti, J., and Quiot, J. M. (1969). *Entomophaga* **14**, 457.

Durchon, M., and Boilly, B. (1964). *C. R. Acad. Sci.* **259**, 1245.

Durchon, M., Boilly, B., and Dhainaut, A. (1965). *C. R. Soc. Biol.* **159**, 106.

Fahimi, H. D., and Drochmans, P. (1965). *J. Microsc. (Paris)* **4**, 725.

Filshie, B. K., and Rehacek, J. (1968). *Virology* **34**, 435.

Filshie, B. K., Grace, T. D. C., Poulson, D. F., and Rehacek, J. (1967). *J. Invertebr. Pathol.* **9**, 271.

Firket, H. (1966). *Stain Technol.* **41**, 189.

Glauert, A. M., Rogers, G. E., and Glauert, R. H. (1956). *Nature (London)* **178**, 803.

Gomori, G. (1946). *Amer. J. Clin. Path.* **10**, 177.

Gomori, G. (1955). *In* "Methods in Enzymology" (S. P. Colowick and N. O. Kaplan, eds.), Vol. I. Academic, New York.

Gordon, G. B., Miller, L. R., and Bensch, K. G. (1963). *Exp. Cell Res.* **31**, 440.

Gorycki, M. A. (1966). *Stain Technol.* **41**, 37.

Grace, T. D. C. (1962). *Virology* **18**, 33.

Heyner, S. (1963). *Stain Technol.* **38**, 335.

Hirumi, H., and Maramorosch, K. (1968). *Proc. Int. Colloq. Invertebr. Tissue Cult., 2nd, 1967* p. 203.

Hoffman, J. A. (1966). *C. R. Acad. Sci.* **262**, 1469.

Howatson, J. A., and Almeida, J. D. (1958). *J. Biophys. Biochem. Cytol.* **4**, 115.

Idelman, S. (1964). *J. Microsc. (Paris)* **3**, 715.

Karnovsky, M. J. (1961). *J. Biophys. Biochem. Cytol.* **11**, 729.

Kay, D. (1965). "Techniques for Electron Microscopy." Blackwell, Oxford.

Kellenberger, E., Ryter, A., and Sechaud, J. (1958). *J. Biophys. Biochem. Cytol.* **4**, 671.

Laschi, R., and Rizzoli, C. (1968). *J. Microsc. (Paris)* **7**, 533.

Leduc, E. H., and Bernhard, W. (1967). *J. Ultrastruct. Res.* **19**, 196.

Luft, J. H. (1961). *J. Biophys. Biochem. Cytol.* **9**, 409.

McCombs, R. M., Benyesh-Melnick, M., and Brunschwig, J. P. (1968). *J. Cell Biol.* **36**, 231.

Maser, M. D., Powell, T. E., and Philpott, C. W. (1967). *Stain Technol.* **12**, 175.

Millonig, G. (1961). *J. Appl. Phys.* **32**, 1637.

Mitsuhashi, J. (1965). *Jap. J. Appl. Entomol. Zool.* **9**, 137.

Mitsuhashi, J. (1966). *Appl. Entomol. Zool.* **1**, 199.

Mitsuhashi, J. (1967). *Nature (London)* **215**, 863.

Monneron, A. (1966). *J. Microsc. (Paris)* **5**, 583.

Monneron, A., and Bernhard, W. (1966). *J. Microsc. (Paris)* **5**, 697.

Moppert, J., and Hamann, W. (1967). *J. Microsc. (Paris)* **6**, 233.

Nishiura, M., and Ragan, S. R. (1960). *J. Biophys. Biochem. Cytol.* **7**, 411.

Palade, G. E. (1952). *J. Exptl. Med.* **95**, 285.

Pease, D. C. (1964). "Histological Techniques for Electron Microscopy," 2nd ed. Academic Press, New York.

Persijn, J. P., and Scherft, J. P. (1965). *Stain Technol.* **40**, 89.

Reynolds, E. S. (1963). *J. Cell Biol.* **17**, 208.

Robbins, E., and Gonatas, N. K. (1964). *J. Cell Biol.* **20**, 356.

Rosen, S. I. (1962). *Stain Technol.* **37**, 195.

Sabatini, D. D., Bensch, K.G, and Barnett, R. J. (1963). *J. Cell Biol.* **17**, 19.

Schultz, R. L., and Karlsson, U. (1965). *J. Ultrastruct. Res.* **12**, 187.

Seligman, A. M., Wasserkrug, H. L., and Hanker, J. S. (1966). *J. Cell Biol.* **30**, 424.

Sternberger, L. A. (1967). *J. Histochem. Cytochem.* **15**, 139.

Sutton, J. S. (1965). *Stain Technol.* **40**, 143.

Terzakis, J. A. (1968). *J. Ultrastruct. Res.* **22**, 168.

Thiery, J. P. (1967). *J. Microsc. (Paris)* **6**, 987.

Vago, C. (1959). *Entomophaga* **4**, 23.

Vago, C., and Croissant, O. (1963). *Ann. Epiphyt.* **14**, 43.

Venable, J. H., and Coggeshall, R. (1965). *J. Cell Biol.* **25**, 407.

Voelz, H., and Dworkin, M. (1962). *J. Bacteriol.* **84**, 943.

Yotsuyanagi, Y. (1960). *C. R. Acad. Sci.* **250**, 1522.

Zagury, D., Zeitoun, P., and Viette, M. (1966a). *C. R. Acad. Sci.* **262**, 1458.

Zagury, D., Zylberberg, L., and Zeitoun, P. (1966b). *C. R. Acad. Sci.* **262**, 2166.

4

ASEPTIC REARING OF INVERTEBRATES FOR TISSUE CULTURE

G. Meynadier

I. INTRODUCTION

Sterile techniques must be rigorously applied for successful tissue culture.

It is, in fact, often possible to dissect a specimen under satisfactorily sterile conditions and to remove a germ-free organ or tissue fragment.

When the size of the organism permits it, such an operation is feasible after thorough disinfection of the epidermis.

Unsuccessful tissue removals can result from several causes, however. Small size, irregular structure of the integument, roughness of the integument, or its folding in the intersegment zones are some examples. Certain internal organs, such as the intestines and trachea, which are normally contaminated and which are difficult to culture, are generally treated with undesirably strong doses of antibiotics. The use of the latter is, of course, excluded when the tissue is destined for *in vitro* pathogenesis studies, such as with rickettsiae or protozoa.

For the above reasons it is desirable to obtain invertebrates totally free of saprophytic germs. Sterile growth of the organisms is the satisfactory solution to this problem.

Sterile growth of organisms for tissue culture has been accomplished in only a limited number of cases. Thus, Vago *et al.* (1961a,b) and Fosset and Chastang (1963) developed sterile techniques for rearing insects, Demal (1961) grew the dipteran *Calliphora erythrocephala* (Meig.), and Mitsuhashi and Maramorosch (1964) grew various leafhoppers under sterile conditions.

Sterile rearing of diverse invertebrates has been developed for other purposes, principally for the study of nutritional factors and their role in the development of organisms. Problems involving the phenomena of symbiosis or of viral latency have also called for the use of this technique. The first studies were undertaken at the beginning of the twentieth century with insects. Delcourt and Guyenot (1911), Guyenot (1917), and Wollman (1911, 1921, 1926) worked with the Diptera and Dictyoptera. Trager (1935, 1948) and, later, Akov (1962) grew larvae of the mosquito *Aedes aegypti* L. under sterile conditions while Glaser (1938) and Monroe (1962) accomplished the same with *Musca domestica* L. For *Drosophila melanogaster* Meig. such studies were undertaken by Sang (1956), David (1959), and Sang and King (1961), while for *Hylemyia antiqua* Meig., Friend *et al.* (1959) and Pascal *et al.* (1967) made similar efforts. Finally, the sterile rearing of the dipteran *Pseudosarcophaga affinis* Fall. was undertaken by House (1954) and House and Barlow (1960).

Among the Lepidoptera, the following have been reared under sterile conditions: *Chilo simplex* Butler (Ishii and Hirano, 1955; Kamano, 1964; Kamano and Fukaya, 1965), *Pectinophora gossypiella* Saund. (Vanderzant, 1957), *Galleria mellonella* L. (Waterhouse, 1959; Vago *et al.*, 1963), *Argyrotaenia velutinana* Walker (Rock *et al.*, 1964), and *Pseudaletia unipuncta* Haw. (Goodwin, 1966).

Attempts at sterile rearing of Coleoptera appear more recently. Thus,

Hill (1965) reared *Ahasverus advena* Walt., Vanderzant (1965) reared *Anthonomus grandis* Boheman, and Charpentier (1968) reared *Aphodius constans* Duft, all under sterile conditions. Among the Homoptera, *Aphis fabae* Scop. was reared under aseptic conditions by Dadd and Krieger (1967).

Finally, only two cases have been mentioned for Orthoptera, those of *Gryllus bimaculatus* De Geer and *Acheta domesticus* L. (Vago and Fosset, 1965).

Apart from insects, there have been a few attempts at sterile rearing of invertebrates. Among these are the crustaceans *Daphnia magna* Strauss (Treillard, 1924, 1925) and *Tigriopus* and *Artemia* (Provasoli *et al.*, 1959), the gasteropod *Australorbis glabratus* Say (Chernin, 1957, 1959; Chernin and Schork, 1959), the annelid *Enchytraeus fragmentosus* Bell (Dougherty and Solberg, 1961), and a rotifer *Lecane inermis* Bryce (Dougherty *et al.*, 1961).

Special notice should be taken of nematodes, which are, after insects, the invertebrates whose sterile growth has most often been attempted. Examples are *Neoaplectana glaseri* Steiner (Glaser and Stoll, 1938; Glaser, 1940), *Radopholus similis* (Cobb) Thorne (Feder, 1958), and *Caenorhabditis briggsae* Dougherty and Nigon (Dougherty *et al.*, 1959; Dougherty and Hansen, 1956; Nicholas *et al.*, 1959, 1962).

Even though the goal of the majority of the attempts at sterile rearing was the study of the physiology of a particular organism, a trying preliminary problem has often been the elimination of microorganisms, as is the case with tissue culture. Therefore, the techniques reported in such cases can be valuable for tissue culture studies.

II. STERILE METHODS FOR REARING INVERTEBRATES

Extensive knowledge of the invertebrate and his environment, coupled with the use of bacteriological techniques, is required for successful sterile rearing.

A. Disinfection before Aseptic Rearing

1. Eggs

Disinfection of the eggs is the first undertaking. All authors are agreed that the eggs must be separated for successful disinfection.

In some cases the eggs are laid individually, without any cementing material, thus facilitating the gathering. Examples of this are flies and crickets, whose eggs can readily be gathered individually on meat or moist cotton.

For certain Lepidoptera (*Mamestra, Pieris*, etc.) the egg is normally deposited on the plant serving as the larva food. One can, however, facilitate the recovery of the eggs by providing strips of muslin or wax paper, to which the eggs do not stick. Beck and Stauffer (1950) used this technique for the lepidopteran *Pyrausta nubilalis* Hbn. as did Goodwin for the lepidopteran *Pseudaletia unipuncta* Haw., for which he provided pleated wax paper. Vanderzant and Reiser (1956) used a sheet of cellophane for the lepidopteran *Pectinophora gossypiella* Saund, while Hill collected eggs of the coleopteran *Ahasverus advena* Waltl on filter paper and then disinfected the ensemble.

In the majority of the above examples the eggs were gathered with tweezers. For the clustered eggs of *Pyrausta nubilalis*, however, Beck and Stauffer recommended separation by digestion of the mucus for a half hour in 2% trypsin buffered to pH 8.

A new technique was found by Mitsuhashi and Maramorosch (1963a) to deal with the laying problems of leafhoppers. A female is put in a mesh cage composed of two magnetic elements enclosing a small zone of the host plant leaf. A few days after the eggs are laid the leaf is shredded with a needle and the eggs are removed and deposited, before sterilization, on paper covered with albumin, to which they adhere.

The eggs, gathered by one of the above procedures, are put into test tubes, and the next step is their disinfection. The goal in this is to completely rid the chorion of germs without disturbing the development of the embryo for a satisfactory eclosion. The success of this operation consequently depends on several factors: the choice of an efficient general-purpose disinfectant, its concentration, the duration of the treatment, and the time chosen for the operation.

For the eggs of each species and for each disinfectant, Vago *et al.* (1961a) consider it necessary to determine hatching and disinfecting curves as a function of disinfectant concentration and duration of treatment and to stand in the overlapping zone of these curves. With the lepidopteran *Bombyx mori* L., selected as a prototype, these authors also determined the harmfulness of the treatment as a function of embryo development. Eggs of the same age which had been put in incubation the same day were divided into equal lots and subjected, at one day intervals, to identical disinfections. The fourth day of incubation was found to be the best time for disinfection; hatchings diminished rapidly thereafter to nil on the eighth day.

Authors generally do not emphasize the importance of the choice of the right time for this treatment. Beck and Stauffer (1950), however, disinfected *Pyrausta nubilalis* before appearance of the "blackhead" stage, while Barlow (1966) so treated *Musca domestica* L. eggs laid less than seven hours previously.

The disinfectants used all seem to be of about equal efficiency. Among them sodium hypochlorite (NaClO), of different forms and brands, potassium permanganate ($KMnO_4$), hydrogen peroxide (H_2O_2), mercuric chloride or "sublimate" ($HgCl_2$), formalin, alcohol, and quaternary ammonium compounds are frequently cited.

Thus, for sodium hypochlorite, Glaser (1940) disinfected eggs of the nematode *Neoaplectana glaseri* Steiner with Labaraque's solution while Chernin (1957) used a 5.25% solution for the mollusc *Austalorbis glabratus*. For eggs of Lepidoptera, Orthoptera, and Diptera, Vago et al. (1961a) diluted an 18° chlorometric titrating solution to 5%, allowing contact time to vary according to the organism. Monroe (1962) and Hill (1965) disinfect with sodium hypochlorite; Monroe uses 0.1% for 20 minutes with *Musca domestica* eggs, and Hill uses 1.0% for one minute with eggs of the coleopteran *Ahasverus advena*.

As for mercuric chloride, eggs of the dipterans *Calliphora vomitoria* L. and *Lucilia cesar* L. were disinfected with it by Wollman (1921), while it was used in the form of the solution of White (1931) to disinfect eggs of *Aedes aegypti* L. (Peleg and Trager, 1963) and of the lepidopteran *Pectinophora gossypiella* (Vanderzant and Reiser, 1956).

Trager (1935) simply used 80% alcohol to disinfect *Aedes aegypti* eggs.

The conjugated action of more than one disinfectant, used together or successively, is often recommended. For example, *Musca domestica* eggs have been disinfected by a 15-minute immersion in a solution composed of 5% sodium hypochlorite and 10% formalin followed by a one hour soak in White's solution (Glaser, 1938).

A mixture of sodium hydroxide and formalin coupled with a 70° alcohol rinse was used for *Pyrausta nubilalis* (Beck and Stauffer, 1950).

Eggs of *Bombyx mori* have been successively treated with potassium hydroxide and potassium permanganate because of the viricidal action of these compounds (Vago, 1954).

Eggs of the lepidopteran *Chilo suppressalis* Walker were disinfected with mercuric chloride and alcohol by Hirano and Ishii (1957), and those of the dipteran *Calliphora*, with caustic soda 2% and alcohol (Demal, 1961). Goodwin (1966) used successively formalin, detergent, and sodium hypochlorite on eggs of *Pseudaletia unipuncta*.

The above incomplete enumeration shows the variety of materials and techniques used for disinfecting eggs. In the same way, Greenberg

(1970) gives useful data in a paper concerning different chemicals used for maintaining the health of insect mass rearings.

The recent application of quaternary ammonium compounds (Hyamine, Zephiran, etc.) to this purpose deserves special mention. A comparative study of them for tissue culture work has been done by Martignoni and Milstead (1960). Akov (1962, 1963), Mitsuhashi and Maramorosch (1963b), and Barlow (1966) have since used these compounds to disinfect eggs of various Diptera and Homoptera.

2. Oothecae, Newly Hatched Invertebrates, Viviparous Invertebrates, and Nematodes

On certain occasions, relatively rare, the egg is not the starting material for sterile rearing. Such is the case with the oothecae of Dictyoptera and viviparous invertebrates. Disinfection is, however, accomplished with the same products as used on eggs.

For oothecae, the technique of soaking is simlar to that used with eggs (Wollman, 1926; Gier, 1947).

Few examples exist of disinfection of viviparous invertebrates for sterile rearing. For the dipteran *Agria* (*Pseudosarcophaga*) *affinis* Fall., House (1954) disinfects the gravid females in a 2.5% formalin bath before extracting the larvae, which are themselves given a similar bath before going into culture.

The same technique, but with sodium hypochlorite as disinfectant, permitted Vago *et al.* (1961a) to recover aseptically the embryo–larvae of aphids. The liberation of the larva was brought about in a sterile enclosure by pressing lightly on the abdomen.

For the nematode *Radopholus similis* (Cobb) Thorne, the females are disinfected with mercuric chloride, then rinsed by centrifugation in sterile water, with the young being recovered in a piece of sterile sponge (Feder, 1958).

The dilution technique was recommended by Treillard (1924) for gathering the young larvae of the cladoceran *Daphnia magna* Straus. The mature parthogenetic females are subjected repeatedly over a period of several days to baths in sterile water followed by rapid immersion in 10% hydrogen peroxide. The larvae obtained after such treatment are generally aseptic.

More recently, successive baths of antibiotic solutions have been used for the crustacean *Tigriopus* (Provasoli *et al.*, 1959), for the annelid *Enchytraeus fragmentosus* Bell (Dougherty and Solberg, 1961), and a species of Rotifera (Dougherty *et al.*, 1961). The antibiotics generally are based on penicillin and streptomycin sulfate.

Whatever the material disinfected and the mode of disinfection, the consensus is that repeated rinsings or rinsings in running distilled water (Sang, 1956) are necessary at the end of the operation. The objective in this is to rapidly stop all harmful action of the products used and to completely eliminate them from the surface of the material disinfected. Some authors, however, do not use such rinsings; instead they terminate the disinfection by an alcohol bath.

Experiments by the present writer on eggs of various insects indicate that alcohol adds nothing to the efficiency of the disinfection and that it can have a harmful effect, judging from the decrease seen in hatching yield. This effect is observed even if the alcohol treatment is followed by rinsing in sterile water (unpublished observations).

When the disinfection is finished the water is poured out; any remaining drops are taken up with a sterile pipette. One must avoid droplets adhering to the eggs or eggs sticking together at the bottom of the tube. Tapping the tube obliquely in the palm of the hand aids in separating the eggs and in throwing them up on the wall of the tube where they cling. They are then ready to be incubated.

3. Testing for Sterility

The disinfection over, the process of sterile growth should be accompanied by bacteriological and mycological testing. A few disinfected eggs, oothecae, embryos, or larvae are placed on samples of the media to verify the absence of germs. These media are the agars or nutritive broths of microbiology. If, after a few days of incubation, the control group reveals the presence of contamination, the corresponding lot of material has to be rejected as unfit for sterile rearing. If the material is found to be free of contamination the eggs or larvae are transferred aseptically onto the raising medium with tweezers or a seeder. A bit of agar sticking to the tip of the instrument aids in the operation. It also helps to avoid damaging the items transferred.

If a larva happens to hatch on the control medium, it can be transferred aseptically into the sterile enclosure for growth.

A test for sterility at the end of growth is recommended by some authors. In tissue culture experiments such testing can be done at the time the tissue is removed. During the growing period, food or dejecta can be tested by the above methods.

B. Rearing Conditions

The accomplishment of sterile rearing demands satisfactory conditions for development of the intended organism as well as avoidance of contamination by pathogenic or saprophytic germs.

1. Growth Vessels

This choice will be limited by the living conditions of the organism and the nature of the growth medium. Test tubes are useful for small organisms reared individually. Erlenmeyer flasks and other glassware serve for larger invertebrates or groups of organisms or when a large volume will be needed for a plant intended as food.

Whatever the vessel chosen, it should have an opening, easily stoppered with cotton, which is convenient for the manipulations of transplanting, sample taking, testing, etc. In all cases its cleansing should be easy and it should be disinfectable and autoclavable. Pyrex is recommended, but in some cases sterilizable transparent plastics such as polycarbonates (Makrolon) are convenient.

2. Growth Media

In the majority of studies with sterile rearings for physiological experiments, the objective has been to replace the natural food for the invertebrate by a food of chemically determined composition (holidic media: Dougherty, 1959). By so doing, the different factors necessary for the complete development of the organism can be isolated by varying the quantity of each constituent in the feed.

It is sometimes difficult to maintain a balance between the requirements of such investigations and that of having enough living material for the experiment envisioned. The use of less complicated feeds (oligidic and meridic media: Dougherty, 1959) should be considered in such cases.

On occasion, for example with phytophaga, the plant material for the nutritional needs of the animals under experiment can be conveniently reared under sterile conditions.

a. Aseptic Plant Cultivation. This technique has been recommended by several authors both for obtaining sterile living material for tissue culture (Vago et al., 1961a,b; Mitsuhashi and Maramorosch, 1964) and for the study of the transmission of plant viruses (Mitsuhashi and Maramorosch, 1963a,b) (Fig. 1). In addition, Feder (1958) has reared the nematode Radopholus similis under sterile conditions on root fragments maintained in culture using plant organ culture methods.

The sterile culture of plants requires the construction of a sterilizable unit convenient for the plant base and medium.

i. PLANT BASE. Experimenting has been done to develop a loose and homogeneous base giving good imbibition of the nutritive solution and assuring sufficient root penetration for supporting plants. It must not interfere with the behavior of the animal, e.g., the prenymphal bur-

FIG. 1. Aseptic rearing of the leafhopper *Euscelis plebejus* Fall. fed on *Pisum sativum*. The plant is cultivated on sand soaked with nutritive solution; l. leafhopper.

rowing of some Lepidoptera, and it should be convenient for the experiment intended.

Agar would seem to be the preferred material for a plant base, particularly for plants feeding invertebrates which do not move down on the substrate, such as aphids and leafhoppers. Other materials, however, are superior when there is a risk, particularly for the young, of drowning. Among these, Vago *et al.* (1961a) recommend fine river sand screened with a 0.6-mm mesh. The sand is washed and dehydrated in an oven and then put in the growth chamber. The unit is then given a preliminary sterilization in the autoclave at 130° for 30 minutes. In order to assure sufficient imbibition and avoid excessive saturation by the support solu-

tion, a strict ratio between weight of sand and volume of solution must
be maintained. This ratio has been established at 4 gm of sand for each
milliliter of solution.

    ii. SUPPORT SOLUTION. The nutritive solution, added to the plant base,
is composed of minerals (nitrogen, sulfur, potassium, phosphorus, magnesium, and calcium) necessary for plant growth. These materials are
used by Vago et al. (1961a) in the form of Heller and Knop's solutions.
To avoid certain deficiencies, they add 10 drops of Berthelot's solution,
a dilute mixture of rare elements, per liter of support solution. Their
nutritive solution also contains 4% glucose and growth factors (cysteine
hydrochloride $10^{-5} M$, naphthylacetic acid $10^{-6} M$, thiamine $(10^{-6} M)$.
These additions are all balanced out so that the above ratio of sand to
solution is kept.

    Rice plant (Oriza sativa L.) culture has been done, incidentally, using
simply a modified Kimura mineral solution containing $12\%_0$ agar (Mitsuhashi, 1965).

    After the above additions, the growth chamber is stoppered with cot-
ton and autoclaved 30 minutes at 110°. The ensemble is then a sterile
unit ready for use or storage.

    iii. SEED. The seed for the plants to be cultivated must be sterilized.
Several materials are suitable for this. The duration of treatment is a
function of the structure and convolutions of the integument. A calcium
hypochlorite solution was maintained at a concentration of $70\%_0$ by
Vago et al. (1961a) while stirring the seed in it to effect complete disinfection. With their process, times required are 10 minutes for Brassica
napus L.; 15 minutes for Cucumis melo L., Phaseolus vulgaris L., Raphanus sativus L., Trifolium repens L., and Zea mays L.; 20 minutes for
Pisum sativum L. and Ricinus communis L.; 30 minutes for Lactuca
sativa L.; and 60 minutes for Nicotiana glutinosa L.

    Sterilization of seeds of Secale cereale L., Callistephus chinensis Nees.,
Lactuca sativa L., Zea mays L., Medicago sativa L., and Trifolium
incarnatum L. can be had by a one-minute immersion in 70° ethanol and
then in a 0.1% solution of Hyamine 2389 (Mitsuhashi and Maramorosch,
1963b).

    Rice seed (Oriza sativa L.) can be disinfected by a one-minute im-
mersion in 70° ethanol followed by 10 minutes in a solution of 0.1%
mercuric chloride and 5% sodium chloride (Mitsuhashi, 1965).

    The elimination of the disinfectant, whatever its nature, from the seed
is brought about by repeated dipping (at least three times) or continuous
rinsing in sterile water.

    Planting of the seeds in the sterile unit can be carried out according to bacteriological practices, working beside a flame. It is, however, preferable to do the seeding in a sterile enclosure such as used in tissue culture laboratories or in a glove box which has been disinfected with hypochlorite solution and ultraviolet lamps. Before starting, the operator's hands should be thoroughly washed with soap and rinsed with alcohol.

The seed is planted deep so that the plants will be well rooted in the medium. For this, special long tweezers or pipettes convenient to the set-up may be desirable.

Tests to assure that the seeds are aseptic are done on microbiological culture media. This kind of test becomes very important when a number of grains are sown in the same enclosure. One should, in such a case, test the germination of each grain individually. The seedlings are not transferred into culture until 5 or 6 days after showing no fungal or bacterial development on these media.

The seeded units are incubated until the plants are large enough to serve as the animal food. When growth is at 20°–25°, this can be conveniently done using ultraviolet lamps which closely duplicate sunlight. (In France, Phytorel tubes are used.)

The preparation of the plants needs to be planned in advance since they should have a certain size before introducing the animals. The optimum feeding age varies among plants, being 8 days for *Zea mays*, 15 days for *Pisum sativum*, 25 days for *Ricinus communis*, 30 days for *Lactuca sativa*, 80 days for *Solanum lycopersicum*, 90 days for *Brassica napus*, etc.

b. Media Based on Natural Products. Sterile rearing on such media is relatively simple, even for nonphytophagous invertebrates.

Such is the case for the dictyopteran *Blattella germanica* L., which Wollman (1926) grew aseptically for long periods of time in glass flasks containing sterile feed (bran, bread, and milk).

The same applies to the lepidopteran *Galleria mellonella* L., whose larvae Vago et al. (1963) reared individually in large test tubes (20 × 200 mm) on a medium composed simply of one part pollen and two parts wax. The tubes, well stoppered with cotton, each contained 5 gm of the mixture. Sterilization was at 110° for 20 minutes. Subsequent addition of a few drops of yeast extract, filtered through a sterilizing membrane, is recommended. The resulting medium was solidified in slanted tubes covered with flame-sterilized aluminum foil.

For sterile rearing of the orthopterans *Gryllus bimaculatus* De Geer and *Acheta domesticus* L., Vago and Fosset (1965) used a medium composed as follows:

bran	25 gm
chopped salad leaves	25 gm
chopped carrots	25 gm
complete diet for lab animals	25 gm
water	70 ml

The mixture is homogenized and sterilized 20 minutes at 110°; subsequent addition of filtered yeast extract is counseled.

Few aseptic rearings of Coleoptera have been done. A medium for *Ahasverus advena* Walt proposed by Hill (1965) had the following composition:

9 parts rolled oats
9 parts wheatfeed
1 part dry yeast
vitamin B

Sterilization is done in propylene oxide vapor or by autoclaving 20 minutes at 115°. Rearing conditions are 30° and 80% relative humidity.

The coprophagous coleopteran *Aphodius constans* Duft. was successfully reared aseptically by Charpentier (1968) on an enriched natural medium composed as follows:

bull dung (40% H_2O)	250 gm
casein	15 gm
soya flour	10 gm
dry brewers' yeast	10 gm
deionized water	200 ml

The medium, set in 25-ml test tubes on the slant, is sterilized 20 minutes at 120°.

The following easily prepared sterile culture medium was proposed by David (1959) for *Drosophila melanogaster* Meig.:

yeast, dry weight	96 gm
corn flour, dry weight	96 gm
agar	15 gm
Nipagin	6 gm
H_2O to total weight of 1200 gm	

After mixing, the medium is autoclaved 15 minutes at 115°.

For *in vitro* studies of organ morphogenesis, Demal (1961) rears the dipteran *Calliphora erythrocephala* on the slightly modified medium (Demal, personal communication) given in Table I. The medium is homogenized, brought to boiling three times, and poured into erlenmeyer flasks. A trace of Nipagin and a small piece of lean meat are then added. The flasks, stoppered with cotton, are sterilized 20 minutes at 120°. The quantities in Table I serve for four flasks, each adequate for feeding 40 to 50 insects.

TABLE I
REARING MEDIUM FOR *Calliphora erythrocephala* MEIG.[a]

Substances	Concentration (gm)	(ml)
NaCl	0.9	
CaCl$_2$	0.02	
NaHCO$_3$	0.02	
NaH$_2$PO$_4$·2H$_2$O	0.65	
KH$_2$PO$_4$	0.75	
Casein	10	
Bakers' yeast	1	
Agar	1	
Marmite[b]	10	
Distilled water		1000

[a] From Demal (1961).
[b] The Marmite Food Extract Company, Ltd., London.

Another dipteran, *Hylemyia antiqua* Meig., was reared under sterile conditions by Pascal *et al.* (1967) on a medium composed as follows:

ground whole onions	20 gm
potato starch	0.6 gm
whole soya flour	0.4 gm
lactic casein	0.4 gm
sucrose	0.4 gm
brewers' yeast	0.5 gm
agar	1 gm

The onion is obtained from mature bulbs which have been autoclaved 20 minutes at 120° and then run through a blender. The medium is poured into erlenmeyer flasks and sterilized 20 minutes at 120°.

Sterile rearing of larvae of *Aedes aegypti* in a medium composed of 0.5% liver extract in distilled water was done by Trager (1935). After adjusting the pH to 7 he added enough brewers' yeast for a concentration of 1%. The adults were fed with defibrinated blood (Trager in Glaser, 1943).

More recently, media based on liver extract have been successfully used for raising various nematodes, especially after chicken embryo extract was added to the medium. In some cases this modification permitted several generations to be reared aseptically (Nicholas *et al.*, 1959; Dougherty *et al.*, 1959).

Liver extract was also employed for the annelid *Enchytraeus fragmentosus* Bell in a two-phase medium. The medium is composed of a semisolid layer of 1.5% agar–agar which is enriched with liver extract during cooling; this is then covered with a thin liquid layer of liver extract (Dougherty and Solberg, 1961).

Another liver extract medium was fortified with malted milk and vitamins and used with success for the sterile rearing of the rotifer *Lecane inermis* Bryce (Dougherty *et al.*, 1961).

c. **Meridic and Holidic Media.** These media are made either from simple constituents to which chemical products of defined composition are added (meridic media) or totally from chemical compounds of definite composition (holidic media). For the first of these, preparation is relatively easy. For the second, however, the formula is often long and the preparation tedious because of the number of ingredients and problems of compounding the mixture. The more easily prepared media tend to be preferred even though the holidic media do play an important role in nutritional studies and sometimes in tissue culture rearings (Figs. 2 and 3).

i. MEDIA FOR DIPTERA. The medium for *Aedes aegypti* L. of Trager (1948) and the derivative one of Akov are composed as indicated in Table II. The casein is finely ground in a mortar and screened. Portions of 50 mg are put in each 5-ml tube, which is then stoppered with cotton and sterilized 1½–2 hours at 160°.

FIG. 2. Aseptic rearing of *Lycophotia saucia* Hb. The medium is solidified in the slanted tube.

FIG. 3. Aseptic rearing of *Lycophotia saucia* Hb. in erlenmeyer flasks. The medium is placed in small cases of aluminum foil. Hygrometry is maintained by an humidified absorbent cotton.

The cholesterol is prepared for 100 tubes by dissolving 3 mg of cholesterol in 2 ml of alcohol, then emulsifying this in 18 ml of distilled water containing 5 mg of Tween 40.

The solutions of the various salts, except the phosphates, are autoclaved and added to the sterilized casein tubes. The RNA (from yeast) in quantity sufficient for 100 tubes (0.5 gm) is first mixed in 20 ml of water and then dissolved by the addition of $0.1\,N$ NaOH. The pH is adjusted to 7.0 and the volume brought to 50 ml. The solution is then autoclaved, and 0.5 ml is distributed to each tube.

A solution, 10 times final concentration, of the vitamins, phosphates, L-cystine, sucrose, and glutathion is sterilized by filtration. Of this filtrate 0.5 ml is added to each tube, which finally contains 5 ml of liquid medium.

The composition of this medium for *Agria* ($= Pseudosarcophaga$) *affinis* Fall. from House and Barlow (1960) is found in Table III.

This medium is prepared in 2 parts. The first, composed of a solution of sugar and water-soluble vitamins, is filtered through a sterilizing membrane. The second contains the amino acids, salts, RNA, cholesterol. and agar. To prepare this second part the amino acids, salts, and agar are dissolved in warm water and the RNA in $2\,N$ NaOH. The cholesterol

TABLE II
MEDIA FOR *Aedes aegypti* L.[a]

Substances	Trager's diet (μg/ml)	Akov's diet (μg/ml)
KH_2PO_4	600	600
K_2HPO_4	600	600
$FeSO_4 \cdot 7H_2O$	12	12
$MnSO_4 \cdot 4H_2O$	12	12
NaCl	12	12
$CaCl_2$	12	12
$MgSO_4 \cdot 7H_2O$	200	200
Ribonucleic acid	1000	1000
L-Cystine	200	—
Cholesterol	30	6
i-Inositol	40	—
Sucrose	2000	—
Pyridoxamine–2HCl	0.02	—
Pyridoxine–HCl	4.0	4.0
Riboflavin	2.0	2.0
Thiamine–HCl	2.0	2.0
Niacin	2.0	—
Calcium pantothenate	6.0	10.0
Pteroylglutamic acid	0.6	0.6
p-Aminobenzoic acid	2.0	—
Niacinamide	10.0	10.0
Choline chloride	20.0	100.0
Biotin	0.05	0.1
Glutathion	10.0	—
Casein: 50 mg/5-ml tube for both Trager's and Akov's		

[v] From Akov (1962).

is first dissolved in a small quantity of 95° alcohol and then emulsified along with the fatty acids in an aqueous solution of polyoxyethylene sorbitan monoleate (Tween 80). These three portions of the second part are then mixed and autoclaved, and the first part is mixed in during the cooling.

The medium of Friend *et al.* (1957) for *Hylemyia antiqua* is indicated in Table IV. The authors used as a base the medium developed by House (1954) for the rearing of *Agria affinis* and the compounding techniques are similar. A few aspects, however, were modified. Except for aspartic acid, glutamic acid, tryptophan, and tyrosine, the amino acids are weighed and ground together in a mortar. Tyrosine is dissolved in a 3% aqueous solution of concentrated HCl. Tryptophan and aspartic and glutamic acids are dissolved in warm water. Thymine and inosine are dissolved in hydrochloric acid (2.5 ml conc. HCl/75 ml warm water).

TABLE III
MEDIUM FOR *Agria* (= *Pseudosarcophaga*) *affinis* FALL.[a]

Substances	mg/100 ml distilled water	Substances	mg/100 ml distilled water
L-Amino acids (total)	1254.7	Lipids (total)	770
Alanine	64.5	Cholesterol	100.0
Arginine–HCl	52.9	Linoleic acid	60.0
Aspartic acid	76.5	Linolenic acid	20.0
Cysteine–HCl	18.0	Oleic acid	192.0
Glutamic acid	137.1	Palmitic acid	88.0
Glycine	17.6	Stearic acid	40.0
Histidine–HCl	17.6	Polyoxyethylene sorbitan	270.0
Hydroxyproline	24.0	monoleate	
Isoleucine	76.5	Vitamins (total)	11.12009
Leucine	140.3	Biotin	0.00009
Lysine–HCl	88.2	Calcium pantothenate	0.44
Methionine	47.3	Choline chloride	2.00
Phenylalanine	70.1	Folic acid	0.34
Proline	100.2	Inositol	5.96
Serine	88.2	Nicotinic acid	0.30
Threonine	47.3	p-Aminobenzoic acid	0.9
Tryptophan	23.6	Pyridoxine–HCl	0.9
Tyrosine	82.2	Riboflavin	0.16
Valine	82.6	Thiamine–HCl	0.12
Inorganic salts (no. 2, USP XII) (total)	66.0	Miscellaneous (total)	1572
		Glucose	500.0
Calcium biphosphate CaH$_4$(PO$_4$)$_2$	8.96	Ribonucleic acid	75.0
		Potassium hydroxide, 2 N	247.0
Calcium lactate	21.58	Agar	750.0
Ferric citrate (17.5% Fe)	1.96		
Magnesium sulfate	9.04		
Potassium phosphate K$_2$HPO$_4$	15.83		
Sodium biphosphate	5.76		
Sodium chloride	2.87		

[a] From House and Barlow (1960).

Vitamins and cofactors are dissolved individually: folic acid in 20° alcohol, thioctic acid in 95° alcohol, riboflavin in warm 0.02 N acetic acid, and the other vitamins in water. The medium is sterilized by autoclaving 15 minutes at 115°.

When the above medium for aseptic rearing of *Hylemyia antiqua* was used, 80% of the larvae developed to adults and viable eggs were laid.

Media for *Drosophila melanogaster* are given in Table V. Medium C, without MgSO$_4$ and NaCl but with 3% agar added, is used by Sang for

TABLE IV

MEDIUM FOR *Hylemyia antiqua* MEIG.[a]

Substances	Concentration (mg/100 ml diet)
Agar	2000
RNA	100
Inosine	30
Thymine	0.4
Cholesterol	10
Dextrose	1500
Mineral mixture USP XIII No. 2	200
Amino acid mixture (see below)	2421
Vitamin mixture (see below)	77.96
Distilled water q.s.p.	100 ml

Amino acid mixture	mg/ml diet	Vitamin mixture	μg/ml diet
L-Alanine	1.09	Biotin (aqueous solution)	0.020
L-Arginine (free base)	0.80	B 12	0.040
L-Aspartic acid	1.22	Calcium pantothenate	6.0
L-Cysteine (free base)	0.48	Choline chloride	20.0
L-Glutamic acid	4.42	Coenzyme A	1.5[b]
Glycine	1.75	Folic acid	6.0
L-Histidine (free base)	0.48	Nicotinic acid	10.0
L-Hydroxyproline	0.38	Pyridoxine–HCl	30.0
L-Isoleucine	1.26	Riboflavin	2.4
L-Leucine	2.35	Thiamine–HCl	1.5
L-Lysine–HCl	1.34	DL-6-Thioctic acid	0.5
L-Methionine	0.34	Total	77.96
L-Phenylalanine	1.01		
L-Proline	1.68		
L-Serine	0.88		
L-Threonine	0.38		
L-Tryptophan	1.75		
L-Tyrosine	1.24		
L-Valine	1.36		
Total	24.21		

[a] From Friend *et al.* (1957).
[b] 217×10^{-6} Lipmann units.

rearing the larvae of *Drosophila*. For rearing adults the agar medium, not being suitable, is replaced by another substrate such as carefully washed nonabsorbent cotton. This imbibes medium C at the rate of 5 ml medium/0.3 gm cotton.

Medium D, less rich than C, is sufficient for the maintenance of larvae and the emergence of adults.

After autoclaving the preparation 15 minutes at 120°, the casein is mixed in during the cooling.

TABLE V
MEDIA FOR *Drosophila melanogaster* MEIG.

Substances	Medium C[a] (μg/ml)	Medium D[b] (μg/ml)
Casein (low vitamin)	55,000	55,000
Fructose	7500	7500
Lecithin	4000	4000
RNA	4000	4000
Thiamine–HCl	2	0.3
Riboflavin	10	1.2
Nicotinic acid	12	1.6
Calcium pantothenate	16	2.4
Pyridoxine–HCl	2.5	0.1
Biotin	0.16	0.025
Folic acid	3	0.3
NaHCO$_3$	1400	1400
KH$_2$PO$_4$	1830	1830
Na$_2$HPO$_4$	1890	1890
MgSO$_4$	810	—
NaCl	130	—

The authors studied the substitution of casein by the following amino acids:

Amino acid mixture	μg/ml		μg/ml
Arginine	3025	Alanine	3300
Histidine	1650	Aspartic acid	3300
Isoleucine	3850	Cystine	1100
Leucine	4675	Glutamic acid	8525
Lysine–HCl	4400	Glycine	1650
Methionine	1650	Proline	4400
Phenylalanine	3025	Serine	4400
Threonine	3025	Tyrosine	3300
Tryptophan	1100		
Valine	3850		

[a] From Sang (1956).
[b] From Sang and King (1961).

A medium for *Musca domestica* L. (Monroe, 1962) is composed as follows:

Ingredients	Parts
micropulverized casein	70.0
celluflour	3.0
sodium oleate	2.0
RNA	1.0
Wesson's salts	4.0
agar	20.0
cholesterol	0.2
B vitamins	0.5 ml/5 gm of diet

The components, vitamins and cholesterol excepted, are homogenized in dry state, then mixed with distilled water at the rate of 15 gm/100 ml water. The medium is sterilized by autoclaving 20 minutes at 121°. To avoid sedimentation the vessels are shaken and then cooled in ice water.

The medium was shown to be suitable for sterile rearing not only of *M. domestica* but also of *Calliphora vicina* R. D. and *Phormia regina* Meig.

ii. MEDIA FOR LEPIDOPTERA. Medium for *Pseudaletia unipuncta* Haw. (Goodwin, 1966) is given in Table VI.

TABLE VI

MEDIUM FOR *Pseudaletia unipuncta* HAW[a]

Substances	Concentration
Fraction A	
Agar	2 gm
Soluble casein	3.5 gm
Folic acid	0.5 mg
Water	72 ml
Fraction B	
α-Tocopherol acetate	25 mg
Linseed oil	0.5 gm
Polysorbate-80	0.3 gm
Fraction C	
Germ flour	3 gm
Wesson salts	1.3 gm
"Alphacel"	1.8 gm
Sucrose	3.5 gm
β-Sitosterol powder	0.2 gm
Cholesterol powder	0.2 gm
Fraction D	
Potassium hydroxide 4 *M*	1.5 ml
Fraction E	
Ascorbic acid	2 gm
Vitamin solution (see below)	2 ml
Water	8 ml
Vitamin solution	
Choline chloride	10 gm
Inositol	2 gm
Nicotinic acid	100 mg
Calcium pantothenate	100 mg
Riboflavin-5-phosphate	50 mg
Thiamine–HCl	25 mg
Pyridoxine–HCl	25 mg
Cyanocobalamin	0.2 mg
Biotin	2 mg
Water	100 ml

[a] From Goodwin (1966).

To prepare 100 gm of feed, fraction A is heated and shaken to dissolve the casein. It is then mixed with fraction B for one minute in a blender and the bowl of the blender is covered with paper to await sterilization. The components of fraction C are first mixed in the dry state, then wrapped in autoclave paper for sterilization. After autoclaving 15 minutes at 118° these three fractions are combined in a sterile enclosure. Fraction C is added to the sterilized blender bowl and the mixture is shaken for five minutes. At 40°, fractions D and E (previously filtered through a millipore filter) are added with gentle mixing in the blender.

A medium composition for *Chilo simplex* Butler (Ishii and Hirano, 1955) is indicated in Table VII. The author indicates that casein is very satisfactory for development of the insects and that it gives better results than a mixture of amino acids. The complete medium is sterilized by autoclaving on three successive days: 30 minutes the first day, 20 minutes the second, and 10 minutes the third. Larvae are reared in darkness at 25° in flasks containing 10 ml of medium.

Table VIII shows the composition of medium for *Pectinophora gossypiella* (Vanderzant, 1957). With the exception of L-cystine and L-tyrosine, which are dissolved respectively in concentrated HCl and 2 N KOH, the constituents are dissolved in water. The medium is prepared in two portions; one is sterilized by filtration, the other by heat.

TABLE VII

MEDIUM FOR *Chilo simplex* BUTLER[a]

Substances	Concentration	
Water	10	ml
Casein (or casein hydrolysate)	0.35	gm
Agar	0.1	gm
Cellulose	0.3	gm
Glucose	0.5	gm
Sucrose	0.2	gm
Cholesterol	0.006	gm
Wesson's inorganic salt mixture	0.06	gm
Vitamins		
Thiamine	50	μg
Riboflavin	25	μg
Nicotinic acid	50	μg
Pyridoxine	25	μg
Calcium pantothenate	50	μg
Folic acid	5	μg
Choline chloride	1000	μg
Inositol	500	μg
p-Aminobenzoic acid	50	μg
Biotin	5	μg

[a] From Ishii and Hirano (1955).

TABLE VIII

COMPOSITION OF AN AMINO ACID DIET FOR *Pectinophora gossypiella* SAUND.[a]

Solution No.[b]	Constituent	mg/100 ml medium	Solution No.	Constituent	mg/100 ml medium
		Portion sterilized by filtration			
1	L-Arginine	311	6	Niacinamide	1.0
	L-Histidine–HCl	75		Calcium pantothenate	1.0
	L-Isoleucine	113		Thiamin–HCl	0.25
	L-Leucine	175		Riboflavin	0.50
	L-Lysine–HCl	113		Pyridoxine–HCl	0.25
	L-Methionine	75		Folic acid	0.25
	L-Phenylalanine	150		Biotin	0.02
	L-Threonine	100		Vitamin B_{12}	0.002
	L-Tryptophan	75			
	L-Valine	138	7	K_2HPO_4	160
				NaH_2PO_4	90
2	L-Alanine	150		NaCl	20
	L-Aspartic acid	100			
	L-Glutamic acid	125	8	$MgSO_4 \cdot 7H_2O$	100
	Glycine	150			
	L-Proline	50	9	$FeSO_4 \cdot 7H_2O$	20
	L-Serine	50			
			10	$CuSO_4 \cdot 5H_2O$	0.25
3	L-Cystine	50		$MnSO_4 \cdot 5H_2O$	2.50
				$ZnCl_2$	0.12
4	L-Tyrosine	50		D-Glucose 2.5 gm	
				Water to 50 ml	
5	Choline chloride	50			

Solution No.	Portion sterilized by autoclaving Constituent	mg/100 ml medium
11	Corn oil (Mazola)	300
	Tween 80	150
	Cholesterol	50
	α-Tocopherol	10
12	KI	0.4
	$CaCO_3$	120
	Water to 50 ml	
	Agar, 3 gm	

[a] From Vanderzant (1957).

[b] The constituents of Nos. 1 and 2 were each present in a volume of 10 ml, Nos. 3 and 4 each in 5 ml, Nos. 5–10 and 12 each in 1 ml, and No. 11 in 25 ml.

The table indicates the order that must be followed in combining the solutions (amino acids, vitamins, choline, sodium chloride, sodium phosphate, potassium phosphate, and magnesium sulfate). After the addition of glucose the volume is 48 ml and the pH is 6.1–6.2. The mixture is then filtered through a Seitz filter. Next, the Cu, Fe, Mn, and Zn solutions are filtered and added, bringing the volume to 50 ml.

For the fraction sterilized by heat, the corn oil and Tween 80 are put in an erlenmeyer flask and 1 mg of α-tocopherol is added per milliliter of ethanol. A few milliliters of ethyl ether to dissolve the lipids (the ether is later eliminated by aspiration) and 25 ml of water are added. The potassium iodide solution, calcium carbonate, agar, and water are mixed in a flask which is then stoppered with cotton and sterilized by autoclaving for 15 minutes at 110°.

TABLE IX

MEDIUM FOR *Anthonomus grandis* BOHEMAN[a]

Substances	Concentration[b] (mg/100 ml)	Substances	Concentration[b] (mg/100 ml)
L-Arginine–HCl	150	Nicotinamide	1.0
L-Histidine–HCl·H$_2$O	75	Calcium pantothenate	1.0
L-Isoleucine	113	Thiamine–HCl	0.25
L-Lysine–HCl	113	Riboflavin	0.50
L-Leucine	175	Pyridoxine–HCl	0.25
L-Methionine	75	Folic acid	0.25
L-Phenylalanine	150	Biotin	0.02
L-Threonine	100	Vitamin B$_{12}$	0.002
L-Tryptophan	75	K$_2$HPO$_4$	160
L-Valine	138	NaH$_2$PO$_4$·H$_2$O	80
L-Alanine	150	NaCl	20
L-Aspartic acid	100	MgSO$_4$·7H$_2$O	100 (50)
L-Cysteine–HCl·H$_2$O	50	FeSO$_4$·7H$_2$O	20 (10)
L-Glutamic acid	125 (325)	CuSO$_4$·5H$_2$O	0.5
Glycine	150	MnSO$_4$·H$_2$O	2.5
L-Proline	50	Zn(C$_2$H$_3$O$_2$)$_2$·H$_2$O	0.5
L-Serine	50	CoCl$_2$·6H$_2$O	0.25
L-Tyrosine	50	Na$_2$MoO$_4$·2H$_2$O	0.25
D-Glucose	2500 (0)	KI	0.5
Sucrose	0 (3500)	CaCO$_3$	120
Linolenic acid	20	Agar	3000
Choline chloride	50	KOH to pH 6.2	
Inositol	20	Water to 100 ml	
Cholesterol	50		

[a] From Vanderzant (1965).

[b] There are two versions of this medium. When the concentration of any substance varies for version 2, that concentration appears in parentheses.

After autoclaving, the two portions are combined and the medium is distributed aseptically into cotton-stoppered sterile test tubes at the rate of 2 ml medium/tube.

iii. MEDIA FOR COLEOPTERA. *Anthonomus grandis* Boheman can be cultured in a medium of Vanderzant (1965). The composition is given in Table IX.

After adjusting the pH the portion containing the amino acids, vitamins, sodium, potassium and magnesium salt solutions, and sugar is sterilized by filtering through a membrane. The iron and trace element solutions are added just before the end of the filtration in order to avoid precipitation in the medium.

The filtered portion is then added to the heat sterilized portion (water, agar, calcium carbonate, cholesterol, and fatty acids) during the cooling of the latter. The fatty acids are sometimes filtered before being incorporated into the agar. Finally, the medium is distributed into 17- by 60-mm sterile test tubes. The development of the insect takes about 35 days.

According to the author, this complex medium, particularly version 2,

TABLE X
MEDIUM FOR *Caenorhabditis briggsae* DOUGHERTY AND NIGON[a]

Substances	Concentration (mg/1000 ml)	Substances	Concentration (mg/1000 ml)
Essential amino acids		Salts	
L-Arginine	520	$CaCl_2 \cdot 2H_2O$	440
L-Histidine	470	$CuCl_2 \cdot 2H_2O$	6
L-Isoleucine	790	$Fe(NH_4)_2(SO_4)_2 \cdot 6H_2O$	725
L-Leucine	1280	K_3-citrate	1460
L-Lysine	1100	KH_2PO_4	1220
L-Methionine	450	$MgSO_4 \cdot 7H_2O$	740
L-Phenylalanine	1230	$MnCl_2 \cdot 4H_2O$	20
L-Threonine	630	NaOH	150
L-Tryptophan	310	$ZnCl_2$	10
L-Valine	970	Vitamins	
Nonessential amino acids		(highest concentrations)	
Sodium-L-glutamate	5750	Biotin	37.5
Glycine	560	Cyanocobalamin	37.5
Miscellaneous		Folic acid	75
Choline-H_2-Citrate	885	Niacinamide	75
i-Inositol·$2H_2O$	648	Calcium pantothenate	75
		Pyridoxine	75
		Riboflavin-5-PO_4Na	75
		Thiamine-Cl-HCl	75

[a] From Nicholas *et al.* (1962).

gives results comparable to those obtained with the casein based medium (Vanderzant, 1963a,b).

iv. MEDIA FOR NEMATODES. A medium for *Caenorhabditis briggsae* Dougherty and Nigon (Nicholas *et al.*, 1962) is given in Table X. This medium is prepared from concentrated stock solutions of the different constituents. The resulting mixture is pipetted into test tubes, 0.5 ml/tube. Then 0.1 ml of vitamin solution and 0.3 ml of filtered distilled water are added. Next, the tubes are autoclaved at 0.67 kg/cm² (10 psi). During cooling the medium is enriched by the addition of 0.1 ml of chicken embryo extract. To obtain this extract, 11-day-old chicken embryos are mixed with an equal weight of water, the suspension is homogenized and centrifuged at low speed, and the supernatant is sterilized by filtration (Nicholas *et al.*, 1959).

III. CONCLUSIONS

The different techniques described make it possible to obtain aseptic invertebrates for physiological or pathological studies or for tissue culture.

All tissues taken from such organisms, including those, such as the intestines, trachea, and integument, that are normally contaminated can be cultured without additional disinfection.

These techniques facilitate the culture of tissues or organs from very small invertebrates where external disinfection is extremely difficult if not impossible.

Sterile rearing, ideally the best method of preparing aseptic raw material for biological experiments, is still far from being generally practiced. In fact, only a limited number of invertebrates, most of them insects, have been reared under such conditions.

Successful sterile rearing calls for thorough familiarity with the living conditions and especially the nutritional requirements of the organism. To this end, experiments to define the nutritional needs of invertebrates will broaden the range of studies possible, thanks to the choice of media now available.

REFERENCES

Akov, S. (1962). *J. Insect Physiol.* **8**, 319.
Akov, S. (1964). *Bull. Wld. Hlth. Org.* **31**, 463.
Barlow, S. S. (1966). *Can. J. Zool.* **44**, 775.
Beck, S. D., and Stauffer, J. F. (1950). *J. Econ. Entomol.* **43**, 4.
Charpentier, R. (1968). *Ann. Epiphyt.* **19**, 533.

Chernin, E. (1957). *Proc. Soc. Exp. Biol. Med.* **96**, 204.

Chernin, E. (1959). *Ann. N.Y. Acad. Sci.* **77**, 237.

Chernin, E., and Schork, A. R. (1959). *Amer. J. Hyg.* **69**, 146.

Dadd, R. H., and Krieger, D. L. (1967). *J. Econ. Entomol.* **60**, 1512.

David, J. (1959). *Bull. Biol. Fr. Belg.* **93**, 472.

Delcourt, A., and Guyenot, E. (1911). *Bull. Sci. Fr. Belg.* **45**, 249.

Demal, J. (1961). *Bull. Soc. Zool. Fr.* **86**, 522.

Dougherty, E. C. (1959). *Ann. N. Y. Acad. Sci.* **77**, 27.

Dougherty, E. C., and Hansen, E. L. (1956). *Proc. Soc. Exp. Biol. Med.* **93**, 223.

Dougherty, E. C., and Solberg, B. (1961). *Nature (London)* **192**, 184.

Dougherty, E. C., Hansen, E. L., Nicholas, W. L., Hollet, J. A., and Yarwood, E. A. (1959). *Ann. N. Y. Acad. Sci.* **77**, 176.

Dougherty, E. C., Solberg, B., and Ferral, J. D. (1961). *Experientia* **17**, 131.

Feder, W. A. (1958). *Phytopathology* **48**, 392.

Fosset, J., and Chastang, S. (1963). *Ann. Epiphyt.* **14**, 35.

Friend, W. G., Backs, R. H., and Cass, L. M. (1957). *Can. J. Zool.* **35**, 535.

Gier, H. T. (1947). *J. Bacteriol.* **53**, 173.

Glaser, R. W. (1938). *J. Parasitol.* **24**, 177.

Glaser, R. W. (1940). *Proc. Soc. Exp. Biol. Med.* **43**, 512.

Glaser, R. W. (1943). *In* "Micrurgical and Germfree Techniques," Vol. 1, pp. 164–187. Thomas, Springfield, Illinois.

Glaser, R. W., and Stoll, N. R. (1938). *Science* **87**, 259.

Goodwin, R. H. (1966). *Nature (London)* **212**, 799.

Greenberg, B. (1970). *Bull. Entom. Soc. Amer.* **16**, 31.

Guyenot, E. (1917). *Bull. Biol. Fr. Belg.* **51**, 1.

Hill, S. T. (1965). *Bull. Entomol. Res.* **55**, 681.

Hirano, C., and Ishii, S. (1957). *Bull. Nat. Inst. Agr. Sci. Jap.* **88**, 99.

House, H. L. (1954). *Can. J. Zool.* **32**, 331.

House, H. L., and Barlow, J. S. (1960). *J. Nutrition* **72**, 409.

Ishii, S., and Hirano, C. (1955). *Bull. Nat. Inst. Agr. Sci. Jap.* **5**, 35.

Kamano, S. (1964). *Jap. J. Appl. Entomol. Zool.* **8**, 101.

Kamano, S., and Fukaya, M. (1965). *Jap. J. Appl. Entomol. Zool.* **9**, 89.

Martignoni, M. E., and Milstead, J. E. (1960). *J. Insect Pathol.* **2**, 124.

Mitsuhashi, J. (1965). *Kontyû* **33**, 271.

Mitsuhashi, J., and Maramorosch, K. (1963a). *Proc. Int. Congr. Zool., 16th, 1963* Vol. 1, p. 3.

Mitsuhashi, J., and Maramorosch, K. (1963b). *Contrib. Boyce Thompson Inst.* **22**, 165.

Mitsuhashi, J., and Maramorosch, K. (1964). *Contrib. Boyce Thompson Inst.* **22**, 435.

Monroe, R. E. (1962). *Ann. Entomol. Soc. Amer.* **55**, 140.

Nicholas, W. L., Dougherty, E. C., and Hansen, E. L. (1959). *Ann. N. Y. Acad. Sci.* **77**, 218.

Nicholas, W. L., Hansen, E., and Dougherty, E. C. (1962). *Nematologica* **8**, 129.

Pascal, M., Kuhl, G., and Missonnier, J. (1967). *Ann. Soc. Entomol.* **3**, 1141.

Peleg, J., and Trager, W. (1963). *Amer. J. Trop. Med. Hyg.* **12**, 820.

Provasoli, L., Shiraishi, K., and Lance, J. R. (1959). *Ann. N. Y. Acad. Sci.* **77**, 250.

Rock, G. C., Glass, E. H., and Patton, R. L. (1964). *Ann. Entom. Soc. Amer.* **57**, 617.

Sang, J. H. (1956). *J. Exp. Biol.* **33**, 45.

Sang, J. H., and King, R. C. (1961). *J. Exp. Biol.* **38**, 793.

Trager, W. (1935). *Amer. J. Hyg.* **22**, 18.
Trager, W. (1948). *J. Biol. Chem.* **176**, 1211.
Treillard, M. (1924). *C. R. Acad. Sci.* **179**, 1090.
Treillard, M. (1925). *C. R. Soc. Biol.* **93**, 1592.
Vago, C. (1954). *C. R. Soc. Biol.* **148**, 255.
Vago, C., and Fosset, J. (1965). *90th Congr. Soc. Sav. Nice, 1965* Vol .2, p. 501.
Vago, C., Fosset, J., and Meynadier, G. (1961a). *Rev. Pathol. Veg. Entomol. Agr. Fr.* **40**, 111.
Vago, C., Fosset, J., and Meynadier, G. (1961b). *C. R. Acad. Sci.* **252**, 2579.
Vago, C., Fosset, J., and Meynadier, G. (1963). *Rev. Pathol. Veg. Entomol. Agr. Fr.* **42**, 99.
Vanderzant, E. S. (1957). *J. Econ. Entomol.* **50**, 219.
Vanderzant, E. S. (1963a). *J. Econ. Entomol.* **56**, 357.
Vanderzant, E. S. (1963b). *J. Insect Physiol.* **9**, 683.
Vanderzant, E. S. (1965). *J. Insect Physiol.* **11**, 659.
Vanderzant, E. S., and Reiser, R. (1956). *J. Econ. Entomol.* **49**, 7.
Waterhouse, D. F. (1959). *Ann. N. Y. Acad. Sci.* **77**, 283.
White, G. F. (1931). *J. Parasitol.* **18**, 133.
Wollman, E. (1911). *Ann. Inst. Pasteur* **25**, 79.
Wollman, E. (1921). *Arch. Int. Physiol.* **18**, 194.
Wollman, E. (1926). *C. R. Soc. Biol.* **95**, 164.

II

Cell Culture

5

THE MORPHOLOGY AND PHYSIOLOGY OF
CULTURED INVERTEBRATE CELLS

T. D. C. Grace

I. INTRODUCTION

A multicellular organism consists of a number of cells which adhere to one another and aggregate in specific patterns to form organized structures, i.e., the tissues and organs. The fate of each cell in the organism is determined not only by its genetical makeup but also by environmental factors acting upon it during embryonic development and throughout its life. Morphology is the study of the mechanisms involved in the aggregation of cells and their development into the structures which give the organism its form. Physiology is the study of the specific functions which are carried out by the various organs. The relation between structure and function is exceedingly close, and during the life of the organism, changes in structure can be and are produced by changes in function, while many functions can only take place in the presence of special structures. It is unwise, therefore, to draw a sharp distinction between morphology and physiology, indeed, morphology has been considered "a method of physiology" (Mayer, 1963), while Grobstein (1965) has suggested that "structure is function viewed in a single time plane."

To gain some insight, therefore, into the dynamics of structure and function, one needs to study the mechanisms of cell movements which lead to aggregation and adhesion, the growth of cells and the changes which occur in them during development (cytodifferentiation), the ways in which tissues and cells convert the nutrients available to them into energy and other products of metabolism, and how they distribute these products throughout the body. An obvious way to study these problems is to place tissues or organs from the body in an environment which simulates the environment within the organism but which can be varied or controlled as desired. When such an operation is carried out and a piece of tissue or an organ is placed in a medium under *in vitro* conditions, it will generally behave in one of two ways:

1. It may continue to grow, develop, differentiate, and maintain, fairly closely, normal physiological functions much as it would have done in the whole animal.

2. Or its cells may multiply rapidly, migrate away from the explant, and exist as more or less independent units.

In such cultures, the explant sooner or later loses its organization, and the cells, after a time, adapt themselves to their new surroundings, lose many of their specific functions, and become generalized or dedifferentiated. Thus, in this chapter on the morphology and physiology of cultured invertebrate cells we are concerned with a discussion of structure and function in, on the one hand, organized tissues in which the cells have retained their differentiated state (the first case above) and, on the other hand, in cells and cell populations in which most of the organization and specific functions have been lost and which resemble, in some respects, bacterial cultures (the second case above).

In recent years, and especially in the last decade or so, there has been an upsurge of interest in invertebrate cell culture. There have been several reasons for this increased activity, but the one which is of importance in this chapter is the renewed interest in the problems of development and differentiation, sparked off partly by the amazing progress in molecular biology, partly by the current research into the causes and cure of cancer, and partly by research into the ways in which cells recognize and distinguish between each other and foreign material (immunology). However, the progress has been much slower than many would have wished. One of the hopes behind this chapter is to provoke interest and stimulate some readers to begin research in invertebrate cell culture. It is worth pointing out that much of the early work on the behavior of cells and their relations with one another was carried out using invertebrates—mainly, sponges (Wilson, 1907) and marine embryos (Herbst, 1900).

The chapters which follow will describe in detail the techniques for growing the tissues and cells of different groups of invertebrates and the results of such studies. I will concern myself with giving a general survey of what is known of the morphology and physiology of cultured invertebrate cells and will concentrate only on those aspects in which I feel invertebrate cell culture has played an important part in the study of structure and function. No attempt will be made to give a complete review of the literature on invertebrate tissue culture, and I shall regard as "tissue cultures" only those cultures which have survived for at least 24 hours or longer in a reasonably normal state.

II. SOURCES AND TYPES OF CELLS USED

It would generally be true to say that the invertebrates provide a much wider range of tissue to choose from and a broader field in which to study morphology and physiology than do the vertebrates. Starting with the subkingdom Parazoa [sponges (Porifera)], which are the most primitive of the multicellular animals, we see the beginnings of specialization and differentiation, in that various functions such as feeding, reproduction, and providing a protective layer are carried out by different types of cells. The cells, however, show far less specialization and dependence upon one another than is found in the cells of the Metazoa. One of the most significant features of the sponges is that there is very little organization into tissues: Many of the cells become amoeboid and assume various shapes, and in many respects, the sponges are more or less colonies of Protozoa. As there is no nervous system and because of the lack of organization, very little coordination is evident, or indeed possible, in the sponges. It is not until we study the members of the subkingdom Metazoa that we really see the evolution of the organization of cells into structures (tissues and organs) which carry out specific functions. The Metazoa are distinguished by their large size and their high degree of morphological differentiation. Along with the increase in morphological complexity has gone the specialization of the various organs in the body to perform definite functions for the whole organism. This has resulted in the organs' losing much of their "independence," which, however, is compensated for by an increase in efficiency of the function carried out by the organ. Within the Metazoa, there is a division between those animals whose bodies consist of only two cell layers, the coelenterates or Diploblastica, and the vast majority of animals who possess bodies consisting of three layers of cells, the Triploblastica. The coelenterates, the most primitive animals of the Metazoa, show a much greater degree of organization and coordination than do the sponges. They possess a simple nervous system, and cells of the same kind associate together to form tissues. Their bodies are relatively simple, and the two cellular layers are separated by a noncellular layer, the mesoglea. The outer layer, the ectoderm, consists of two cell types, i.e., the epithelial–muscular cells and, lying between them, the interstitial cells. Interstitial cells are of great importance because they preserve their embryonic character and are able to differentiate into either epithelial–muscular cells, nematoblasts, or, during the sexual phase, germ cells. The endodermis, or inner layer, consists of the gland cells and mucous cells, which secrete enzymes into the lumen where digestion of the captured prey begins, and the digestive–muscular cells, which engulf the partly digested food and complete the digestion.

In the triploblastic Metazoa there is, between the ectoderm and endoderm, a third layer of cells, the mesoderm, which forms the greater part of the body and has made possible, to a great extent, the increasing complexity and efficiency in the activities of the higher animals. The most primitive members of the triploblastic Metazoa, the phylum Platyhelminthes (the flatworms), show relationships to the coelenterates in the lack of a coelom (acoelomate), the use of one opening as both a mouth and an anus, and in the general similarity of the nervous system. In other respects, however, the flatworms show a number of advances in organization, the most notable being bilateral symmetry, the beginning of an excretory system, well-developed organs of reproduction, and the aggregation of nerve cells at the anterior end which could be the beginning of a central nervous system.

In the platyhelminths we also see for the first time how structures can be modified and adapted to suit changes in function. Of the three classes into which the phylum is divided, the Turbellaria, with few exceptions, are free living, while the Trematoda and Cestoda are all parasites. In the Turbellaria, which are considered to show the typical organization of the phylum, the outer covering of the body, the ectoderm, is covered with cilia. In both the parasitic groups the cilia have been lost and the ectoderm is covered by a thick cuticle. The parasites also have suckers by which they cling to their hosts. The most radical changes to the parasitic mode has occurred in the Cestoda, where the gut has been lost (the animals apparently absorb food directly through the skin) and the reproductive system is highly modified.

It is among the members of the coelomate phyla of the invertebrates, i.e., the Annelida, Arthropoda, Mollusca, and Echinodermata, that we see most clearly the variety and complexity of organs and structures developed to serve specific functions. One of the main consequences of the development of the coelom or body cavity, and one which contributed to a marked degree to the great body complexity of the coelomates, was the separation of the digestive system from the other organs. In the coelenterates and some of the smaller Metazoa, dissolved foodstuffs could be transported to other parts of the body by diffusion, but the intervention of a body cavity made this no longer possible. Also, as the size of animals increased, there eventually came a point at which the transport of oxygen to, and carbon dioxide from, the tissues by simple diffusion was inadequate. In the annelids, molluscs, echinoderms, and arthropods other than the insects, a blood vascular system was developed in which dissolved food and gases were actively transported about the body. This system also served to transport waste products of metabolism to the excretory organs. The development of a vascular system made it possible for organs to develop which were concerned with specific functions such as respiration and excretion. In the insects the circulatory system has no important role in the transport of the respiratory gases to or from the tissues. The respiratory system of the insects consists of a system of tubes or tracheae by which air is brought into direct relationship with the organs and tissues. In many insects the gases move by diffusion alone, but in those insects which exceed a certain size or are very active, there are supplementary mechanisms which help to circulate the gases.

Along with the increase in body size and complexity there occurred an increase in the size and complexity of the central nervous system. This, in turn, led to the development of more efficient locomotor organs and more sensitive sense organs, which enabled the animals to respond to small and subtle changes in their environment, and allowed them to carry out a greater variety of coordinated actions, many of which may be quite intricate.

This is not the place to delve any deeper into the evolution of the different organs and physiological systems in the invertebrates. Enough has been said in the brief outline given above to show that within the invertebrate phyla there are very rich sources of material for a wide variety of studies in morphology and physiology. There are, however, several difficulties, connected with using invertebrate tissues for *in vitro* studies, which have, in fact, precluded their use by many workers in morphological and physiological investigations. The most serious disadvantage, and one which includes the majority of invertebrates, is their relatively small size, which makes it difficult and, in many cases, quite impractical to obtain sufficient tissue to culture. This is especially true when embryos or embryonic tissues are used. In some instances, when specific tissues are not required, the difficulty of obtaining enough tissue can be partly overcome by breeding or catching large numbers of organisms, e.g., sponges, insect eggs, or *Drosophila* eggs, larvae, or pupae, etc., and mincing or cutting them up. Another difficulty often encountered is that many invertebrates cannot be bred in the laboratory or can only be obtained at certain periods of the year so that their usefulness is limited by their availability.

Determining from which animal to take tissues or organs can be a much more difficult task in the invertebrates than it would be in the vertebrates. A comparison of the excretory organs in vertebrates and invertebrates will illustrate this point. With regard to function, the organs of both groups are principally involved in the elimination of nitrogenous wastes and the regulation of water loss. The kidneys of vertebrates, whether from reptiles, birds, or mammals, are very similar in their general plan although their structures may vary somewhat with the environment and with the evolutionary level of the organism. The invertebrates, on the other hand, show a wide array of organs involved in excretion, both between phyla and within phyla. In the platyhelminths, some annelids, and some molluscs, the main excretory organ is the nephridium, an ectodermal derivative with an intracellular lumen ending in a flame cell. In other annelids and molluscs, most arthropods, and the echinoderms, the principal organs of excretion are the coelomoducts, which are paired structures of mesodermal origin with an intercellular lumen which does not end in a flame cell. In the insects the excretory organs are the malpighian tubules, which are diverticula of the gut.

The stage in the life cycle at which the tissues or cells are removed can be very important in invertebrate tissue culture. This is especially so where the immature or larval forms may be very different, both structurally and functionally, from the adults, as is often found in many of the arthropods and molluscs. In general, tissues from the immature stages have produced better growth and survived longer *in vitro* than adult tissues although adult tissues have been used extensively in invertebrate tissue culture. Some of the earliest work on the behavior of cells and the way they aggregate and adhere to one another was done with the cells of adult sponges (Wilson, 1907). More recently, sponges have been used to study cell recognition and to determine what the substance(s) is which causes cells specifically to aggregate (Curtis, 1962; Moscona, 1963, 1968). The adult stages of the coelenterate *Hydra* have been used in many studies on regeneration (Papenfuss and Bokenham, 1939), the organization of cell movement, and cell adhesion (Cerame-Vivas and Bookhout, 1961; Campbell, 1967; Lenhoff, 1968; Haynes *et al.*, 1968). *Hydra*, along with many other coelenterates, are extremely easy to rear in the laboratory, but their most important qualities are that they continue to grow throughout their life and have an amazing ability to regenerate lost parts. Consequently, in most of the investigations referred to above, the whole animal was used. Usually, the experiments involved cutting or removing pieces from the hydroid and observing the regeneration and reorganization of the lost parts. Although these studies have contributed valuable information to several fields of developmental biology, they have given little information on the roles played by the various types of cells in the developmental processes. It was mainly to gather such information that there have been several attempts in recent years to culture the cells of coelenterates *in vitro*. Although it is a simple matter to culture intact *Hydra* and some other coelenterates (both fresh- and saltwater forms), not very much success has been achieved in culturing their cells *in vitro* (Burnett *et al.*, 1968). Philips (1961) had some success in culturing the cells from a sea anemone *Anthopleura elegantissima*, and R. Martin and Tardent (1963) observed the multiplication for up to 50 days of nematoblasts and the partial development of nematocysts from the marine hydroid *Tubularia larynx* in a semiartificial medium. Apparently, the main problem of culturing the cells of freshwater coelenterates *in vitro* has been the development of a medium which provides all the necessary nutrients for growth and yet is not osmotically deleterious. In the intact animals all the ionic requirements are obtained from the digestion of food, very little being provided or available in the freshwater in which the animals live. Li *et al.* (1963) found that *Hydra* cells tended to shrink when placed in Earle's saline solution as its osmotic pressure was too great. Eventually, they developed a medium which was a mixture of Eagle's medium, Earle's solution, horse serum, phosphate buffer, and antibiotics and in which the cells were not osmotically damaged. The cells survived in this medium, but to obtain growth, it was necessary to add a "*Hydra* bud extract," which consisted of a homogenate of *Hydra* buds added at a concentration equivalent to 10 buds/ml of growth medium. The composition of the medium is given in Chapters 1 and 13.

An important recent contribution to the culture of coelenterate tissues was made by Burnett *et al.* (1968), who developed a chemically defined medium which contained no serum or protein. In this medium epidermal cells, digestive cells, interstitial cells, and epithelio-muscular cells of the stem tissue of Tubularia underwent growth and differentiation in a normal fashion. However, when individual cells were placed in fresh medium they died, which suggests that the medium had to be "conditioned" so that individual cells could survive.

The planarians are another group of animals the adults of which have been used extensively in studies on both regeneration and the mechanisms involved in the differentiation and development of parts of the body. As in *Hydra*, the majority of experiments with planarians have used whole animals or large parts of them. Murray (1927, 1931) was the first to attempt to culture specific tissues of planarians. She kept the cells of the parenchyma (mesenchyme) surviving for up to four weeks in a medium consisting of several salts and an extract of planarian tissues. If the extract was left out, the cells did not survive for more than two weeks. The parenchyma is a very interesting tissue; it lies between the endoderm and ectoderm and consists of a loose network of cells which fills the spaces between the organs. Many of the parenchyma cells are amoeboid, and they probably serve to transport food materials. Their most interesting feature, however, is that they remain in an undifferentiated condition and whenever there is a wound they gather about it and play an intimate role in regenerating and repairing the injured parts. They are, to a great extent, totipotent (Chandebois, 1963, 1968).

The ability to regenerate lost parts decreases as we pass from the planarians to the higher invertebrates, and therefore, fewer attempts have been made to study the processes of repair and regeneration in the higher organisms, Gatenby (1931, 1932) and his colleagues (Gatenby and Duthie, 1932; Gatenby and Hill, 1933; Hill and Gatenby, 1934) studied regeneration of the wall of the pulmonary cavity of the common snail (*Helix aspersa*). A much more interesting technique was developed by Luscher (1947, 1948). He amputated the leg of a fifth instar nymph of *Rhodnius prolixus* Stal. and then inserted a capillary tube into the stump. The tube and the stump were then immersed in a physiological salt solution. Within 24 hours epithelial cells had formed a network along the tube. Marks (1968), Marks and Reinecke (1964, 1965a,b), and Marks *et al.* (1968) have studied regeneration in the regenerating tissues from the legs of fifth instar nymphs of the Madeira cockroach (*Leucophaea maderae*).

The most extensive use of cultures of invertebrate tissues has been in studies of the mechanisms involved in the aggregation, adhesion, and cohesion of cells. This subject will be dealt with in more detail later in this chapter, but at this time some of the tissues used in these studies will be mentioned. The sponges, and the tissues of many invertebrate embryos, especially sea urchin embryos, have proved exceptionally suitable for studies of aggregation (Herbst, 1900; Wilson, 1907; Galstoff, 1923, 1925a,b; Curtis, 1962; Moscona, 1963). Sponges can be very simply dissociated by pressing them through a fine mesh such as silk. These treatment causes less damage to the cells' surface than chemical or enzymic methods which are essential to dissociate the cells of vertebrate tissues. Sea urchin embryos and those of other marine invertebrates will dissociate into separate cells if they are placed in calcium-free seawater; and when the calcium ions are restored, the cells reaggregate (Herbst, 1900). The sponges have the added advantages that species of different colors can be obtained so that the specificity of cellular aggregation and behavior can be studied (Moscona, 1963, 1968) and that they can be kept alive for considerable periods in media as simple as sterilized seawater.

The blood cells of many invertebrates will aggregate when placed in their own blood or body fluids in hanging drop cultures. In most, if not all cases, the cells responsible for the agglutination are the amoebocytes or plasmatocytes, a type of cell found in the blood of most invertebrates. These cells wander, by amoeboid movements, around the body and appear to be involved in phagocytic activities as well as in wound healing. The cells studied have been taken from the marine annelids *Arenicola* and *Nephthys* (Fauré-Fremiet, 1925, 1934); the King crab *Limulus* Loeb, 1922, 1927), and the insects *Samia advena* (Jones and Cunningham, 1960), *Antheraea polyphemus*, and *Hyalophora cecropia* (Walters and Williams, 1966).

The phagocytic amoebocytes appear to be deeply involved also in the cellular defense mechanisms in the invertebrates (Tripp, 1960, 1963).

Tripp *et al.* (1966) and Tripp and Kent (1968) have cultured the amoebocytes of the oyster *Crassostrea virginica* Gmelin primarily in order to study the ways in which phagocytes are able to distinguish substances which are foreign to them, such as pathogens (bacteria, viruses, etc.) and many parasites, and to react so as to destroy them or nullify their effects. The amoebocytes were obtained from either the ventricular tissue or, in larger numbers, by trypsinizing the mantles of several large oysters. A large number of media were tested, and in the best one, a mixture (45:45:10) of Scherer's medium (Difco), a basal salt solution, and chicken serum, the amoebocytes phagocytosed bacteria and red blood cells at comparable rates to those measured *in vivo*. Most of the investigations of immunity in invertebrates have been carried out on whole animals (Glaser, 1925; Zernoff, 1934; Briggs, 1958; Stephens, 1959, 1963; Bang, 1966; Acton and Evans, 1968), and although much work has been done, there is still a great deal of confusion and little understanding of the immune response in invertebrates. Immunity in invertebrates appears to be quite different from that in vertebrates (Chadwick, 1967; Landureau and Jolles, 1970; Mohring and Messner, 1968). One of the main reasons for the slow progress in the field of invertebrate immunity is that most investigations have attempted to interpret their results in terms of the theories of vertebrate immune mechanisms. *In vitro* studies of the phagocytic amoebocytes may be one of the keys to a better understanding of immunity in the invertebrates.

For some purposes it is desirable to culture entire organs rather than tissues or cells. The organs from a variety of invertebrates have been cultured but the majority have come from the insects. The areas in which organ cultures have been used extensively are the study of growth and differentiation, physiological studies concerned with nutrition and the effects of hormones, and pathology. In those studies in which the interest has been confined to differentiation and development, the majority of workers have used either the gonads [especially the spermatocytes from the testes (Goldschmidt, 1915, 1916; Lewis and Robertson, 1916; Frew, 1928; Schmidt and Williams, 1953; Lender and Duveau-Hagege, 1962, 1963; Demal and Leloup, 1963)] or the imaginal discs from several species of insects (Fischer and Gottschewski, 1939; Gottschewski and Fischer, 1939; Stern, 1940; Kuroda, 1954a,b; Kuroda and Yamaguchi, 1956; Demal and Leloup, 1963). Sengel and Kieny (1963) obtained some differentiation of the ovocytes from the immature hermaphrodite organs of an ascidian (*Molgula manhattensis*). These organs were cultured in a medium containing the "neural gland–neural ganglion–vibratile organ complex" from the ascidian. If the gonads are cultured without the complex, the differentiation ceases.

The effects of radiation on the growth and differentiation of organs have been studied for a number of years. Carlson (1946, 1956, 1961) and Gaulden and Carlson (1947) used the neuroblasts from embryos of the grasshopper (*Chortophaga*) to study mitosis and the effects of radiation, both ionizing and ultraviolet, on mitosis and differentiation. The neuroblasts form a layer on the ventral surface of the prospective nerve cord in each segment of the embryo. They are large cells with large chromosomes, which makes them easy to irradiate; and they also maintain a fairly constant position relative to neighboring neuroblasts so that individual cells can be watched over a period. Horikawa and Sugahara (1960) carried out an extensive study of the effects of X irradiation on the development and differentiation in culture of organs from third instar *Drosophila*. The organs used were the brain, salivary glands, fat body, eye, wing, leg, and testis imaginal discs. Larsen (1963, 1964) has used fragments of the heart of the cockroach *Blaberus craniifer* not only to study the effects of gamma irradiation on the organ but also to test the efficiency and effect of various radiation-protecting substances on the irradiated organs.

It is in physiological studies that most use has been made of organ culture. Schmidt and Williams (1953) used cultures of the testes from diapausing pupae of the cecropia moth (*Hyalophora cecropia*) in an assay system to test the effect of the prothoracic gland hormone on sperm development. Bucklin (1953) also attempted to study diapause by culturing fragments of grasshopper (*Melanoplus*) embryos. Schneiderman et al. (1953) used cultures of cecropia testes to study oxygen requirements and utilization in spermatogenesis. They found that spermatogenesis proceeded at a normal rate at oxygen tensions between 21 and 1% of an atmosphere, but below 1% the process was inhibited.

A number of experiments have been carried out in which organs have been cultured to determine the nutritive value of various substances on growth and differentiation. Demal and Leloup (1963) cultured the male and female gonads (at three stages of development), fragments of the heart, and imaginal discs of *Calliphora erythrocephala* and the salivary glands of *Drosophila melanogaster* in several media, one of which consisted of a simple physiological salt solution containing chick embryo extract, while the other media had been designed specifically for growing insect tissues (Vago and Chastang, 1958; Trager, 1959). The best growth was obtained from the gonads in the medium containing chick embryo extract, which the authors suggested may have contained factors necessary for growth and which were not present in the other media. Similar experiments of this type have used organs of the King crab (*Xiphosura polyphemus*) (Wolff, 1963), the leafhoppers *Agallia constricta* and

Macrosteles fascifrons (Hirumi and Maramorosch, 1963), and the earthworms (Lumbricides) (Gay, 1963). In all these experiments some growth, development, and differentiation has taken place and some organs have shown better survival, growth, or differentiation than others, but in general, the results have not been as successful or as productive as one would have hoped from the great amount of labor that must have gone into carrying them out.

The establishment of diploid cell lines of *Drosophila melanogaster* by Echalier and Ohanessian (1969) has fulfilled one of the fond wishes of many geneticists and embryologists who have hoped that some day it would be possible to maintain and grow *Drosophila* tissues *in vitro* for long periods. The vast background of information on the genetics, embryology, and development of *Drosophila* encouraged many to attempt to culture its organs and tissues. On the one hand, there have been those who have concentrated on true organ culture of the imaginal discs of *Drosophila* so as to study their differentiation (Fischer and Gottschewski, 1939; Gottschewski and Fischer, 1939; Stern, 1940; Kuroda, 1954a,b) or the effects of various substances, such as hormones, and radiation on growth and development (Kuroda and Yamaguchi, 1956; Horikawa, 1958; Horikawa and Sugahara, 1960). Others have been more interested in the genetic control of differentiation and in the role played by the genes in synthetic processes within the cells. In these cases tissues and cells, rather than organs, have been cultured (Horikawa and Kuroda, 1959; Castiglione and Raimondi, 1961; Horikawa and Fox, 1964; Horikawa *et al.*, 1966; Seecof and Unanue, 1968; Seecof and Teplitz, 1971). The tissues and cells have been obtained almost invariably from the dissociation of embryos although Horikawa and Kuroda (1939) cultured hemocytes obtained from third instar larvae. The *Drosophila* cell lines of Echalier and Ohanessian (1969) are being used for genetic studies as well as in studies on the multiplication of the sigma virus of *Drosophila*.

In the majority of attempts to culture the tissues and cells of invertebrates, the primary interest has not been to study the tissues or cells themselves but rather to use them as a means of studying the growth and development of viruses and parasites which are either pathogenic to insects or grow in the insects and are pathogenic to man, animals, or plants. This is certainly true in the case of insect tissue culture and tick tissue culture (for a complete survey of the use of tissue cultures in pathology, see Vol. II, Chapters 7–10). Recent attempts to culture oyster (Tripp *et al.*, 1966; Perkins and Menzel, 1964) and snail tissues (Burch and Cuadros, 1965) have been made to provide a technique in which parasites and pathogens of these organisms may be studied. Besides being able to make primary cultures of the tissues, organs, and cells from many groups of invertebrates, there are available several lines of cells which have been established for a number of years (Grace, 1962, 1966, 1967; Mitsuhashi, 1967; Chiu and Black, 1967; Singh, 1967; Ohanessian and Echalier, 1967; Peleg, 1968; Schneider, 1969; Varma and Pudney, 1969). There is no reason why the cell lines and many primary cultures should not be used for physiological and morphological studies. Grace (1958a) studied the effect of several substances on the growth of silk-worm (*Bombyx mori*) ovarian cells in primary cultures, and Grace and Brzostowski (1966) and Clements and Grace (1967) have used the cells from the established line of *Antheraea eucalypti* ovarian cells to deter-mine which amino acids and sugars are used during growth. Ball (1947, 1948, 1954) has been interested for many years in studying the develop-ment of the mosquito phase of the malaria parasite *Plasmodium relictum* in organ cultures of the gut of *Culex tarsalis*. Concurrently with these studies, he and his colleagues (Ball and Chao, 1957, 1960; Clark and Ball, 1952, 1954, 1956) have made quite an intensive investigation of the composition of the mosquito body fluids, various types of media, and culture conditions. The information obtained has been very useful in prolonging the survival of the guts of *Culex tarsalis* in culture, and it has also helped in designing media for the culture of organs and tissues from other species of mosquito (Grace, 1967; Singh, 1967; Kitamura, 1964).

One of the most puzzling features of insect tissue culture and, I should imagine, of the culture of other invertebrates as well is the small number of organs and tissues which have grown or even survived for long periods. Insect tissues which have been cultured but which have shown very little growth are muscle (Schmidtmann, 1925), nerve tissue (Pfeiffer, 1927, 1939, 1943; Mitsuhashi, 1965), fat body (Grace, 1954; Mitsuhashi, 1965), hypodermis (Grace, 1954; Mitsuhashi, 1965), and gut (Collier, 1920; Gavrilov and Cowez, 1941; Mitsuhashi, 1965). Many, many attempts have been made to culture insect hemocytes. In most instances they have survived and shown limited multiplication for only short periods although Mitsuhashi (1967) and Chao and Ball (1971) have established a line of cells from the hemocytes of the rice stem borer (*Chilo suppressalis* Walker). There is no doubt that many studies of both a morphological and physiological nature would be undertaken if many of the above organs or tissues could be cultured.

The tissue which has given the most successful growth in insect tissue culture is undoubtedly the ovarian tissue from last instar larvae about to pupate (Wyatt, 1956; Grace, 1962, 1967). However, Singh (1967), Chiu and Black (1967), and Ohanessian and Echalier (1967) established cell lines from either embryonic or very early (just after hatching) first instar larvae. The tissues which grew in these cultures have not been determined in any instance.

III. MORPHOLOGY OF CELLS IN PRIMARY CULTURES

When we look through the microscope at living cells in culture we must realize and keep constantly in mind that the cells are not static but are constantly moving, changing their shape and their behavior in response to many factors in the culture system. The most important factors affecting the morphology of cells in culture are the type of cell itself, the nature of the substrate on which the cells are growing, the medium which surrounds the cells, and the presence of cells of the same and other types in the culture. The best way to observe the movements and behavior of cells *in vitro* is by the use of time-lapse cinematography, and in recent years there have been several films made of insect cells in culture which show cellular activity very well (Grace and Day, 1963; Vago, 1964).

A tissue culture may consist either of pieces of one type of tissue such as ovary, heart, muscle, etc., or it may contain pieces of many tissues. Cultures of the latter type are made simply by chopping a whole animal into small pieces and adding the explants to culture medium. The types of cells found in primary cultures appear to be very similar, irrespective of the group of invertebrates from which the donor comes, the age of the donor (embryo, larva, pupa, or adult), or the tissue used.

Within 24–48 hours after setting up a culture, a number of cells will have migrated from the tissue. In most instances the cells adhere to and move over the substrate, which is usually glass or plastic, but in several cases (Grace, 1962; Singh, 1967) the cells have floated in the medium and remained round in outline. The migrated cells represent several cell types. The first type of cell to move away from the explant is usually spindle shaped (Fig. 1). In a number of papers these cells have been referred to as fibroblasts. Since true fibroblasts, as recognized in vertebrates, are not present in invertebrates and since what is meant is that the cells are spindle shaped, a plea is made here to call such cells "spindle-shaped cells" or at least not to call them fibroblasts or fibroblast-like cells. The spindle-shaped cells tend to move actively over the substrate, and if they come into contact with other cells of the same type, they will either move away or form very open networks of cells.

Another type of cell which migrates at an early stage from the explant is the epithelial cell (Fig. 2). Cells of this type have been reported in

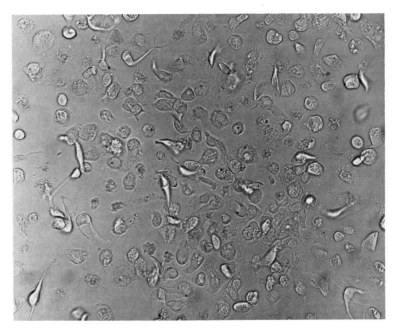

FIG. 1. Spindle-shaped cells from a primary culture of *Antheraea eucalypti* ovarian tissue. Some of the cells have attached to the glass and some are floating. ($\times$252.)

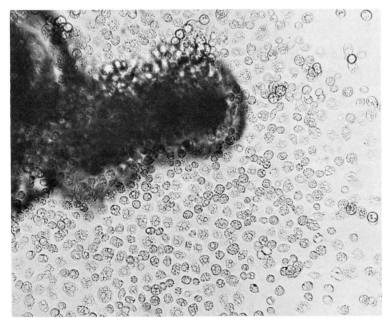

FIG. 2. Cells of epithelial type migrating from an explant of *Antheraea eucalypti* ovarian tissue. The cells have attached to the culture surface but not to each other. ($\times$252.)

cultures of mollusc tissues (Flandre and Vago, 1963) and in most insect tissue cultures (Jones and Cunningham, 1961; Vago and Flandre, 1963; Mitsuhashi and Maramorosch, 1964; Mitsuhashi, 1965). These cells are usually more round than spindle shaped and adhere more firmly to the substrate. They tend to aggregate and are the main cell type involved in forming sheets of cells (Fig. 3). Mitsuhashi (1965) has described several types of epithelial cells from the tissues of several species of leafhoppers. The epithelial type of cell is usually the most abundant in tissue cultures and often survives the longest.

In cultures which consist of chopped up animal tissues or dissociated cells, a number of types of cells will naturally be present at initiation of the culture, but after two or three days many will die, and by the fifth to seventh days only a few types will be left, such as spindle-shaped cells, epithelial cells, and often, the cells which have been termed amoe-

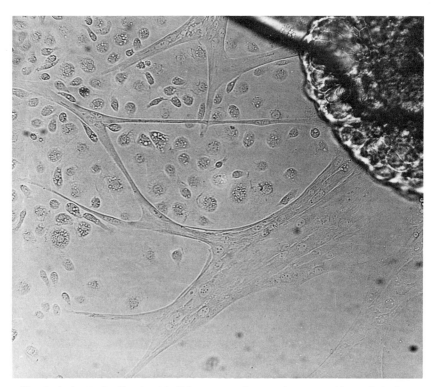

FIG. 3. A sheet of cells of epithelial type growing out from an explant of *Antheraea eucalypti* ovarian tissue. Also present are "free" epithelial cells and spindle-shaped cells. Note the prominent nuclei and the absence of cell membranes in the sheet. (×288.)

boid cells, amoebocytes, phagocytes, plasmatocytes, or wandering cells (Hirumi and Maramorosch, 1964; Mitsuhashi, 1965; Marks and Reinecke, 1964; Tripp *et al.*, 1966). This type of cell wanders over the culture; they do not aggregate and have no definite shape but move by pseudopodial action. The main function of the wandering cells is to phagocytose dead cells and foreign material, they also play a very important role in wound healing and in immunity in invertebrates.

The formation of vesicles have been reported in cultures of cockroach tissues (Larsen, 1964; Marks and Reinecke, 1964) and leafhopper tissues (Mitsuhashi and Maramorosch, 1964; Mitsuhashi, 1965). The vesicles in all the cultures were hollow spherical structures filled with fluid and covered by a monolayer of cells. Marks and Reinecke (1964) stated that the covering layer consisted of epithelial cells interlaced with fiber-like cells and covered with a thin membrane of gelatinous secretion. In the leafhopper cultures the monolayer also consisted mainly of epithelial cells but other types of cells that migrated from the explants could also be recognized. In the older vesicles of the leafhopper explants, several cell layers formed. The vesicles most commonly appeared in the explants about three to four days after the cultures were set up and continued to enlarge over a period of several days.

The cells in the covering layer in the leafhopper vesicles multiplied on the surface of the vesicle, but if they came into contact with the glass surface of the culture vessel, they migrated across it and multiplied on the glass.

Cells such as nerve cells and fat body cells usually have not survived for more than several days *in vitro* and are among the first types of cells to disappear from the cultures.

For the first 7–14 days after a culture is set up, mitotic figures are quite common in all the cell types. By about the tenth day, due to mitosis and cell migration, there are usually sheets of cells adhering to the substrate. The cells in the sheets are very flat and the cytoplasm is often finely granulated. In some cultures the surface membranes may disappear so that a syncytium is formed (Grace, 1958b).

In cultures of ovarian tissue of the cynthia moth (Grace, 1958b), *Antheraea eucalypti* (Grace, 1962) and the silkworm *Bombyx mori* (Grace, 1967) it was noticed that between 9 and 16 days after initiation of the cultures, the muscles of the ovarioles started to contract. The contractions were regular and strong, and in the case of the *A. eucalypti*, tissues continued for well over a year.

In most reports, the migration of cells from the explants and the frequency of cell divisions fell off between two and three months after the cultures were set up. Many cells showed degenerative changes, such as vacuoles and fat droplets in the cytoplasm, and usually by the end of the third month the majority of cultures had died or so few cells were alive that the cultures were discarded.

As stated above, one of the factors which affects the shape of cells is the substrate on which they are grown. It has been observed many times that the most successful growth and migration is achieved in primary cultures in cells which attach to the surface of the culture vessel. If the cells do not become attached, they tend to round up and do not divide. The most usual surface for growing cells is glass, but it must be scrupulously clean or the cells will not attach to it. In recent years, disposable plastic culture vessels, the same as are used in vertebrate tissue culture, have been widely used for growing invertebrate tissues. The cells adhere to the plastic very well and, in general, grow and multiply as well as on glass. In an effort to ensure that the tissues and cells came into very close contact with the substrate, many workers have partly embedded the explants in plasma clots made by adding to the medium chick embryo extract and fowl plasma or plasma from other vertebrates such as the guinea pig (Trager, 1938). Such clots have been used for growing insect tissues by Trager (1938), Gottschewski and Fischer, (1939), Gavrilov and Cowez (1941), Flandre et al. (1962), and Vago and Flandre (1963). Flandre and Vago (1963) cultured tissues from the foot, heart, and mantle of the snail *Helix aspersa* in a semisolid medium, and Gay (1963) cultured tissues from the earthworm in a medium solidified by the addition of 1% agar. In all these cases, cells which became attached to the surface of the clot grew well, and their shape was similar to cells grown in liquid medium. Flandre et al. (1963) cultured silkworm cells in media containing fowl plasma at dilutions of 1:20, 1:15, 1:10, 1:5, and 1:2. The amount of cell migration was abundant after 24 hours on the liquid medium and in the medium containing 1:20 plasma, but it fell off as the amount of plasma and, consequently, the firmness of the clot increased. In the firmest clot (1:2) very few cells migrated. There does not appear to be any advantage in growing invertebrate cells in plasma clots, and it is doubtful if the technique will ever have wide use.

The temperature at which cells are grown can have a marked effect on their shape. Insect cells are normally grown in culture at temperatures between 24°–30°. Within this range there is little variation in shape, the most notable difference being that cells at the lower temperature do not have as many processes, which fact probably indicates that they are less active. If the cells are placed in a refrigerator at 4°, within 48 hours most cells will have rounded up, but they generally remain attached to the surface of the culture vessel; the surfaces of the cells are very smooth, and no processes are at all evident. Although cell multiplication is very slow at 4°, it does not stop, and as the cells do not move, or only very little, small colonies are formed as the cells multiply. At temperatures above 32° the cells do not survive for long. Within 48 hours at 37° the cells become detached from the culture vessel. They do not round up but, rather, tend to remain spread out and flat. The cells would not survive longer than seven days at 37°.

The medium, or at least substances in it, can alter the shapes of cells. The most obvious effect is on the ability of the cells to adhere to the culture surface or to other cells to form aggregates. Jones and Cunningham (1961) observed that hemocytes of a silkmoth, when placed in a medium containing 10% heat-treated silkmoth hemolymph, preferentially attached to the glass surface and did not aggregate. However, the hemocytes formed aggregates in 15 minutes when placed in citrated hemolymph. The aggregates could not be dispersed by mechanical means but only by chemical means. Chick embryo fibroblasts also clumped when placed in the citrated hemolymph after the hemocytes had been removed, but they did not aggregate as firmly as the hemocytes and could be dissociated by mechanical means. In general, the presence of insect hemolymph enhances the attachment of insect cells to the surface of the culture vessel.

Herbst (1900) showed very clearly the effect of a substance on the shape and form of cells when he demonstrated that the dissociated cells of sea urchin embryos would reaggregate when placed in seawater containing calcium ions. If the embryos were placed in seawater in which there was no calcium, they dissociated. The ability of cells to adhere to one another to form organized structures makes it possible for multicellular organisms to exist. However, a cell will not cohere indiscriminately with any other cells in the population but will show a high degree of selectivity. How cells recognize each other is one of the most intriguing questions in biology. That cells can react selectively was shown many years ago by Wilson (1907) in a series of classic experiments in which he dissociated two species of sponge and then mixed the cells of each species together. Aggregates soon formed which were composed entirely of cells from one species or the other. Galstoff (1925a,b) and several others, most notably Moscona (1963, 1965), have postulated that substances produced by the cells and acting at the cell surface are responsible for selectively attracting and binding cells into histogenetic patterns. Galstoff (1925b) called the substance "hyaloplasm" and Moscona (1963) referred to it as "extracellularly functioning materials" or "ECM." Working with two species of sponge, *Microciona prolifera*, which is red, and *Haliclona occulata*, which is a light, purple-brown, Moscona (1963) was able to show that the sponge cells had on their surfaces an exudate that not only had high cell-binding activity but also was species selective. If the exudate was removed from the cells of either species of sponge, they could not reaggregate until fresh exudate had been secreted or the exudate from cells of the same species was added. The ECM is apparently bound to the cell surface by specific bonds involving the divalent cations Ca and Mg. More recently, Margoliash *et al.* (1965) have further characterized the ECM from both species of sponge. The material consists of roughly spherical particles 20–24 Å in diameter and with a molecular weight of 15,000–20,000. A determination of the amino acid and sugar components of the particles from both *Microciona* and *Haliclona* showed that, although they were qualitatively similar, they differed quantitatively. The *Microciona* particles contained 72–75 amino acid residues whereas in *Haliclona* there were 51–54. It appears that the particles consisted predominantly of a glycoprotein, but it is also possible that it was a lipoglycoprotein since lipid in small amounts was detected; but its significance was not determined.

An interesting observation was made by Walters and Williams (1966) on the reaggregation of dissociated fat body cells from pupae of two species of silkmoth, *Hyalophora cecropia* and *Antheraea polyphemus*. Within 24 hours after placing fat body cells from either species in drops of hemolymph in culture, practically all the cells had reaggregated into large masses. As the fat body cells are not motile it was puzzling as to how they managed to aggregate, until it was observed, and later confirmed by time lapse cinematography, that amoeboid plasmatocytes became incorporated into the fat body masses. The aggregation was completely inhibited if chelating agents were added to remove divalent cations, but when the cells were washed and placed again in fresh hemolymph, aggregation occurred.

It was also observed that the plasmatocytes would clump positively charged diethylaminoethyl(DEAE)-Sephadex beads, which were about the same size as fat body cells, but only in the presence of divalent cations. The cells did not clump G-Sephadex beads which had no charge and showed only a little affinity for the negatively charged beads of CM- and SE-Sephadex. When fat body cells or DEAE-Sephadex beads were gently shaken in hemolymph it was found, surprisingly, that the fat body cells would adhere to each other in the absence of plasmatocytes, as long as divalent cations were present, but the Sephadex beads required the presence of plasmatocytes. Apparently, the dissociated fat body cells possessed an intrinsic adhesiveness not present in the Sephadex beads.

Fox *et al.* (1967), in a study of the aggregation of embryonic cells of *Drosophila*, have noted some observations which are similar to those found by Walters and Williams (1966). In stationary cultures the yolk cells had a spontaneous tendency to aggregate while the blastoderm cells did not. When the primary cultures were shaken, however, two types of aggregates were formed, i.e., large spherical aggregates containing more than one type of cell and small irregular aggregates which consisted mainly of small cells. The process of aggregation was quite rapid—the whole process took less than 10 hours. It was shown that a number of external factors affected aggregate formation. It was necessary to add either yolk or newborn calf serum (10%), but high concentrations of serum inhibited aggregation. It did not appear to matter if the pH varied within the range of 6.5–7.5 and the temperature between 5° and 18°. If the cells were subjected to long and intense centrifugation or uv irradiation before being shaken, then aggregation would not occur. Apparently also, the cells gradually lost their ability to aggregate if they were kept for 1–10 days in stationary cultures before being shaken. Perhaps the most important observation made in the study was the effects of Actinomycin D and puromycin on cell aggregation. Actinomycin D inhibits RNA synthesis and puromycin inhibits protein synthesis. In the presence of either of these substances the cells formed normal aggregates, but their subsequent behavior was profoundly affected. In the presence of puromycin the aggregates dissociated after they had reached their maximum size of 2 mm in about three hours. Presumably, there were enough of the proteins required for the completion of aggregation in the medium, but the synthesis of new protein to maintain the aggregates was blocked by the puromycin. Similar results were obtained with the Actinomycin D except that the aggregates dissociated after 10 hours.

Although there has been a great deal of progress in recent years in determining some of the factors involved in the aggregation of cells, it is obvious that there is much to be learned. Besides being able to adhere to each other, cells must also have the ability to move away from each other and to reassort themselves into tissues and organs. I have not attempted to give a completely detailed account of the process of aggregation as I am not competent to do so. For those who wish for more details it is recommended that they consult the papers by Moscona mentioned above and the section on cell aggregation in invertebrates by Jones (1966).

IV. CELL LINES

A. Adaptation of Cells in Culture

In the previous section we have seen that after a piece of tissue or dissociated cells have been set up in culture they pass through a fairly definite sequence of events which ends, in the vast majority of cases, in their dying out after a period which may last from one week to many months. In a few instances, however, the cells do not die out but undergo a change, after which cell growth increases, and the cultures may exist indefinitely. Such cultures have been termed "established cell lines." At the present time the only established lines in the invertebrates are of insect tissues (Grace, 1962, 1966, 1967; Chiu and Black, 1967; Singh, 1967; Mitsuhashi, 1967; Ohanessian and Echalier, 1967; Peleg, 1968; Schneider, 1969; Varma and Pudney, 1969).

The question of how an established cell line originates is not only of interest to invertebrate tissue culturists but has puzzled vertebrate tissue culturists for many years. It appears that some cells are able to adapt to culture conditions, but what is actually meant by adaptation is not known. It could be selection, transformation, or mutation. It is evident a short time after a primary culture is set up that some cells seem better adapted to grow in the artificial culture conditions than others. It is possible that these cells are less demanding or more flexible in their life requirements so that they can adjust quickly to culture conditions. But the problem appears to be much more complex than simply some cells being able to adjust to the medium because such adjusted cells are present at a relatively early stage in all cultures which survive for a reasonable time, and yet it is only rarely that they give rise to an established line. It may be that by selection, only the most adaptable cells survive and that as time passes a very small number of cells continues to adjust their metabolism, structures, enzyme systems, etc., to such an extent that eventually they are able to live and multiply with no difficulty in the culture conditions. There is also the possibility that, by mutation, cells could arise which would be able to adapt more readily and successfully to the culture conditions.

The development of the invertebrate cell lines, especially those which arose from moth tissues (Grace, 1962, 1967; Mitsuhashi, 1967), was very similar to many of the vertebrate cell lines. In the four *Antheraea euca-lypti* cell lines (Grace, 1962) the times required for each of the cultures to adapt were 9, 10, and 11 months for the cultures containing dissociated cells and 10 months for the culture containing whole ovaries. The line of hemocytes from the rice stem borer (*Chilo suppressalis*) established by Mitsuhashi (1967) developed after it had been in culture six months. It is rather interesting that all the established lines of mosquito tissues (Grace, 1966; Singh, 1967) adapted after very short periods. In the line of *Aedes aegypti* cells and *Aedes albopictus* cells developed by Singh (1967), the cells continued to multiply practically from the time the cultures were set up. Chiu and Black (1967), who established a number of lines of cells from the leafhopper *Agallia constricta*, stated that most of their lines were established about two months after the primary cultures were set up.

In none of the insect cell lines except that of Mitsuhashi (1967) has it been determined from which tissues or cells the lines developed. A comparison of the morphology of the cells from all the established lines shows that they are all very similar in size and consist of either spindle-shaped or epithelial cells.

B. Clones

When a line of cells is established, it frequently consists of several types of cells which in their morphology, metabolism, ability to support the growth of viruses, and other properties may be very different from the cells set up in the primary cultures from which the line developed. For many studies such a mixed population of cells is not important, but in other studies it may be important to work with a pure strain of cells. The best way to obtain such a pure population is to grow it from a single cell. Such a population is known as a clone. Although the cells of a clone will initially be genetically and morphologically homogeneous, after several generations cells of different shapes and genetic make-up will often appear and it is necessary to clone the cells again.

By using some of the methods developed for cloning vertebrate cells (see Paul, 1961), Suitor et al. (1966) and Grace (1968) have cloned cells from the established lines of Aedes aegypti cells (Grace, 1966) and Antheraea eucalypti cells (Grace, 1962), respectively. The capillary method, devised by Sanford et al. (1948), was used by Suitor et al. (1966) to clone the spindle-shaped cell type in the mosquito cell line. The capillary method, in which a single cell is sealed inside a capillary tube, ensures that the clone obtained has arisen from a single cell, but it is a most tedious method and only a very small number of cells grow. Suitor et al. (1966) made many attempts before they managed to obtain a clone, and it took 82 attempts before they succeeded in cloning a cell from the cloned line. Several characteristics of the clone were compared with the uncloned cells. The growth rate of the cloned cells at 22°, 28°, and 34° was much slower at each temperature than in the uncloned cells. As the parent clone contained several types of cells, Suitor et al. (1966) suggested that the differences in growth rate could be due to the presence in the mixed population of a cell with a growth rate faster than that of the cells in the clone. In their morphology the cloned cells very closely resembled the spindle-shaped cells in the parent line. A comparative study of the chromosome complements showed that there was very little differ-

ence between the cloned and uncloned cells, i.e., both groups contained
no diploid cells and all the cells examined had about 100 chromosomes,
which was very close to the 96 (32n) found by Grace (1966) in the
mosquito line.

The method used by Grace (1968) to clone the cells of the *Antheraea
eucalypti* line was the dilution method and was based on the technique
described by Paul (1961). The method consists very simply of placing
a small number of cells (about 100) in a petri dish so that they are well
separated from each other. It is important in this method to leave the
cultures completely undisturbed for about seven days so that any cells
which float or are only lightly attached to the culture vessel will not come
into contact with each other or other cells. After several days the cultures were examined and each colony which appeared morphologically
distinct was placed in a vessel by itself and allowed to multiply up to
about 100 cells. These cells were then transferred back to a petri dish.
This procedure was repeated three times, after which the clones were
transferred to culture bottles and allowed to multiply until the population had reached about 5×10^5 cells/ml of medium. Samples of each
population were then examined, and if there was any marked variation
in shape, the cells were again diluted out. By repeating the clones at
frequent intervals it was possible to reduce the danger, inherent in this
technique, of contamination by cells migrating from other colonies.

Ten clones were established which could be grouped into the three
types of cells originally described by Grace (1962, 1968). Six of the
clones are spindle-shaped, and two consist of cells which are round to
spindle-shaped and which usually remain in aggregates and adhere to
the substrate. The cells of one clone were round and showed very little
variation in shape or size. In another clone, the cells were very variable
and irregular in shape and size, and yet, each time they were recloned
the variability persisted and it was not possible to select subclones. The
clones showed differences in their growth rates over a seven-day period;
three of the clones (two spindle-shaped and one round to spindle-shaped)
grew faster than the other seven clones, which all grew at about the same
rate.

It is possible that when the cell lines were first established there were,
in fact, only three types of cell and that over the years cells have been
selected which show different morphological characters.

Grace (1968) found no difficulty in growing populations from single
cells. The efficiency of cloning was not measured accurately but was
certainly over 85%. It was also found to be unnecessary to use conditioned medium (i.e., medium in which cells had previously grown).
Quite frequently it was possible, when using the capillary method in early

attempts to clone the *Antheraea eucalypti* cells, to obtain colonies of up to 20 or 30 cells, but they would not continue to grow and would gradually die away. The reasons why such colonies died are unknown, but it is possible that they required the presence of cells of another type to supply them with some essential factor.

Although cloning the cells on morphological characteristics is generally the easiest method, it should be borne in mind that it is possible that cells with quite different characters, such as their ability to support virus growth or their possession of particular enzymes, may not be distinguishable by their shape alone. The ability to clone cells also can be used to advantage for assessing cellular response to physical and chemical factors and for determining the nutritional requirements of cells. One warning, which has been made many times in reports on the cloning of vertebrate cells and which is also relevant when cloning invertebrate cells, is that it must be realized that in most instances the cells which are cloned cannot be considered as normal and that in extrapolating any results obtained either to other cultures or to the cells from the original host, care should be taken.

C. Internal Morphology

Electron microscope examinations of thin sections of spindle-shaped cells of the silkworm (*Bombyx mori*), (Vago and Croissant, 1963) and of cells from the *Antheraea eucalypti* cell lines (Grace, 1963) grown *in vitro* showed very few specialized inclusions and in their general appearance were very like the undifferentiated cells found in mammalian cell cultures. A study of Figs. 4 and 5 show the following features. The mitochondria (M) can be exceedingly long, and in the *A. eucalypti* cells, they were oriented in the direction of the cytoplasmic processes. The cytoplasm also contained Golgi apparatus and a number of dense vesicles (V) which were periodic acid-schiff reagent (PAS) positive. The vesicles are membrane covered, and in some can be seen what could be cell debris. They resemble lysosomes, but their precise function and nature have not been determined. The endoplasmic reticulum (ER) is in fairly small amount, and there is little ribosome covered ER(RER). Most of the ribosomes (R) lie free in the cytoplasm. The nuclei (N) are large, round, and in the *A. eucalypti* cells, contain usually more than one nucleolus, (NU) which are very variable in shape. The large nuclear/cytoplasmic ratio found in these cells is consistent with their being undifferentiated. In many of the spindle-shaped cells microtubules were present. Like the mitochondria they were usually oriented in the long axis of the cells.

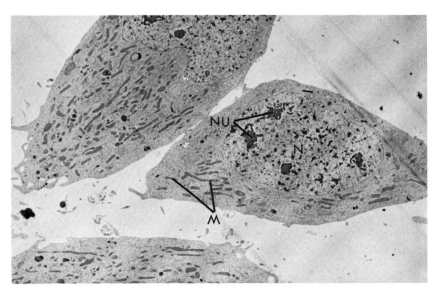

FIG. 4. Electron micrograph of spindle-shaped cells from the *Antheraea eucalypti* cell line. Note the numerous mitochondria, large nuclei, and numerous nucleoli. M. mitochondria; N, nucleus; NU, nucleolus. (Approx. ×2040.)

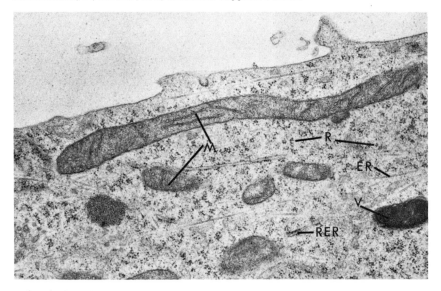

FIG. 5. Magnified section of part of a cell from the *Antheraea eucalypti* cell line. ER, endoplasmic reticulum; M, mitochondria; N, nucleus; NU, nucleolus; RER, "rough" (ribosome covered) endoplasmic reticulum; R, ribosomes; V, vesicles. (Approx. ×20,400.)

V. GROWTH OF CELLS IN CULTURE

A. Mitosis

The term *growth* can have different meanings in tissue culture. In organ cultures, growth may, and often does, mean an increase in the size of an organ due to development and differentiation, without necessarily an increase in the number of cells. To the tissue and cell culturists, growth almost invariably means an increase in tissue mass or cell number due to the multiplication of cells by mitosis. No intensive studies have been made of the mitotic process in invertebrate cells in culture, but a number of interesting observations have been made which are worth noting. One of the most depressing features noticed when reading about invertebrate tissue culture is the number of papers in which it is stated that the tissues or cells survived for several days but that no mitoses were seen, or were seen only during the first two or three days after the cultures were set up. There is no doubt that the very poor growth and survival obtained in the early years was due in a large degree to the unsuitable media in which the cells and tissues were cultured. As the media improved, so did the growth and survival, and mitotic figures could often be seen in cultures which had been set up for several months.

Jones and Cunningham (1960, 1961) measured the mitotic index of cells in hanging drop cultures of ovarian tissue from diapausing pupae of a silkmoth over a 21-day period. During the first 12 days, the first two days of which the cells were in lag phase, the average mitotic index was 0.5%. The maximum mitotic index of 1.0% was reached on the fifth and sixth days and fell to a minimum of less than 0.3% by the 21st day. These authors maintained that this was the first time that it had been shown conclusively that cell growth had taken place in cultures of insect tissues. It is a pity the cultures did not continue to grow.

In general, mitoses in cells in culture do not appear to be different from those in cells taken directly from the intact animal. In cultures of the embryonic tissues of the green rice leafhopper (*Nephotettix cincticeps* Uhler) Mitsuhashi (1965, 1967) studied the process of mitosis and the formation of binucleate cells. The tissues were grown in sitting drop cultures, and as the cells moved across the glass surface they became very flat, making it easy to follow each stage in mitosis. The tissues were grown at 25° and the duration of each stage was measured at this temperature. Prophase lasted at least 30 minutes, and at the end of it the nuclear membrane disappeared "almost instantaneously." The period of prometaphase (Firket, 1965), which starts from the time of disappearance of the nuclear membrane and in which the chromosomes arrange themselves into an equatorial plate, took from 10 to 150 minutes. Polyploid cells took a much longer time to complete this stage than diploid cells. The cells also shrank in size and became thicker and rounder. The true metaphase stage, in which the chromosomes are arranged along the equator of the cell, varied from 10 to 60 minutes. Mitsuhashi did not state whether the variation in this stage depended also upon the ploidy of the cell. Anaphase, the stage where the chromosomes split longitudinally and the chromatids move to opposite poles, was completed in 10 minutes. The last stage is telophase, in which the nucleoli and the nuclear membrane reappear and the cell divides into two daughter cells under normal conditions. Mitsuhashi does not give an explicit time for this stage but states that about 30 minutes after the cell divided the nuclear membrane reformed. It appears that at the temperature of 25° mitosis took a total time of between 90–280 minutes. In vertebrates the duration of mitosis is about 30–100 minutes at 37° for warm-blooded animals and between 90–120 minutes at 20°–26° for frogs and newts (Firket, 1965). Grace (1963) estimated the duration of mitosis in cells from the *Antheraea eucalypti* cell line (Grace, 1962) by time-lapse cinematography and found it to be about 120 minutes at 28°. As in the vertebrate cells, the phase of shortest duration is anaphase and the other phases are of about the same duration as each other except that prometaphase in the leafhopper seems to be very slow and prolonged. Occasionally, Mitsuhashi also found that the number of multipolar (especially tripolar) mitoses increased if the tissue cultures were maintained at 32°, which is too high a temperature for normal growth of insect tissues. The presence of abnormal and multipolar mitoses in vertebrates is also increased by exposure to high temperatures (Stillwell, 1947; Firket, 1965).

Tokumitsu and Maramorosch (1967) studied the formation of protuberances (blebs) and bubbling on the surface of dividing cells in cultures of embryonic tissues of the six-spotted leafhopper *Macrosteles fascifrons* Stal. In most instances, the blebs appeared first during metaphase, but during late anaphase and early telophase, the frequency of bleb formation was at its height and then decreased as telophase ended. The stage of metaphase was prolonged when bubbling and bleb formation occurred, taking 45–75 minutes, whereas in cells in which no protuberances appeared metaphase took only 22–36 minutes.

Carlson and his colleagues (Carlson, 1946, 1958, 1961; Carlson and Hollaender, 1948) have studied, under culture conditions, the effect of X irradiation on proliferating neuroblasts of embryonic grasshoppers. When a dose of 3 R (roentgens) was given to neuroblast cells, cell division was arrested at late prophase. Even a single α particle passing through a dividing cell could stop mitosis at prophase. Gaulden and Kokomoor (1955) showed that the recovery of neuroblasts from the effects of irradiation could be hastened if the cells were cultured in a medium containing yolk from grasshopper eggs. Gaulden (1956) found that the delay in mitosis induced by irradiation could be prevented if the neuroblasts were placed in a hypertonic salt solution. This observation supported a hypothesis that irradiation affected the permeability of the cell surface so that cations necessary in the mitotic process leaked away and that, if the concentrations of the necessary cations could be maintained in the culture medium, the delay in mitosis would be prevented (see Trowell, 1966).

Necco and Martin (1963) studied the mitotic activity of the white body cells of the octopus (*Octopus vulgaris*) and found that they have a very low mitotic rate, only one cell in a thousand begins mitosis per hour.

It is a pity that mitosis and cell division have not been more thoroughly studied in cultures of invertebrate cells. A strong stimulus to begin such studies should be provided by the establishment of lines of *Drosophila* cells (Ohanessian and Echalier, 1967).

B. Polyploidy

There are not many reports in invertebrate tissue culture to polyploidy, which is perhaps rather surprising in view of the fact that in insects, at least, cells of the gonads, which have often been used in culture, are frequently polyploid (White, 1954). The most thorough study to date of the cytology and cytochemistry of cultured cells was made by Thomson and Grace (1963) on the cells of the *Antheraea eucalypti* cell lines (Grace, 1962). The reason for making the study was to see if the cells of an established line of insect cells showed a high degree of polyploidy, in view of the fact that most established mammalian cell lines are polyploid.

The haploid number of chromosomes in *A. eucalypti* is 25. In squash preparations of cells from the gonad sheath of pupal testis and ovary, the ploidy ranged from 2n (50 chromosomes) up to approximately 128n (3000 chromosomes). Most commonly the nuclei contained either tetraploid (100), octoploid (200), or 16n (400) chromosomes.

When the cells from the line were examined, they showed a range of chromosome complements from 2n to 128n with the most frequently encountered numbers being 4n, 8n, and 16n; that is, they showed the same range of ploidy as the cells from the pupal tissues. When it is realized that the cells from the line had passed through about 120 generations in a period of 15–20 months under *in vitro* conditions, it is rather surprising that there had been no change in the chromosome complements.

An effort was also made in this study to correlate the number of chromosomes with the cell morphology. In order to do this, cells were grown on cover glasses and, after fixation, were stained with Feulgen. The relative amounts of DNA in each cell type were then estimated quantitatively by cytophotometry (Lison, 1950). There were, at this stage, three types of cells in the line. Type 1 cells were polygonal in outline, rather flat, the cytoplasm was finely granulated, and they were about 20–40 μ in diameter. These cells showed intermediate ploidy ranging from 2n up but never reaching the levels attained in the other types. The type 2 cells were spindle-shaped, 15–20 μ in diameter, and had a finely granular cytoplasm. Most cells of this type had a DNA content indicating at least a tetraploid condition, and in some cells the ploidy was the highest observed. The type 3 cells were small, round, 10–15 μ in diameter, and had a DNA content which suggested they might be diploid or, at least, that they did not have a high level of polyploidy.

It is interesting that the spindle-shaped cells, which were the most abundant cells in the lines, should have also had the greatest level and range of polyploidy. Landureau (1966) found that in cultures of embryonic cells from the cockroach *Blabera fusca* Brunner, some cells became polyploid and that after several weeks they were the only cells which remained active.

In the mosquito cell line (Grace, 1966) all the cells examined were polyploid. Whereas the diploid number in *Aedes aegypti* is 6, most of the cells had 96 (32n) chromosomes. Some had 48 (16n) and a few more than 96. A similar state of affairs was found in the silkworm cell line (Grace, 1967), where most cells, examined 18 months after the line was established, contained well over 100 chromosomes. The diploid number in the silkworm is 56.

C. Multinucleate Cells

It is not uncommon in tissue cultures to observe binucleate and, more rarely, multinucleate cells. Mitsuhashi (1967), who followed the formation of binucleate cells in cultures of the green rice leafhopper *Nephotettix cincticeps*, believed that they were derived from cells which had migrated out from the explant rather than having been present in the explant when it was set up in culture. The binucleate and some multinucleate cells were only rarely seen when cell migration first began and later were found mostly at the edge of the cell sheets. The cell which became binucleate was very large (120 μ in diameter) and was thought to be tetraploid. After the chromosomes had passed into metaphase it was noticed that they started to rotate, along with the poles and spindles, and after 20 minutes they had rotated through 90° so that they came to lie along the long axis of the cells. After anaphase was completed a large mass of cytoplasm came to lie between the separated chromosomes and then a cleft appeared, cutting the mass of cytoplasm. Eventually the mass of cytoplasm disappeared along with the cleft and the cell passed into telophase and two daughter nuclei formed in the one cell. The cell did not divide. The bipolar mitosis took 155 minutes at 25°.

Varma and Pudney (1967) also observed multinucleate cells in cultures of embryonic cells from the bug *Triatoma maculata* (Erichson) which had grown for 74 days. Some of these cells had their nuclei arranged "like peas in a pod."

The formation of multinucleate cells appears to be one of the consequences of growing cells *in vitro*. It would be interesting to see if such cells survived longer than other cultured cells.

VI. METABOLISM OF CULTURED CELLS

A. Nutritive Requirements

The invertebrates are a very diverse group of animals, and yet, there is no reason to believe that the fundamental pathways of synthesis and of obtaining energy are basically different between a sponge cell and an insect cell. In fact, it is interesting that a medium recommended for growing dissociated cells of the coelenterate *Hydra* contained horse serum and a mixture of saline solutions designed for growing vertebrate cells (Li et al., 1963). Vaughn, in this volume, Chapter 1, has discussed in detail the media that have been used for growing invertebrate cells, and there is no point in repeating this information. There are, however, some general remarks which can be made concerning designing and choosing media for growing invertebrate cells. For cells to grow for long periods *in vitro* it is obvious that they will need to be supplied with all the factors necessary for their growth or which they can use to synthesize essential materials. As it would have been surprising if many of the media designed for growing vertebrate cells did not also maintain to some extent the growth of invertebrate tissues, many of the early workers used vertebrate media for their cultures. They realized, especially those

working with insect tissues, that there were important differences between
the composition of insect hemolymph and vertebrate plasma (Martignoni,
1960), and in many instances they modified the media used to make them
more suitable for the growth of insect tissues. One of the major differences between insect hemolymph and vertebrate plasma is the high concentrations of amino acids in the hemolymph (up to 50 times higher
than in human plasma). To increase the concentrations, many workers
simply added such substances as hydrolysates of yeast or lactalbumen.
In some instances these media have maintained the tissues for a number
of months (Hirumi and Maramorosch, 1963; Mitsuhashi and Maramorosch, 1964), but generally, they have not been particularly successful.
Similar results have been obtained with mollusc tissues (Burch and
Cuadros, 1965; Tripp et al., 1966) and tick tissues (H. M. Martin and
Vidler, 1962; Rehacek, 1963).

More successful media have consisted of a solution of salts whose ions
such as sodium, potassium, calcium, and magnesium have been adjusted
to those found in the host's sera plus various hydrolysates and vertebrate
sera. In such media Chiu and Black (1967) established lines of leafhopper
tissues and Singh (1967) established lines of mosquito tissues.

If one wishes to use tissue cultures simply as a technique, then media
such as these are the best to use since they are comparatively cheap and
very easy to make up, but for many studies on the nutrition of cells *in
vitro* or for biochemical and physiological studies, media which are completely synthetic or in which most of the components are known are
preferable. Some attempts have been made in insect tissue culture (Grace
and Brzostowski, 1966; Landureau, 1969; Landureau and Jolles, 1969)
to determine which components in a medium are used, and it is hoped
that further studies of the nutritive requirements of invertebrate cells
will be made.

B. Role of Growth Factors

A large number of substances have been added to media in the hope
that they will provide factors that will promote growth in the cells, but
in the majority of instances, the hoped-for results have not eventuated.
Vertebrate sera from both mammalian and avian sources have been the
most common supplement added for culturing many types of invertebrate
cells. The role of the serum in the media is not known, but there is little
doubt that it provides factors, most likely proteins, which help the cells
to attach to the culture vessel, which, in turn, has been shown to promote
growth. The main reason why vertebrate sera have been used is because

they are readily available in large quantities, whereas it is usually impractical and often practically impossible to obtain large amounts of hemolymph or blood from invertebrates. However, when invertebrate sera have been used they have usually had a growth-promoting effect (Grace, 1962, 1966, 1967). Sen Gupta (1963) discussed the role of hemolymph in insect tissue culture and came to the conclusion, which I believe is the right one, that the hemolymph is a source of protein to aid the cells in attaching to the culture surface. Many attempts have been made to replace the hemolymph in Grace's established cell lines with substances from vertebrate sources which are more readily available. Yunker *et al.* (1967) succeeded in adapting the *Antheraea eucalypti* cells to grow in medium containing 10% whole egg ultrafiltrate and 10% heat-inactivated calf serum, instead of insect hemolymph. The cells took several months to adapt to the new medium, but when they did, they grew faster than the cells in the medium containing hemolymph. Nagle *et al.* (1967) grew the cells in suspension in a medium in which the hemolymph had been replaced by 10% fetal bovine serum and methylcellulose to increase the viscosity. The mosquito cell lines established by Singh (1967), Peleg (1968), and Varma and Pudney (1969) were grown, from the beginning, in media which contained, instead of hemolymph, fetal bovine serum.

In regard to the question of hormones being essential for growth, there is no evidence that they are required for the growth of invertebrate tissues. Grace (1958a) found that the addition of "endocrine organ extracts" to cultures of silkworm tissues increased the number of mitoses but the cells did not survive any longer than those in cultures without extracts. The increased number of mitoses could have been due to the presence of protein material in the extract. Further evidence against the need for hormones is the fact that the *A. eucalypti* cell lines were developed from tissues which were taken from diapausing pupae, and the hemolymph used in the medium in which they have grown for over 10 years was also obtained from diapausing pupae.

Although the hormones are not necessary for the growth of undifferentiated cells, there is evidence that the presence of endocrine glands can produce morphogenetic changes in organs such as imaginal discs. Burdette *et al.* (1968) showed that the addition of ecdysones prolonged the survival and caused the differentiation of the eye imaginal discs of *Drosophila melanogaster* (Oregon R) cultured *in vitro*. The discs developed better when the entire brain complex was intact, irrespective of whether the ecdysones were added. This suggested that for normal development some type of hormonal interaction is necessary as well as the addition of ecdysone. Lender and Laverdure (1967) and Ittycheriah and Stephanos

(1968) obtained results that indicated that the addition of explants of
the brain, corpus cardiacum, corpus allatum, or synthetic juvenile hormone induced vitellogenesis in cultures of ovaries from several species
of insects; and several workers have reported that the presence of
ecdysone in cultures of epithelial tissues has stimulated the production
and deposition of cuticle (Sengel and Mandaron, 1969; Agui et al., 1969;
Marks and Leopold, 1970).

In an effort to supply all the necessary factors for growth, various extracts of tissues, eggs, whole animals, etc., have been added to media.
Murray (1931) added extracts of planarian tissues to her cultures of
parenchyma tissue from planarian worms and increased the survival
time from two to four weeks. However, extracts of tapeworms, clams,
isopods, and sheep were harmful. In insect tissue cultures extracts from
every stage of the life cycle have been added, but the results have been
consistently unsuccessful (Pfeiffer, 1927; Gavrilov and Cowez, 1941;
Grace, 1958a).

Certain compounds, such as nucleic acids, and important metabolites
such as adenosine triphosphate, and various purines and pyrimidines
which are essential in many metabolic processes had absolutely no effect
when added to cultures of silkworm cells (Grace, 1958a).

C. Phagocytosis

In the invertebrates, which do not have the ability to make antibodies
against invading agents, the wandering phagocytic cells play an extremely important part in the immune mechanism. Phagocytic cells are
found in all phyla of the invertebrates from the sponges up. That the
phagocytes are capable of eliminating dead or foreign material was
beautifully shown in the time-lapse movie of the *Antheraea eucalypti*
cells in culture (Grace and Day, 1963). Within a very short time of a
cell dying, a number of phagocytic cells moved on to the cell and started
ingesting it.

Tripp and his associates (Tripp, 1960, 1963; Tripp et al., 1966; Tripp
and Kent, 1968) have made a detailed study of phagocytosis in the
oyster and other molluscs, both *in vivo* and *in vitro*.

In *in vivo* studies Tripp (1960) found that bacteria, yeast, and red
blood cells were not only rapidly phagocytosed by the oyster cells but
they were also digested. In *in vitro* studies Tripp and Kent (1968)
studied the ability of the oyster phagocytes to ingest and digest the
bacterium *Escherichia coli* and chicken red blood cells. The bacteria
were phagocytosed as rapidly in culture as they were *in vivo*, and most

of them digested as rapidly also, but some live bacteria did persist within the phagocytes for several days. The red blood cells were ingested and digested as rapidly *in vitro* as *in vivo*.

One of the difficulties, apparently, in growing oyster tissues and, consequently, in studying the action of phagocytes is that it is very difficult to maintain sterile conditions. This is probably due to the persistence of viable bacteria within the phagocytes when they are removed from the host.

The phagocytic action of the oyster cells is influenced by the conditions of culture. If calf serum is added at a concentration of 10%, phagocytosis is drastically reduced. However, phagocytosis can be greatly enhanced if the blood cells are placed in oyster hemolymph prior to being phagocytosed.

It is rather remarkable that phagocytosis has not been studied in insect tissue cultures. There is no doubt that cells from *Antheraea eucalypti* and *Bombyx mori* cell lines are capable of phagocytosing virus particles and bacteria (Grace, 1962b). Very useful studies could also be made using the dissociated cell cultures of *Hydra* described by Li *et al.* (1963).

REFERENCES

Acton, R. T., and Evans, E. E. (1968). *In Vitro* **3**, 139.
Agui, N., Yagi, S., and Fukaya, M. (1969). *Appl. Entomol. Zool.* **4**, 156.
Ball, G. H. (1947). *Amer. J. Trop. Med.* **27**, 301.
Ball, G. H. (1948). *Amer. J. Trop. Med.* **28**, 533.
Ball, G. H. (1954). *Exp. Parasitol.* **3**, 359.
Ball, G. H., and Chao, J. (1957). *J. Parasitol.* **43**, 409.
Ball, G. H., and Chao, J. (1960). *Exp. Parasitol.* **9**, 47.
Bang, F. B. (1966). *J. Immunol.* **96**, 960.
Briggs, J. D. (1958). *J. Exp. Zool.* **138**, 155.
Bucklin, D. H. (1953). *Anat. Rec.* **117**, 539.
Burch, J. B., and Cuadros, C. (1965). *Nature (London)* **206**, 637.
Burdette, W. J., Hanley, E. W., and Grosch, J. (1968). *Texas Rep. Biol. Med.* **26**, 173.
Burnett, A. L., Ruffing, F. E., and Zongker, J. (1968). *J. Embryol. Exp. Morphol.* **20**, 73.
Campbell, R. D. (1967). *J. Exp. Zool.* **164**, 379.
Carlson, J. G. (1946). *Biol. Bull.* **90**, 106.
Carlson, J. G. (1958). *Biology* **29**, 106.
Carlson, J. G. (1961). *Ann. N. Y. Acad. Sci.* **95**, 932.
Carlson, J. G., and Hollaender, A. (1948). *J. Cell. Comp. Physiol.* **31**, 149.
Castiglione, M. C., and Raimondi, G. R. (1961). *Atti Ass. Genet. Ital.* **6**, 139.
Cerame-Vivas, M., and Bookhout, C. G. (1961). *J. Elisha Mitchell Sci. Soc.* **77**, 117.
Chadwick, J. M. (1967). *Fed. Proc., Fed. Amer. Soc. Exp. Biol.* **26**, 1675.
Chandebois, R. (1963). *Ann. Epiphyt.* **14**, 141.

206 T. D. C. GRACE

Chandebois, R. (1968). *J. Embryol. Exp. Morphol.* **20**, 175.
Chao, J., and Ball, G. H. (1971). Paper given at "Symposium on Arthropod Cell Cultures and their Application to the Study of Viruses."
Chiu, R. J., and Black, L. M. (1967). *Nature (London)* **215**, 1076.
Clark, E. W., and Ball, G. H. (1952). *Exp. Parasitol.* **1**, 339.
Clark, E. W., and Ball, G. H. (1954). *Physiol. Zool.* **27**, 334.
Clark, E. W., and Ball, G. H. (1956). *Physiol. Zool.* **29**, 522.
Clements, A. N., and Grace, T. D. C. (1967). *J. Insect Physiol.* **13**, 1327.
Collier, W. A. (1920). *Z. Wiss. Insektenbiol.* **16**, 1.
Curtis, A. S. G. (1962). *Nature (London)* **196**, 245.
Demal, J., and Leloup, A. M. (1963). *Ann. Epiphyt.* **14**, 91.
Echalier, G., and Ohanessian, A. (1969). *C. R. Acad. Sci.* **268**, 1771.
Fauré-Fremiet, E. (1925). *C. R. Soc. Biol.* **92**, 1287.
Fauré-Fremiet, E. (1934). *Arch. Exp. Zellforsch. Besonders Gewebezuecht.* **15**, 373.
Firket, H. (1965). *In* "Cells and Tissues in Culture" (E. N. Willmer, ed.), Vol. 1, pp. 203–237. Academic Press, New York.
Fischer, I., and Gottschewski, G. (1939). *Naturwissenschaften* **27**, 391.
Flandre, O., and Vago, C. (1963). *Ann. Epiphyt.* **14**, 161.
Flandre, O., Vago, C., and Chastang, S. (1962). *C. R. Soc. Biol.* **255**, 1654.
Fox, A. S., Horikawa, M., and Ling, L.-N. L. (1967). *In Vitro* **3**, 65.
Frew, J. G. H. (1928). *J. Exp. Biol.* **6**, 1.
Galstoff, P. S. (1923). *Biol. Bull.* **45**, 143.
Galstoff, P. S. (1925a). *J. Exp. Zool.* **42**, 183.
Galstoff, P. S. (1925b). *J. Exp. Zool.* **42**, 223.
Gatenby, J. B. (1931). *Nature (London)* **128**, 1002.
Gatenby, J. B. (1932). *Nature (London)* **130**, 628.
Gatenby, J. B., and Duthie, E. S. (1932). *J. Roy. Microsc. Soc.* **52**, 395.
Gatenby, J. B., and Hill, J. C. (1933). *Quart. J. Microsc. Sci.* **76**, 331.
Gaulden, M. E. (1956). *Ioniz. Radiat. Cell Metab., Ciba Found. Symp.* pp. 206, 207, and 303.
Gaulden, M. E., and Carlson, J. G. (1947). *Genetics* **32**, 87.
Gaulden, M. E., and Kokomoor, K. L. (1955). *Proc. Soc. Exp. Biol. Med.* **90**, 309.
Gavrilov, W., and Cowez, S. (1941). *Ann. Parasitol. Hum. Comp.* **18**, 180.
Gay, R. (1963). *Ann. Epiphyt.* **14**, 61.
Glaser, R. W. (1925). *J. Immunol.* **10**, 651.
Goldschmidt, R. (1915). *Proc. Nat. Acad. Sci. U. S.* **1**, 220.
Goldschmidt, R. (1916). *Biol. Zentralbl.* **36**, 161.
Gottschewski, G., and Fischer, I. (1939). *Naturwissenschaften* **27**, 584.
Grace, T. D. C. (1954). *Nature (London)* **174**, 187.
Grace, T. D. C. (1958a). *Aust. J. Exp. Biol.* **11**, 407.
Grace, T. D. C. (1958b). *J. Gen. Physiol.* **41**, 1027.
Grace, T. D. C. (1962a). *Nature (London)* **195**, 788.
Grace, T. D. C. (1962b). *Virology* **18**, 33.
Grace, T. D. C. (1963). Ph.D. Thesis, unpublished.
Grace, T. D. C. (1966). *Nature (London)* **211**, 366.
Grace, T. D. C. (1967). *Nature (London)* **216**, 613.
Grace, T. D. C. (1968). *Exp. Cell Res.* **52**, 451.
Grace, T. D. C., and Brzostowski, H. W. (1966). *J. Insect Physiol.* **12**, 625.
Grace, T. D. C., and Day, M. F. (1963). *Ann. Epiphyt.* **14**, 27.
Grobstein, C. (1965). *In* "Cells and Tissues in Culture" (E. N. Willmer, ed.), Vol. 1, pp. 463–488. Academic Press, New York.

Haynes, J. F., Burnett, A. L., and Davis, L. E. (1968). *In Vitro* **3**, 49.
Herbst, C. (1900). *Wilhelm Roux' Arch. Entwicklungsmech. Organismen* **9**, 424.
Hill, J. C., and Gatenby, J. B. (1934). *Arch. Exp. Zellforsch. Besonders Gewebezuecht.* **18**, 195.
Hirumi, H., and Maramorosch, K. (1963). *Ann. Epiphyt.* **14**, 77.
Hirumi, H., and Maramorosch, K. (1964). *Contrib. Boyce Thompson Inst.* **22**, 259.
Horikawa, M. (1958). *Cytologia* **23**, 468.
Horikawa, M., and Fox, A. S. (1964). *Science* **145**, 1437.
Horikawa, M., and Kuroda, Y. (1959). *Nature (London)* **184**, 2017.
Horikawa, M., and Sugahara, T. (1960). *Radiat. Res.* **12**, 266.
Horikawa, M., Ling, L. N. L., and Fox, A. S. (1966). *Nature (London)* **210**, 183.
Ittycheriah, P. I., and Stephanos, S. (1968). *Indian J. Exp. Biol.* **7**, 17.
Jones, B. M. (1966). *In* "Cells and Tissues in Culture" (E. N. Willmer, ed.), Vol. 3, pp. 397–457. Academic Press, New York.
Jones, B. M., and Cunningham, I. (1960). *Nature (London)* **187**, 1072.
Jones, B. M., and Cunningham, I. (1961). *Exp. Cell Res.* **23**, 386.
Kitamura, S. (1964). *Kobe J. Med. Sci.* **10**, 85.
Kuroda, Y. (1954a). *Zool. Mag.* **63**, 75.
Kuroda, Y. (1954b). *Idengaku Zasshi* **29**, 163.
Kuroda, Y., and Yamaguchi, K. (1956). *Idengaku Zasshi* **31**, 98.
Landureau, J. C. (1966). *Exp. Cell Res.* **41**, 545.
Landureau, J. C. (1969). *Exp. Cell Res.* **54**, 399.
Landureau, J. C., and Jolles, P. (1969). *Exp. Cell Res.* **54**, 391.
Landureau, J. C., and Jolles, P. (1970). *Nature (London)* **225**, 968.
Larsen, W. (1963). *Ann. Entomol. Soc. Amer.* **6**, 442.
Larsen, W. (1964). *Life Sci.* **3**, 539.
Lender, T., and Duveau-Hagege, J. (1962). *C. R. Soc. Biol.* **254**, 2825.
Lender, T., and Duveau-Hagege, J. (1963). *Develop. Biol.* **6**, 1.
Lender, T., and Laverdure, A. M. (1967). *C. R. Acad. Sci.* **265**, 451.
Lenhoff, H. M. (1968). *In Vitro* **3**, 33.
Lewis, M. R., and Robertson, W. R. B. (1916). *Biol. Bull.* **30**, 99.
Li, Y. Y. F., Baker, F. D., and Andrew, W. (1963). *Proc. Soc. Exp. Biol. Med.* **113**, 259.
Lison, L. (1950). *Acta Anat.* **10**, 333.
Loeb, L. (1922). *Science* **56**, 237.
Loeb, L. (1927). *Protoplasma* **2**, 514.
Luscher, M. (1947). *Nature (London)* **160**, 873.
Luscher, M. (1948). *Rev. Suisse Zool.* **55**, 227.
Margoliash, E., Schenk, J. R., Hargie, M. P., Burokas, S., Richter, W. R., Barlow, G. H., and Moscona, A. A. (1965). *Biochem. Biophys. Res. Commun.* **20**, 383.
Marks, E. P. (1968). *Gen. Comp. Endocrinol.* **11**, 31.
Marks, E. P., and Leopold, R. A. (1970). *Science* **167**, 61.
Marks, E. P., and Reinecke, J. P. (1964). *Science* **143**, 961.
Marks, E. P., and Reinecke, J. P. (1965a). *J. Kans. Entomol. Soc.* **38**, 179.
Marks, E. P., and Reinecke, J. P. (1965b). *Gen. Comp. Endocrinol.* **5**, 241.
Marks, E. P., Reinecke, J. P., and Leopold, R. A. (1968). *Biol. Bull.* **135**, 520.
Martignoni, M. E. (1960). *Experientia* **16**, 125.
Martin, H. M., and Vidler, B. O. (1962). *Exp. Parasitol* **12**, 192.
Martin, R., and Tardent, P. (1963). *Rev. Suisse Zool.* **70**, 312.
Mayer, E. (1963). "Introduction to Dynamic Morphology." Academic Press, New York.

Mitsuhashi, J. (1965). *Jap. J. Appl. Entomol. Zool.* **9,** 107.

Mitsuhashi, J. (1967). *Nature (London)* **215,** 863.

Mitsuhashi, J., and Maramorosch, K. (1964). *Contrib. Boyce Thompson Inst.* **22,** 435.

Mohring, W., and Messner, B. (1968). *Biol. Zentralbl.* **87,** 439.

Moscona. A. A. (1963). *Proc. Nat. Acad. Sci. U. S.* **49,** 742.

Moscona, A. A. (1965). *In* "Cells and Tissues in Culture" (E. N. Willmer, ed.), Vol. 1, pp. 489–524. Academic Press, New York.

Moscona, A. A. (1968). *In Vitro* **3,** 13.

Murray, M. R. (1927). *J. Exp. Zool.* **47,** 467.

Murray, M. R. (1931). *Arch. Exp. Zellforsch. Besonders Gewebezuecht.* **11,** 656.

Nagle, S. C., Crothers, W. C., and Hall, N. L. (1967). *Appl. Microbiol.* **15,** 1497.

Necco, A., and Martin, R. (1963). *Ann. Epiphyt.* **14,** 23.

Ohanessian, A., and Echalier, G. (1967). *Nature (London)* **213,** 1049.

Papenfuss, E. J., and Bokenham, A. H. (1939). *Biol. Bull.* **76,** 1.

Paul, J. (1961). "Cell and Tissue Culture," 2nd ed., p. 312. Williams & Wilkins, Baltimore, Maryland.

Peleg, J. (1968). *Virology* **35,** 617.

Perkins, F. O., and Menzel, R. W. (1964). *Nature (London)* **204,** 1106.

Pfeiffer, H. H. (1927). *Arch. Exp. Zellforsch. Besonders Gewebezuecht.* **20,** 225.

Pfeiffer, H. H. (1939). *Naturwissenschaften* **27,** 389.

Pfeiffer, H. H. (1943). *Naturwissenschaften* **31,** 47.

Phillips, J. H. (1960). *Ann. N. Y. Acad. Sci.* **90,** 760.

Rehacek, J. (1963). *Ann. Epiphyt.* **14,** 199.

Sanford, K. K., Earle, W. R., and Likely, G. D. (1948). *J. Nat. Cancer Inst.* **9,** 229.

Schmidt, E. L., and Williams, C. M. (1953). *Biol. Bull.* **105,** 174.

Schmidtmann, M. (1925). *Z. Ges. Exp. Med.* **45,** 714.

Schneider, I. (1969). *J. Cell Biol.* **42,** 603.

Schneiderman, H. A., Ketchel, M., and Williams, C. M. (1953). *Biol. Bull.* **105,** 188.

Seecof, R. L., and Teplitz, R. L. (1971). In press.

Seecof, R. L., and Unanue, R. L. (1968). *Exp. Cell Res.* **50,** 654.

Seecof, R. L., and Teplitz, R. L. (1971). Proceedings of a symposium in honor of the late Earle C. Suitor, Jr., in press.

Sengel, P., and Kieny, M. (1963). *Ann. Epiphyt.* **14,** 95.

Sengel, P., and Mandaron, P. (1969). *C. R. Acad. Sci.* **268,** 405.

Sen Gupta, K. (1963). *Ann. Epiphyt.* **14,** 39.

Singh, K. R. P. (1967). *Curr. Sci.* **36,** 506.

Stephens, J. M. (1959). *Can. J. Microbiol.* **5,** 203.

Stephens, J. M. (1963). *J. Insect Pathol.* **5,** 129.

Stern, C. (1940). *Growth* **4,** 377.

Stillwell, E. F. (1947). *Anat. Rec.* **99,** 227.

Suitor, E. C., Jr., Chang, L. L., and Liu, H. H. (1966). *Exp. Cell Res.* **44,** 572.

Thomson, J. A., and Grace, T. D. C. (1963). *Aust. J. Biol. Sci.* **16,** 869.

Tokumitsu, T., and Maramorosch, K. (1967). *J. Cell Biol.* **34,** 677.

Trager, W. (1938). *Amer. J. Trop. Med.* **18,** 387.

Trager, W. (1959). *Ann. Trop. Med. Parasitol.* **53,** 473.

Tripp, M. R. (1960). *Biol. Bull.* **119,** 210.

Tripp, M. R. (1963). *Ann. N. Y. Acad. Sci.* **113,** 467.

Tripp, M. R., and Kent, V. E. (1968). *In Vitro* **3,** 129.

Tripp, M. R., Bisignani, L. A., and Kenny, M. T. (1966). *J. Invertebr. Pathol.* **8,** 137.

Trowell, O. A. (1966). *In* "Cells and Tissues in Culture" (E. N. Willmer, ed.), Vol. 3, pp. 64–149. Academic Press, New York.

Vago, C. (1964). "Insect Tissue Culture," a film.

Vago, C., and Chastang, S. (1958). *Experientia* **15,** 110.

Vago, C., and Croissant, O. (1963). *Ann. Epiphyt.* **14,** 43.

Vago, C., and Flandre, O. (1963). *Ann. Epiphyt.* **14,** 127.

Varma, M. G. R., and Pudney, M. (1967). *Exp. Cell Res.* **45,** 671.

Varma, M. G. R., and Pudney, M. (1969). *J. Med. Entomol.* **6,** 432.

Walters, D. R., and Williams, C. M. (1966). *Science* **154,** 516.

White, M. J. D. (1954). *In* "Animal Cytology and Evolution," 2nd ed., pp. 454. Cambridge Univ. Press, London and New York.

Wilson, H. V. (1907). *J. Exptl. Zool.* **5,** 245.

Wolff, E. (1963). *Ann. Epiphyt.* **14,** 113.

Wyatt, S. S. (1956). *J. Gen. Physiol.* **39,** 841.

Yunker, C. E., Vaughn, J. L., and Cory, J. (1967). *Science* **155,** 1565.

Zernoff, V. (1934). *C. R. Soc. Biol.* **116,** 304.

6

CELL CULTURE OF LEPIDOPTERA

K. Aizawa

I. INTRODUCTION

Goldschmidt (1915) first observed the mitosis and gametogenesis of *Cecropia* moth *in vitro* using insect hemolymph, and the first attempt to cultivate insect hemocytes was made by Glaser (1917). Following by several years, *in vitro* cultivation of insect tissues was made using a relatively simple medium, containing inorganic salts, insect hemolymph, and peptone, which resulted in a short survival of tissues.

The second phase was begun by Trager (1935), who succeeded in the cultivation of ovariole tissues of the silkworm *Bombyx mori* using inorganic salts, sugars, egg albumin, and insect hemolymph. During this phase, addition of tissue extracts of insects, plasma and embryo extracts of chicks, amino acids, sugars, and vitamins to media was also attempted, but except for the experiment by Trager (1935), the survival of insect tissues *in vitro* was relatively short.

The third phase was initiated by S. S. Wyatt (1956), who observed the migration, mitosis, and growth of cells of the silkworm using a medium consisting of inorganic salts, organic acids, sugars, amino acids, and heat-treated hemolymph based on the chemical analysis of the silkworm hemolymph. In this period the cultivation of tissues and cells of insects was greatly advanced, and improvements in the composition of media, including semisynthetic media, were made.

The fourth phase was started by Grace (1962), who succeeded in the establishment of four types of cell strains from *Antheraea eucalypti*. He cultivated the ovariole tissues and subcultured 44 times during eight months. A cell line of the rice stem borer (*Chilo suppressalis*) by Mitsuhashi (1967) and a cell line from *Bombyx mori* by Grace (1968a,b) were established. Modifications of medium composition, from semisynthetic to synthetic, is under progress, and the establishment of insect cell lines and strains will be developed further. The cloning of cells as recently realized by Grace (1968a,b), has initiated the fifth phase.

The general aspects of insect cell and tissue culture have been reviewed by a number of writers (Day and Grace, 1959; Hartzell, 1958; Jones, 1962, 1966; Maramorosch, 1962; Martignoni, 1960, 1962; Smith, 1967; Vago, 1959, 1967; Vaughn, 1968). In this chapter, the development and present status of tissue and cell culture of lepidopterous insects which have been widely used for insect tissue culture will be reviewed.

II. MATERIALS AND TECHNIQUES

A. Surface Sterilization of Insect Body

Sublimate, alcohol, potassium permanganate, and other disinfectants have been used for surface sterilizations of insect bodies. It is difficult, however, to sterilize them completely, but by adding antibiotics to culture media, it is possible to avoid microbial contaminations. Recently, acepticly reared insects have been available for tissue culture (Vago *et al.*, 1961a,b; Fosset and Chastang, 1963; Kamano, 1964; Mitsuhashi, 1965a).

B. Tissues and Cells

Most successes in insect tissue culture have been obtained, until recently, by using ovariole tissues of lepidopterous insects; however, use of other organs and cells has been attempted and will be described in Section III,A.

C. Dispersion of Cells

Tissue fragments cut by scissors or minced and then stirred mechanically in salt solutions have been used for *in vitro* cultivation. Tissue fragments were further dispersed by chemical treatment with, for example, trypsin, EDTA, and hyaluronidase (Aizawa and Vago, 1959a). Snail extracts were used for cell dispersion (Martignoni *et al.*, 1958). In *Chilo suppressalis* trypsinization stimulated the production of migrating cells and the adhesiveness of the tissue on the glass surface (Mitsuhashi, 1965b); on the other hand, tissues of some lepidopterous insects are not tolerant to trypsinization.

D. Adhesiveness of Cells

It is necessary to adhere the dispersed cells to the glass surface to obtain good growth, and many methods have been tried. For example, chicken plasma clot, covering the glass surface with agar, slight drying of the tissue fragment, placing tissue fragments in a salt solution lacking Ca^{2+} and Mg^{2+}, and the use of substrates such as mica, plastic, or porous cellophane instead of glass have been attempted.

E. Culture Vessel

The hanging drop culture technique has been widely used, as have the Carrel flask, the test tube (stationary and roller tube), petri dishes, and other special devices such as the V-H tissue culture flask and microslide rings with cover glasses.

F. Culture Media

The compositions of the most prevalent media preparations for *Lepidoptera* are indicated in Tables I–VI.

III. CULTIVATION AND GROWTH OF CELLS

A. Primary Culture and Attempts of Subculture

1. Silkworm (*Bombyx mori*)

Trager (1935) first succeeded in the culture of insect cells, in the modern sense, by using the silkworm. Female larvae were immersed in 0.1% mercuric chloride for 30–45 minutes and were washed in two petri dishes of sterile water. Each fragment of ovariole tissue (about 0.5–1 mm in diameter) was set up in a hanging drop (0.005 ml), and cultures were kept at 27.5°–28.5°. He tried a number of balanced salt solutions for tissue culture and prepared two kinds of media, which had approximately equivalent osmotic pressure ranges and pH values equal to that of silkworm hemolymph. The best growths were obtained when the medium contained silkworm hemolymph (usually 10%). The media contained

TABLE I

MEDIA FOR *Bombyx mori* L.[a]

Substances	Concentration (mg/100 ml)	
	Medium A	Medium B
NaCl	87.6	75.9
$MgCl_2 \cdot 6H_2O$	20.3	20.3
$CaCl_2$	11.0	11.0
$NaH_2PO_4 \cdot H_2O$	20.7	20.7
K_2HPO_4	26.1	26.1
Maltose	2161.8	2161.8
Egg albumin digest, 0.137 M[b]	0	10(ml/100 ml)
	pH: 6.7	pH: 6.7
Freezing-point depression	0.285°	0.290°

[a] From Trager (1935).

[b] The molarity of the digest was calculated from the amount of NaOH needed to neutralize it. Nitrogen content of medium: 1.19 mg/ml.

TABLE II
MEDIUM FOR OVARIAL SHEATH FROM *Bombyx mori* L.[a]

Substances	Concentration (mg/100 ml)
Inorganic salts	
NaH_2PO_4	110
$MgCl_2 \cdot 6H_2O$	304
$MgSO_4 \cdot 7H_2O$	370
KCl	298
$CaCl_2$	81
Sugars	
Glucose	70
Fructose	40
Sucrose	40
Organic acids	
Malic acid	67
α-Ketoglutaric acid	37
Succinic acid	6
Fumaric acid	5.5
Amino acids	
L-Arginine–HCl	70
DL-Lysine	125
L-Histidine	250
L-Aspartic acid	35
L-Asparagine	35
L-Glutamic acid	60
L-Glutamine	60
Glycine	65
DL-Serine	110
DL-Alanine	45
β-Alanine	20
L-Proline	35
L-Tyrosine	5
DL-Threonine	35
DL-Methionine	10
L-Phenylalanine	15
DL-Valine	20
DL-Isoleucine	10
DL-Leucine	15
L-Tryptophan	10
L-Cystine	2.5
Cysteine–HCl	8
Other data	
Homologous hemolymph	10%
pH	6.35
Freezing-point depression	0.53°

[a] From S. S. Wyatt (1956).

TABLE III
Medium for Lepidoptera (Bm XXII)[a]

Substances	Concentration (mg/100 ml)
Inorganic salts	
$NaH_2PO_4·H_2O$	120
KCl	300
$CaCl_2·2H_2O$	100
$MgCl_2·6H_2O$	300
$MgSO_4·7H_2O$	400
Sugars	
Glucose	150
Amino acids	
Lactalbumin hydrolysate	1000
Vitamins	
Choline	0.05
Biotin	0.05
meso-Inositol	0.2
Folic acid	0.05
Riboflavin	0.05
Niacinamide	0.05
Thiamine	0.05
p-Aminobenzoic acid	0.05
Pyridoxine	0.05
Ascorbic acid	0.1
Other data	
Homologous hemolymph	10%
pH	6.4
Freezing-point depression	0.52°
Antibiotics	
Penicillin (when necessary)	60.000 IU
Streptomycin (when necessary)	2 mg

[a] From Vago (1967).

maltose, and the substitution of sucrose or glucose in equimolecular amounts did not give growths as good as those obtained with maltose alone. One of the two media contained an egg albumin digest, and the cell growth was usually better in this medium if the silkworm hemolymph was left out.

In successful cultures, small numbers of wandering connective-tissue-like cells appeared after one to two days incubation. By the third day the living cells were very numerous, and they became more so on the fourth and fifth day. Usually, the cells remained in good condition for one or two more weeks. They had numerous fine pseudopodia and showed slow amoeboid movement, and mitotic figures were seen in some cultures.

TABLE IV

MEDIUM 26C (FOR HEMOCYTES OF *Peridroma saucia* HÜBNER)[a]

Substances	Concentration (mg/100 ml)
Inorganic salts	
KCl	626.2
CaCl$_2$	255.3
MgCl$_2$·6H$_2$O	366.0
H$_2$(HPO$_3$)	114.9
NaOH	106.8
Sugars	
Glucose	70
Fructose	40
D(+)-Trehalose	40
Amino acids	
L-Arginine	1.7
L-Cystine	1.2
L-Histidine	0.77
L-Isoleucine	2.6
L-Leucine	2.6
L-Lysine	2.9
L-Methionine	0.74
L-Phenylalanine	1.7
L-Threonine	2.4
L-Tryptophan	0.41
L-Tyrosine	1.8
L-Valine	2.3
L-Glutamine	29.2
Vitamins	
L-Ascorbic acid	100
Choline	0.1
Folic acid	0.1
Nicotinamide	0.1
Pantothenate	0.1
Pyridoxal	0.1
Thiamine	0.1
Riboflavin	0.01
Inositol	0.2
Gas phase	
O$_2$	1% by volume
CO$_2$	3% by volume
N$_2$	96% by volume
Other data	
Homologous larval hemolymph	15%
Fetal bovine serum	15%
pH	6.45
Antibiotics when necessary	

[a] From Martignoni and Scallion (1961a).

K. AIZAWA

TABLE V

MEDIUM FOR *Philosamia advena*[a]

Substances	Concentration (mg/100 ml)
Inorganic salts	
NaH_2PO_4	110
$MgCl_2 \cdot 2H_2O$	300
$MgSO_4 \cdot 7H_2O$	370
KCl	300
$CaCl_2$	80
Sugars	
Glucose	70
Fructose	40
Sucrose	40
Amino acids	
Lactalbumin (Difco)	1000
Vitamins	
TC yeastolate (Difco)	100
Organic acids	
Malic acid	60
α-Ketoglutaric acid	35
Succinic acid	6
Fumaric acid	5.5
Other data	
Antibiotics (as necessary)	
Homologous pupal hemolymph	10%
pH	6.35

[a] From Jones and Cunningham (1960).

The cultures could not be kept going indefinitely, although a few first subcultures were successful.

No cell growths were obtained using nerve, muscle, fat body, silk-gland, leg and wing bud, or male gonad tissues of the silkworm.

Grace (1954) attempted to cultivate insect tissues, including hemocytes and gonads of *Bombyx mori*, with various media containing adult and embryonic insect tissue extracts in various combinations with vitamins, glutathione, cystine, cholesterol, and amino acids. Techniques such as hanging drops with solid clots of fowl plasma and other ingredients, perforated cellophane sheets covered by liquid medium, and cover slips containing a drop of agar on which were placed drops of liquid medium have been attempted. (All cultures were incubated at 25°.) Survival of various tissues for up to a week was observed, but continued growth was not successful. In *Bombyx mori* hemocytes, a syncytium was formed within 24 hours of setting up the culture, and it survived for six days.

TABLE VI

MEDIUM FOR LEPIDOPTERA[a]

Substances	Concentration (mg/100 ml)
Inorganic salts	
$NaH_2PO_4 \cdot 2H_2O$	114
$NaHCO_3$	35
KCl	224
$CaCl_2$ (separate)	100
$MgCl_2 \cdot 6H_2O$	228
$MgSO_4 \cdot 7H_2O$	278
Amino acids	
L-Arginine–HCl	70
L-Aspartic acid	35
L-Asparagine	35
L-Alanine	22.5
β-Alanine	20
L-Cystine–HCl	2.5
L-Glutamic acid	60
L-Glutamine	60
L-Glycine	65
L-Histidine	250
L-Isoleucine	5
L-Leucine	7.5
L-Lysine–HCl	62.5
L-Methionine	5
L-Proline	35
L-Phenylalanine	15
DL-Serine	110
L-Tyrosine (dissolved in N/1 HCl)	5
L-Tryptophan	10
L-Threonine	17.5
L-Valine	10
Sugars	
Sucrose (in gm)	2.668
Fructose	40
Glucose	70
Organic acids	
Malic acid	67
α-Ketoglutaric acid	37
Succinic acid	6
Fumaric	5.5
(Neutralize organic acids with KOH)	
Vitamins	
Thiamine–HCl	0.002
Riboflavin	0.002
Calcium pantothenate	0.002
Pyridoxine–HCl	0.002

TABLE VI (*Continued*)

Substances	Concentration (mg/100 ml)
p-Aminobenzoic acid	0.002
Folic acid	0.002
Niacin	0.002
Inositol	0.002
Biotin	0.001
Choline chloride	0.02
Antibiotics	
Penicillin "G" (Na salt)	3
Streptomycin sulfate	10
Other data	
Insect plasma from diapausing pupae of *Antherea eucalypti* (heat-treated at 60° for 5 min) pH adjusted to 6.5 with KOH	5%

a From Grace (1962).

The insect cell culture with biological significance was initiated by S. S. Wyatt (1956), and recent progress has been made possible primarily by her investigations. Silkworm larvae were surface-sterilized by immersion for one minute in 0.1% Hyamine and then washed in three changes of sterilized tap water. The ovarioles were cut into pieces of about 1 mm³. Hanging drop cultures were prepared with a single explant in 0.005 ml of medium spread on a glass cover slip and inverted over a 0.8-mm-depth depression slide. In roller tube cultures, 12- by 50-mm culture tubes containing four to six explants and 0.15 ml of medium and closed with rubber stoppers were rotated at 6 rph or occasionally held stationary. Cultures were incubated at 28°–29°.

Transparent cells with few granules and no large fat globules were considered to be healthy. Movement of the cells continued, however, for some time after they had lost their transparency.

S. S. Wyatt (1956) attempted the hanging drop culture of ovarian explants [according to Trager (1935)], positive infection of cells with the silkworm nuclear-polyhedrosis virus, and culture of tissues other than ovary, i.e., muscle, nerve, epidermis, imaginal discs, abdominal ganglia, and testes. The best results were always in cultures from the ovary, but she considered that these cultures were not satisfactory, so more profound modifications of the methods were tried.

S. S. Wyatt (1956) examined the method of inhibition of phenol oxidase in insect hemolymph using recrystallized phenylthiourea, p-aminobenzoic acid, ascorbic acid, glutathione, and disodium ethylenediaminetetra-acetate, and it was found that the supernatant from silkworm hemolymph heated at 60° for five minutes remained clear indefinitely although the enzyme was not completely inactivated. Wyatt modified the physiological saline solution with cations corresponding proportionately to the chemical analysis of hemolymph, including sufficient EDTA, and the cells were more numerous than in Trager's solution. Based on analysis of the content of free amino acids and sugars in silkworm hemolymph (G. R. Wyatt *et al.*, 1956), a physiological solution was prepared. This physiological solution, with the addition of heat-treated hemolymph, was greatly superior to any previously obtained. A number of organic acids were tested, and it was found that the addition of organic acids such as malic, α-ketoglutaric, succinic, and fumaric produced significant stimulation in the cultures. The ratio of aspartic and glutamic acids to their amides was changed because increased aspartate and glutamate might prove helpful by combining with ammonia formed in the medium.

Four- to five-day-old silkworm eggs were surface-sterilized, washed, ground with an equal volume of physiological solution, heated at 60° for five minutes, and centrifuged; and the addition of small amounts of this extract (less than 1%) to the medium improved the cultures. Addition of chick embryo extract (about 0.2%) had a stimulating action but, in larger quantities, produced cellular abnormalities such as binucleates.

In hanging drop cultures, cells increased in number for from five to seven days until they finally covered an area about three to five times the diameter of the explants. The cells ordinarily resembled fibroblasts in open growth, but sometimes, compact brush formations very similar to vertebrate fibroblast cultures were seen. In roller tube cultures, when the new medium was changed twice a week, the cells spread over the glass surface in four or five days, rapid mitoses were observed after two weeks, and transparent active cells were present by the third week. Occasionally in roller tube cultures, a continuous sheet of cells developed resembling the beginning of epithelial development. This was observed in Trager's medium as well as in Wyatt's medium. No attempts were made to subculture the cells. Mitosis in Trager's medium took about 50 minutes from metaphase to the completion of telephase, but in Wyatt's medium this took only 20 to 25 minutes.

Using the silkworm, Grace (1958a) attempted to examine the effect of additives to Wyatt's medium, the effect of age, and other characteristics of the tissues. Larvae were starved for 24 hours and were surface-sterilized by washing twice with 70% alcohol, and then the ovaries were cut into pieces about 1 mm³. The principal culture method used was the hanging drop, and single explants were placed in approximately 0.005 ml of medium. Cultures were also set up in Carrel flasks, roller tubes, hanging drops containing perforated cellophane, and solid clots of fowl plasma.

The addition to Wyatt's medium of the B-vitamin group (thiamine, riboflavin, pyridoxin, niacin, pantothenic acid, biotin, folic acid, *p*-aminobenzoic acid, choline, and *meso*-inositol at 0.01 μg/ml) or only *meso*-inositol at 2 μg/ml improved the appearance of the cells, but there was no increase in mitosis or survival of the tissues. The addition of cholesterol (0.03 mg/ml), nucleic acids (10–30 μg/ml of yeast RNA and thymus DNA added separately or together), or heat-treated embryo extracts (boiled in water for two minutes and centrifuged; 5–10%) and the replacement of either glucose, fructose, or sucrose by trehalose did not appear to have any effect on the growth or survival. The total replacement of sugars in Wyatt's medium by trehalose, vitamin B complex (10 μg/ml), and silkworm embryo extract (2–5%) had a deleterious effect on growth. The addition to the medium of extracts of endocrine organs (ring glands of *Lucilia cuprina* larvae and prothoracic glands from *Periplaneta americana* nymphs) or silkworm ovary increased markedly the number of mitoses in the culture.

In a medium consisting of Wyatt's solution plus 10 components of the B-vitamin group, cholesterol, and extracts of endocrine and ovarian tissues, migration and multiplication of the cells were profuse and mitoses were first noticed 48 hours after the cultures were set up. Mitoses were numerous for 12–14 days and were still observed after 19 days, and cells survived for 29 days. Subculturing was attempted with only partial success.

Cultivation of tissues from silkworm embryos and hemocytes were tried without success, and only ovaries from fourth instar larvae produced cells which grew in culture.

Gaw *et al.* (1959) reported 22 subcultures of cells from male and female gonads of the silkworm. Tissues were cut into pieces about 0.1–0.2 mm in diameter and then washed by centrifuging in Trager's medium A. The tissue fragments were made to stick to the cover slips placed in a petri dish and then incubated at 36° for 10 minutes. The tissue fragments were set up directly on the surface around the edge of the inside of a petri dish covered with a glass jar, the edges of which were sealed with paraffin. Stationary test tube cultures were also set up. After the tissue fragments were made to stick on the glass surface, a medium consisting of 90% Trager's A solution and 10% silkworm hemolymph (pH 6.7) was added. All cultures were incubated at 26°–27°. Male and female gonads, muscle, silk-gland, intestine, and trachea were all successfully grown in hanging drop cultures and in stationary test tube cultures. Monolayer cell cultures in Carrel flasks could be obtained from mechanically dispersed cell suspension and trypsinized cells. Monolayer cultures with test tubes were kept for 7–10 days changing the medium at intervals of three to four days, and surprisingly, 22 attempts at subculture (epithelial cells from male and female gonads) were successful.

Vago and Chastang (1958a) attempted the culture of ovarian tissue of *Bombyx mori* and *Galleria mellonella* with a medium at 30° and observed the formation of networks of fibroblast-like cells. Subculturing was repeated at least 12 times. Vago and Chastang (1958b) cultivated the ovarian tissues of *Bombyx mori* pupae more than 40 days using a modified Bm XVI medium.

Vago (1958) modified the culture vessel by using a medicine bottle (antibiotic type) for the hanging drop culture. Aizawa and Vago (1959b) attempted the cultivation of cells of lepidopterous insects with plastic vessels, and Vago (1961) made a plastic slide for hanging drop cultures which is convenient for exchanging the medium and for continuous perfusion.

Vago and Chastang (1962a) examined the effect of calf serum on the cell growth. They prepared ten culture media consisting of Bm XIX (Vago and Chastang, 1960) or Bm XXVIII each supplemented five different ways: (a) 15% heat-treated *Bombyx mori* hemolymph, (b) 10% hemolymph plus 5% calf serum, (c) 5% hemolymph plus 10% calf serum, (d) 2% hemolymph plus 13% calf serum, and (e) 15% calf serum. In the culture of ovarian tissues of *Bombyx mori, Galleria mellonella,* and *Antheraea pernyi,* the former three proportions resulted in better growths. However, cells grew in the media with 2% hemolymph and 13% calf serum, and nuclear polyhedra were well formed when the virus was inoculated.

Vago and Chastang (1962b) also cultivated fibroblasts of *Lymantria dispar, Bombyx mori,* and *Galleria mellonella* in a medium consisting of Bm XIX and only lyophilized chick embryo extracts (6 mg/100 ml). The medium was changed every five days and mitoses were observed 20 days after cultures were set up. However, after 15–20 days cells in a medium with insect hemolymph or calf serum were more transparent, less vacuolized, and had many more cells than those in a medium supplemented only with chick embryo extracts.

Flandre *et al.* (1962) cultivated the ovarian tissues of *Bombyx mori* on coagulated plasma. Chick plasma was mixed with Bm XXII and chick embryo extract, the dilutions of plasma were 1/20, 1/15, 1/10, 1/5, and 1/2; the 1/20 diluted plasma coagulated and formed a semisolid medium. Fibroblasts were abundant but less than in the culture in a liquid medium. Cells were rare in the more solid coagulated plasma (1/5 and 1/2), and the cell migration was slower than in the control culture.

Medvedeva (1959, 1960) reported the cultivation of ovariole tissues of *Bombyx mori* and *Antheraea pernyi* for from seven months to even more than a year with Trager's, Ringer's, or Clark's solutions with 10–30% hemolymph added. Testicular cysts, immature spermatid, and immature cysts showed mobility and phagocytic activity in the first day of cultivation.

In an *in vitro* culture of silkworm ovary, fibroblasts were well formed in a medium composed of Wyatt's inorganic salts, sugars, amino acids (or lactalbumin hydrolysate), and the dialysate of silkworm hemolymph. Effective substances in the dialysate were resistant to alkali or acid treatment and were not adsorbed on active charcoal (Aizawa *et al.*, 1961; Aizawa and Sato, 1963). The role and indispensibility of hemolymph in insect tissue culture have been discussed by Sen Gupta (1963). He considers unknown growth factors, rather than sources of protein or hormones, to be contained in hemolymph.

Krause (1962) attempted the culture of ovariole tissues and Krause *et al.* (1966) examined cell growth using ovariole tissue in various kinds of media with or without hemolymph, protein hydrolysate, and egg (*Calliphora, Bombyx*) extracts. They pointed out that the following factors were important for insect cell culture: ratio of Na:K, addition of sugars and protein hydrolysate, and certain substances contained in the insect extracts.

Among ovaries and oviducts of the silkworm taken during various stages from the fourth instar to pupal stages, pupal oviduct showed the best formation of fibroblasts (Aizawa *et al.*, 1961).

2. Promethea Moth (*Callosamia promethea*)

A prolonged survival of insect cells *in vitro* was carried out by Grace (1958b) using ovarian tissues of *Callosamia promethea*. Pupae of *Callosamia promethea* were surface-sterilized with 70% alcohol, and ovaries were transferred to a drop of culture medium and were cut into pieces about 1 mm³. The principal culture method used was the hanging drop in slides with a central depression of about 0.8 mm, or Maximov slides. The cover glass containing the tissues in about 0.005 ml of medium was sealed to the slide with a mixture (1:1) of paraffin (mp 54°) and Vaseline. All cultures were incubated at 25°, and the medium was changed every five days. The cell growth was adjudged by mitoses in the migrated cells and an increase in the cell population. Cells were considered to be healthy if the cytoplasm remained clear and movements took place. When fat-like, highly refractive droplets appeared in the cytoplasm, the cells ceased to move, rounded up, and began to degenerate after one or two days.

Forty-eight hours after setting the culture up, many cells moved from the explants and very few cells became attached to the cover glass. These cells were spindle-shaped or irregular in outline and moved quite actively on the glass. Numerous mitoses were observed after 72 hours, and the time from metaphase to completion of cell division was 15 to 20 minutes at 25°.

During six days the number of cells increased and mitoses were very numerous. Six explants and as many cells as possible were transferred to a 25-ml erlenmeyer flask where six explants from freshly dissected ovaries were also placed. The volume of the medium was 1.0 ml, the flask was shaken at 80 rpm for four days, and 10 explants became attached to the glass surface. After four days, the 12 explants and free cells were transferred to a roller tube. Thirty minutes after the explants were introduced, the volume of medium was made up to 1.0 ml. The tube was rotated at 12 rph. Cells began to migrate from the explants and cell numbers increased during the next five days. The cells became attached to the glass surface and formed a halo around the explants. After six days the explants were removed from the tube, washed in a drop of medium, and set up in six hanging drop cultures. According to Grace, this was the first time the tissues were subcultured. The media in the roller tube which contained only cells was renewed, and granules appeared in both the cytoplasm and the nucleus three days after the subculture was set up. By the eighth day every cell was granulated and degenerated. This culture was discarded. Forty-eight hours after subculturing of tissues, cells began to migrate from the explants, increased in number by migration from tissues and by mitoses, and during the first three days, began to clump together. Mitoses were very numerous both in the free-floating cells and in the cells at the edges of the groups. The period from metaphase to the completion of cell division was 15–20 minutes, as in the original cultures.

The hanging drop cultures were again subcultured 10 days after the first subculture. Eleven explants were divided into two hanging drops (five and six explants), and the 12th explant was placed in a culture containing all the cells from the previous cultures because the presence of a piece of tissue was shown to increase growth and prolong survival. Cells migrated from the explants after 48 hours and continued to increase in number, and some cells tended to form groups.

The explants continued to move actively. The number of cells increased slowly, but noticeably, over a period of 16 days, and very few cells showed granulation up to 13 days. By the 17th day many cells granulated and no mitoses were observed after the 18th day, but by the 20th day only a few cells close to the explants were still healthy.

After seven days of the second subculture, the third subculturing was attempted. Four cultures were set up, three of which containing three explants each and the other containing two explants and all the cells from the previous cultures. The migration of cells from explants and the growth of cells were slow, and cell numbers reached about 600 after one week. Cells migrating from explants remained healthy, and mitoses were fairly numerous for 12 days, but by the 19th day the majority of cells were dead.

The fourth subculturing was attempted 13 days after the third subculture was set up. (Three subcultures containing three explants each and the cells and the 12th explant from the second subculture.) After seven days there were not more than 200 cells in each explant culture.

As very little growth occurred, the three remaining explants (two of the cultures containing three explants were discarded owing to fungous contamination) and the two explants from the third subculture were placed in one culture. During 47 days the medium was changed every five days and the five explants slowly grew into mass. Between 100 and 105 days after the cultures were first set up, cell migration from the tissue mass was resumed. Two-hundred-and-fifty cells were present by the 111th day, and on the 126th day four mitoses were observed. On the 140th day subculture was attempted as previously and the explant culture continued to survive but the cell culture died three days later. By the 161st day 20 cells were counted and one division was observed. Subculturing of tissues had been carried out six times during the 186 days, and tissue mass continued to survive without growth and after 336 days still showed activity.

In these experiments Grace (1958b) suggested that the tissues had become adapted to the medium during their long survival and the cells which migrated from explants after 100 days showed considerably longer survival than those in earlier cultures.

Grace obtained superior growth and slightly longer survival in the culture of ovarian tissue of *Bombyx mori* when hormone extracts were added to the medium. However, in the present study the tissues from the diapausing *Callosamia promethea* pupae grew and survived without any growth hormone during the entire culture period.

3. Cynthia Moth (*Samia walkeri*)

Ovarian tissues of *Samia walkeri* were cultivated *in vitro* for long periods by Grace (1959). One whole ovary was used for each culture using, as in the case of *Callosamia promethea,* a medium with 3% hemolymph from diapausing pupae of the cynthia moth. The ovarian sac was torn and completely exposed to the medium immediately before the culture was set up. Cell growth was very slow, but by the fifth day, the cell numbers increased rapidly and mitoses were abundant.

The first subculturing was made on the 12th day after setting up the culture. Explants contracted strongly and the cell growth was abundant. The cell culture survived for only three days. The second subcultures were made nine days later. Two days later processes and many separate cells grew out from the explants, and the processes gradually grew into a sheet of cytoplasm containing many nuclei where abundant mitoses were seen. Forty-three days after the cultures were set up, the processes were large and healthy. On the 52nd day the sheet broke away from the coverslip and became constricted into a knot of tissue. The last mitoses were seen on the 68th day, although the cultures survived for 111 days.

4. Variegated Cutworm (Peridroma saucia = Peridroma margaritosa)

a. Preparation of Cell Suspensions. The liberation of cells from larval integument of the variegated cutworm was reported by Martignoni et al. (1958). The fifth instar larvae were anesthetized for one minute in CO_2, and the external surfaces were sterilized with 5% ethyl alcohol, 4% formaldehyde, and two changes of 70% alcohol. The thoracic segments of 5 to 10 larvae were collected in a modified phosphate-buffered saline solution of Dulbecco and Vogt and were washed five times.

Disaggregation of the tissue was attempted with trypsin and versene; however, the liberated cells were injured by the treatments. Since an extract from the hepatopancreas and crop of the snail *Helix aspersa* is a rich source of hydrolytic enzymes, this was used for the liberation of cells. Snails starved for four to seven days were homogenized with an equal weight of distilled water at approximately 4°, the homogenate was centrifuged at 24,000 g for 15 minutes under refrigeration, and the supernatant was kept at −20°. Prior to use, the extract was centrifuged, diluted with two volumes of saline solution, and sterilized with a millipore filter.

Disaggregation was performed with a magnetic stirrer at room temperature using five thoracic segments and 5 ml of the snail extract. Liberation of cells was completed in five to seven minutes, and the cell suspension was allowed to stand for five minutes and was then decanted into a centrifuge tube and centrifuged for one minute at 1700 rpm. Sedimented cells were washed in the saline. Approximately 1.6×10^5 cells were obtained from each larva, and separated cells appeared round and clear with well-defined nuclear and cytoplasmic membranes.

The cells were recentrifuged and were suspended in the culture medium

(medium 199 modified by increasing amino acids to the level of Wyatt's medium and adding 20% human serum and 5% chick embryo extract). Approximately 4×10^5 cells/ml were seeded and incubated at room temperature. The cells attached themselves readily to the glass surface and were maintained for four to five days in a healthy state and with normal nuclei.

b. Hemocyte Monolayer Culture. Martignoni and Scallion (1961a) attempted the hemocyte monolayer cultures of *Peridroma saucia*. Second to fourth day sixth instar larvae were anesthetized with ethyl ether for about 10 minutes, and body surfaces were sterilized with 0.2–0.4% Hyamine 10-X for five minutes. Three to four milliliters of culture medium were placed in a 12-ml conical graduated tube, hemolymph from 15–20 larvae was added, and the composition of the final culture medium was made up as follows: 15% hemolymph, 15% fetal bovine serum, and 70% maintenance medium.

The cell suspension was distributed in petri dishes (3.5 ml for 60-mm glass petri dishes and 2 ml for 35-mm wettable polystyrene dishes, each containing one Corning 22×22 mm No. 1 cover glass). The petri dishes were incubated in a gas mixture (96% N_2, 3% CO_2, and 1% O_2) at $25° \pm 0.5°$ in darkness. The medium was changed every third day.

Cells attached to glass surface readily and formed a sheet within 12 hours, and cells floating in the culture vessel were discarded when the medium was changed. A continuous monolayer of single cells and polynucleated syncytia was formed (Martignoni and Scallion, 1961b). The cell sheet was composed mainly of plasmatocytes, prohemocytes, spheroidocytes, and other cells including degenerating cells. These monolayers could be maintained for 10 to 15 days, and the prevalent cell was the plasmatocyte (80.35% of the cell population). The plasmatocyte count was used for the estimation of effectiveness of added substances in a series of tests. The addition of kinetin (6-furfurylaminopurine, 2 μg/ml) caused a decrease in plasmatocyte numbers, an increase in spheroidocytes, and no change in prohemocytes, and the mitotic activity did not increase. The addition of DL-carnitine at 5 μg/ml or 0.1% proteose–peptone (Difco) did not cause appreciable change. The addition of egg extracts from the house fly (*Musca domestica*) (8- to 10-hour-old eggs were homogenized with an equal volume of BBS, put through millipore filters, and added at concentrations of 10%) seemed to have a stimulative effect on plasmatocyte numbers. An increase in oxidation–reduction potential of the culture medium was connected with a decrease in plasmatocyte numbers.

Martignoni and Scallion (1961b) obtained good results without insect blood plasma by replacement of 30% fetal bovine serum and 70%

medium at 26°. Based on the striking similarity of cells in cultures from ovariole sheath of *Philosamia advena* (Jones and Cunningham, 1960) with the present cultured hemocytes, they supported the view suggested by Wigglesworth (1959) that the cells migrating from the ovarioles of Lepidoptera maintained *in vitro* hemocytes formerly adherent to the tissue.

5. Silkmoth (*Philosamia advena*)

Jones and Cunningham (1960, 1961) cultivated ovariole tissues of *Philosamia advena*. Pupal ovarioles were cut into two or three pieces. The explants were placed in a drop of the medium spread on a cover glass and left for about 10 minutes to settle against the surface. The cover glass was inverted over a chamber, and the preparations were kept in petri dishes containing moist filter papers and incubated at 25°. The medium contains inorganic salts, sugars, organic acids, TC yeastolate, lactalbumin hydrolysate (or lactalbumin hydrolysate supplemented with DL-lysine, L-histidine, and DL-serine), and pupal hemolymph.

Migration of cells began on the third day and the cellular outgrowths spread over the glass surface from the fourth to ninth day. Cells from ovariole sheath and the intermediate layer were predominant in the outgrowth. Mitosis in the outgrowth seemed to be confined to these cells, but inner follicle cells were also capable of mitosis when they were present in the outgrowths. Many of the sheath cells became binucleate, and the number of binucleate cells increased with the age of the culture. Cells of the inner follicle layer and the extremely large polynucleate nurse cells wandered into the cellular field. Brush-like extensions were formed by the cells of connective tissue cap, and sheet-like epithelium was formed by fusion of cells of the ovariole sheath. The cells survived for four to six weeks when the medium was changed every fifth day.

The mean mitotic index was 1% in five- to six-day-old cultures, 0.5% in eight- to nine-day-old cultures, 0.3% in 12-day-old cultures, and less than 0.3% in 21-day-old cultures. Since cells in culture took about 30 minutes to complete mitosis, cells in the outgrowths that were able to divide produced more than the three to four generations (estimated).

Cellular outgrowth was increased neither by substitution of lysine, histidine, and serine for lactalbumin nor by addition of the B-vitamin group, cholesterol, or glutathione to the medium. The adherence of cells on the glass surface was reduced by the ommission of hemolymph.

6. Greater Wax Moth (*Galleria mellonella*)

Sen Gupta (1961) cultivated intestinal, ovarian, and testicular tissues of *Galleria mellonella* using modified Parker's medium and modified

Trager's medium. Dissected tissues were washed with culture medium several times and were cut into fragments which were transferred to culture vessels (roller tubes or hanging drop cultures).

In intestinal tissue explants, migration and multiplication of cells began within 36–72 hours, and growth stopped by about the fourth week. An outgrowth of cells started in about 48 hours in ovariole tissue, and in some cases, a cell layer was formed from the cut end. A mass of cells surrounding the ovariole sheath formed in about two weeks and degenerated by the end of the third week. The outgrowth of cells with male gonad tissue continued for about two weeks. Using intestinal and gonad tissues, monolayer culture was tried. Tissue fragments were trypsinized (0.2% at 28° for 15 minutes) and were pipetted carefully. A culture medium containing 20% calf serum was added to trypsinized cell suspensions, and they were washed by repeated centrifugations at 700–800 rpm for 10 minutes and then transferred to roller tubes. Cells attached themselves to the surface of stripped slides within 48–72 hours, and their numbers increased by 60–70%, and with multinucleated cells, by the fourth or fifth day, but the cells degenerated after 7–10 days.

Vago and Flandre (1963) cultivated female gonads of *Galleria mellonella* on a coagulated plasma with a salt solution (Gm XVII) which contained mostly sodium and potassium organic salts. Fibroblasts migrated on the second day, and a halo showing mitosis was formed after five to six days. Subcultures were successfully carried out 12–22 times by changing the medium every eighth day. Cells were always of the fibroblast type, accompanied periodically by the macrophage type.

Krejzová (1966a,b) attempted the cultivation of intestinal tissues and ovariole tissue of *Galleria mellonella* with different media, and the best results were obtained in the culture of ovarioles with Eagle's (4 parts) and Vago–Chastang's (1 part) solutions plus 0.1% albumin fraction of calf serum or with Grace's medium. The addition of amino acids to the Vago–Chastang medium was found to be effective.

7. Tussock Moth (*Hemerocampa leucostigma*)

Grace (1959) cultivated ovarian tissues of the last instar larvae of the tussock moth in the same medium as the promethea moth tissues. Explants grew for 80 days and survived for 115 days.

Grace (1958c) used a medium consisted of 2–3% Eagle's solution in Wyatt's medium containing 3% hemolymph of *Hemerocampa leucostigma*. Five days after setting up, the cultures containing hemolymph showed very good growth, but in the cultures without hemolymph the growth was poor.

8. Monarch Butterfly (*Danaus plexippus* = *Anosia plexippus*)

Various tissues of the monarch butterfly were cultivated by Hirumi and Maramorosch (1964). Pupae were surface-sterilized in 70% ethyl alcohol for five minutes, then quickly flamed over a gas microburner. Fragments of organs in sitting drop cultures were prepared in the ,V–H tissue culture flasks with a medium consisting of 20 ml of modified Vago's Bm XXII, 20 ml of TC 199, 13 ml of fetal bovine serum, and TC yeastolate at 0.1% and were kept moist.

a. Subesophageal Ganglion. Numerous neuroblasts from explants attached themselves to the glass surface, grew, and formed network-like outgrowths in which frequent mitoses were observed. Active growth continued for two weeks, and cells began to degenerate after about four weeks.

b. Circulatory Organs. Within 24 hours two cell types appeared from explants of circulatory organs. One type was small, resembled trephocytes, and wandered actively; the other type was large, amoeboid in shape, and was classified as phagocytes. After two weeks the trehocytes stopped growing, and after three weeks they began to degenerate. In amoeboid phagocytes, there was a slow migration of cells until the eight day. No mitoses were observed in these cells, and after 16 days extensive degeneration was evident.

c. Ovarian Tissue. Three cell types appeared from ovarian tissues. One was a large number of fibroblast-like cells which continued to come out from original explants for more than 20 days. The attached cells grew, forming networks and pseudopodia. Many mitoses were observed in these cells for up to three weeks. After four weeks the outgrowth of fibroblast-like cells degenerated. The second cell type appeared after seven to eight days and consisted of compact sheets of epithelial cells. Mitosis was observed, and cells continued to grow slowly for more than 23 days. The third cell type was observed after 10 days of cultivation, in fine networks made up of a small number of cells with very fine irregular pseudopodia. The outgrowth of this type of cell continued very slowly without mitosis.

d. Malpighian Tubules. Large epithelial cells appeared from fragments of Malpighian tubules by the fifth day of cultivation, became attached to the glass surface, and formed cell sheets. During the next 10 days the sheets of epithelial cells grew actively. After 15 days the cells showed no visible changes, and then they began to degenerate.

e. Pupal Wing. Epithelial cells grew from tissue fragments and formed compact cell sheets by the third day. These cells continued to grow actively for more than 14 days. Many mitoses were clearly seen in the epithelial cells. After 15 days the growth of cells gradually lessened, and cells began to degenerate between the 20th and 24th day.

f. Brain and Optic Lobe. No growing cells were observed from tissues of these organs.

9. Cynthia Moth (Samia cynthia)

Hartzell (1961) attempted to cultivate ovarian tissue of the pupae of *Samia cynthia*. Tissue fragments were cultivated in hanging drops with Wyatt's basic medium plus Grace's additives and at $25° \pm 1°$. The tissues grew successfully for 120 hours, and the cell migration was definitely inhibited with arsenic trioxide but was not evident with any of the other compounds, such as thallium sulfate, copper sulfate, and DDT.

Meiosis has never been reported from cultures of lepidopteran ovary but has been observed in testicular cysts cultured *in vitro*. White and Sastrodihardjo (1966) found a meiotic division in a culture of tissues from diapausing pupal ovary of *Samia cynthia* with Grace's medium containing 5% homologous heat-treated (at 60° for five minutes) hemolymph.

10. Polyphemus Moth (Antheraea polyphemus)

Loeb and Schneiderman (1956) could maintain living epidermis from the pupal wing and antenna *in vitro* for 20–35 days at 25° with TC 199 medium. By the addition of 2% Difco Bactopeptone, they achieved much longer survival of epidermis, heart fragments, pericardial cells, and Malpighian tubules (for more than six weeks).

11. Gypsy Moth (Porthetria dispar = Lymantria dispar)

Vago and Bergoin (1963) cultivated the fibroblast derived from larval ovary and pupal oviduct of *Porthetria dispar* using a liquid medium (Bm XIX with 12% bovine serum and 3% insect hemolymph). Subculturing of fibroblasts on a plasma clot was carried out 20 times at two-week intervals. They attempted the culture of dispersed cells derived from pupal oviduct by a combination of pipetting and tryptic digestion. It resulted in a better dispersion of cells than by enzymatic digestions.

12. Spruce Budworm (Choristoneura fumiferana)

Embryonic tissue of *Choristoneura fumiferana* produced three types of growth (hollow vesicles, cell sheets, and free cells) using the Grace's medium supplemented with hemolymph of *Bombyx mori* (10%). Ovarian tissue of sixth instar larvae did not produce any kind of growth (Sohi, 1968).

B. Establishment of Cell Lines

1. Saturniid Moth (*Antheraea eucalypti*)

Grace (1962) established four cell lines from *Antheraea eucalypti*. Ovaries of diapausing pupae of *Antheraea eucalypti* were dissociated in 0.25% trypsin (Difco 1:250) in Puck's saline A. Cells dissociated from four ovaries were placed in a Porter flask with 0.9 ml of Grace's medium. The cultures were incubated at 27°–29° and the medium was changed every 7–14 days for the first seven months. After the cells began to multiply rapidly the medium was changed every four to five days and subcultures were made at 8- to 10-day intervals. For the subculturing the medium was removed from the bottles and the cells were washed once in Puck's saline A. Then 2 ml of 0.1% trypsin in Puck's saline A was added and the cells were incubated at 25°. When a few cells began to detach from the glass surface, 1 ml of medium was added and gently pipetted to free the cells. After centrifugation at 200 g for two minutes, the supernatant was removed and the cells were resuspended in fresh medium. Approximately 5×10^4 to 1×10^5 cells/ml were seeded in a 2-oz half-flat medicine bottle with 3 ml of medium.

In October 1960 dissociated cells from ovaries were placed in a Porter flask. After 48 hours the majority of cells attached themselves to the glass surface. About 50 days after setting up, many cells began to degenerate, and by the 70th day only a few cells were still healthy. During the next four months the cell growth was very poor. Ten months after setting up, healthy cells increased rapidly and the first subculturing was made. The subsequent subcultures were repeated at 14-day intervals for two months. The early subcultures consisted of about 8000 cells in 0.9 ml of medium in Porter flasks. As the growth continued, the cells were transferred to 2-oz medicine bottles. Since November 1961, subcultures have been made at 8- to 10-day intervals. The cell line established had been subcultured 29 times during five months.

The two other lines which derived from dissociated cells have been growing for three months and were subcultured 22 times. The fourth line was derived from cultures of undissociated ovaries and has been growing for eight months and was subcultured 44 times.

After subculturing, the majority of cells remained floating for two to four hours and then attached themselves to the glass surface. After four days there was usually a confluent layer of cells on the surface. Mitotic divisions were numerous, and many cells became attached and multiplied while floating in the medium. The generation time of the cells at the beginning of the establishment was about five to six days, but after about 14 months it has been 60–72 hours.

There are three distinct cell types in the cell lines. The first type is common to all four lines. It is 20–40 μ in diameter, polygonal in outline, and usually forms sheets which adhere strongly to the glass surface. The second type of cell, which is found in three of the lines, is round to fibroblastic (15–20 μ in diameter) with a distinct outline and a finely granular cytoplasm. These cells grow on the glass surface or while floating in the medium. The third type is small and round (10–15 μ in diameter and very little variation in size or shape) with a clear outline and a clear cytoplasm. This type of cell is predominant in only one line and loosely attaches to the glass surface.

Established cells have been deep-frozen in the tissue culture medium supplemented with 10% glycerol at —68° and successfully regenerated.

In establishing cell lines, Grace suggested that certain factors, such as osmotic pressure, pH, and ionic ratios of the hemolymph, should be taken into consideration. The incorporation of extracts of insect hormones into the medium has not increased the growth, but these tissue extracts had no deleterious effects on the cells.

Rahman et al. (1966) maintained Grace's Antheraea cells in monolayer culture for more than two years (about 30 passages). Seven milliliters of Grace's medium supplemented with Antheraea pernyi heat-treated hemolymph (3%) was added to each 1- by 6-in. glass tube, and 4 ml was added to each plastic flask (24 cm² surface). Cells were seeded at 10^3–10^4/ml. The tubes were placed on a slanting board (17°) at 28°–30°, and medium was changed at weekly intervals. Monolayers covering the tube surface have usually been obtained within three weeks after setting up. Antheraea pernyi hemolymph was replaced with hemolymph from Bombyx mori, Callosamia promethea, Hyalophora cecropia, Rothschildia orizaha, or Samia cynthia, but eventual lysis of the cells resulted. Antheraea polyphemus hemolymph was a satisfactory substitute for the Antheraea pernyi hemolymph.

Cells were maintained for more than nine months at 4° or at —185° in Grace's medium supplemented with 20% glycerol.

The adaptation of Grace's Antheraea cells to a medium free of insect hemolymph was achieved by Yunker et al. (1967). The original cells were cultured at 28° in 30-ml disposable tissue culture flasks (Falcon Plastics) containing 4 ml of Grace's medium (Grand Island Biological Co.). Effects on growth of cells were tested with over 60 kinds of empirically selected substances, singly or in combinations. Their effects were judged by inspection by comparison with control cultures grown in the minimal medium enriched with 10% *Antheraea pernyi* hemolymph. (Later, hemolymph concentration was adjusted to 3%.) The most successful result was obtained with a medium containing 10% heat-inactivated fetal bovine serum (Grand Island Biological Co.), 10% whole chicken egg ultrafiltrate (Microbiological Associates, Inc.), and 1% bovine plasma albumin (fraction V, Armour Co.) in the minimal medium. When cells were transferred to this medium, they survived and increased only slowly after 49 days, but their numbers were sufficient for subculture. The growth rate increased with 12 successive passages, and this subline has been subcultured 44 times during 17 months. Addition of rabbit serum and hemolymph of lobsters (*Homarus americanus*) did not permit survival or growth of the cells.

At the 21st passage some of these cells were transferred to the minimal medium containing 10% *Antheraea pernyi* hemolymph instead of the substitute factors. Cells failed to grow, but when bovine and egg factors were offered, these cells resumed their vigorous growth and normal morphology. The growth of those subline cells at the 20th passage that were adapted to bovine and egg factors was compared with that of the cells grown continuously on the medium containing 3% *Antheraea pernyi* hemolymph. Cell numbers were 40,000–60,000 cells/ml (an approximate 1:15 of the original suspension), and 4 ml of the cell suspension was pipetted into 30-ml plastic culture flasks which were then incubated at 26°–28°. Some cells adhered to the vessel surface and were loosened with a 1.5- by 15-mm Teflon-coated stirring bar (Microspinbar) and a magnetic stirrer, and 0.5 ml of the suspension was removed for counting. The cultures had a lag phase of approximately three days, and the adapted subline maintained logarithmic growth for 9–10 days, as compared with 7–8 days for the unadapted line. Population doubling time, calculated from the slope of the curve during the log phase, was 2.5 days for the former and 4.2 days for the latter.

Three other lines of *Antheraea* cells were induced to grow in minimal medium containing either 5% lobster hemolymph, or 5 or 10% rabbit serum. These three lines were maintained for 24 passages (13 months), 58 passages (17 months), and 34 passages (6.5 months), respectively. Growth of cells of these strains was never rapid as with the above-mentioned line and routine maintenance of cultures was difficult.

Hukuhara (1966) cultured the Grace's *Antheraea* cell line with a modified Grace's medium (L-histidine and DL-serine were replaced by DL-histidine and L-serine, respectively, and supplemented with 1% calf serum and 1% heat-treated *Antheraea pernyi* hemolymph). The cells

were successfully subcultured 25 times a year when more than 5×10^3
cells/ml were seeded. No growth of cells took place if less than 5×10^3
cells/ml were seeded. When calf serum or hemolymph of *Antheraea
pernyi* was discontinued, the cell growth was lessened; however, *Antheraea
pernyi* hemolymph in the medium could be replaced with *Bombyx mori*
hemolymph.

Bellett and Mercer (1964) and Bellett (1965a,b) investigated the infection and multiplication of *Sericesthis* iridescent virus using the established Grace's *Antheraea* cells. The cells adapted to grow in Grace's
medium containing 4% heat-treated hemolymph of diapausing pupae of
Antheraea pernyi. The cells grew rapidly at 28° without attaching firmly
to the glass surface and could easily be removed by gentle pipetting.
Subcultures were made at four- to five-day intervals, and a cell suspension of $2–2.5 \times 10^5$ cells/ml was seeded. In the *in vitro* assay of *Sericesthis* iridescent virus, Bellett (1965a) used a modified Grace's medium
supplemented with bovine plasma albumin (10 mg/ml) and with the
hemolymph concentration reduced to 2%.

Suitor (1966) attempted to study the multiplication of Japanese encephalitis virus using Grace's line of *Antheraea* cells. The cells were
cultured at 28° in 2-oz glass prescription bottles or plastic tissue culture
flasks (Falcon Plastics) with a medium consisting of Grace's medium
supplemented with bovine plasma albumin (Armour Co. fraction V, 10
mg/ml) and pupal hemolymph of *Philosamia cynthia pryeri*. Under these
conditions the population doubling time of the cells was two to three
days. In order to maintain the cells for four or five weeks, Grace's medium
supplemented with 10% *Antheraea pernyi* hemolymph was added to the
culture.

Thomson and Grace (1963) made cytological observations on *Antheraea* cell lines for about 120 generations over a period of 15–20 months.
The haploid chromosome number in the male pupa of *Antheraea eucalypti*
is 25, and cells in culture for about 120 generations range from diploid
to at least approximately 128n.

Grace and Brzostowski (1966) and Clements and Grace (1967) made
an analysis of the amino acids and sugars utilized by *Antheraea* cells
grown *in vitro*. Of the 21 amino acids, 14 were utilized, but the other
seven either increased in amount or remained at the same concentration
as those in the unused medium. Trehalose was utilized at approximately
the same rate as glucose; fructose was, at first, utilized at a lower rate
than glucose. During the first two days the utilization of sucrose was
low, but later, it was greatly increased.

Stanley and Vaughn (1967) examined the sensitivity of the cell lines
of the *Antheraea* and *Aedes aegypti* to Fungizone (Amphotericin B). Two

cell lines were very sensitive to Fungizone, mosquito cells being much more sensitive than the moth cells. In this experiment, *Antheraea* cells had been adapted to Grace's Insect T. C. Medium supplemented with 9.1% fetal bovine serum and 1% bovine serum. Although *Antheraea* cells grew poorly in the mosquito medium and their morphology was somewhat altered, they were healthy after three weeks and as sensitive to Fungizone as were mosquito cells grown in the same medium.

2. Rice Stem Borer (*Chilo suppressalis*)

In vitro cultures and the establishment of cell lines have been carried out by Mitsuhashi (1965b, 1966, 1967, 1968). (See Fig. 1.)

a. **Tissues and Organs.** Using *Chilo suppressalis* diapausing larvae reared on an artificial diet under aseptic conditions (Kamano, 1964), dissected organs and tissues such as nervous systems, circulatory organs, alimentary canals, Malpighian tubules, fat bodies, salivary glands, silk glands, prothoracic glands, testes, and ovaries were cultured *in vitro*. The dissected organs or tissues were cut into small pieces in Rinaldini's solution. The tissue fragments were trypsinized with 0.1% trypsin (Difco, 1:250) at about 25° for 10 minutes. Trypsinized tissue fragments were transferred into a modified Ringer–Tyrode's salt solution (Carlson, 1946) in the bottom of a culture vessel which consisted of microslide rings (25-mm diameter and 10-mm height) and cover glasses. The Ringer–Tyrode's solution was then replaced with the culture medium, and the medium was carefully changed several times. Cultures were kept at 25° without control of light conditions, and the culture medium was changed every week.

The explanted abdominal ganglion produced wandering cells which migrated within 24 hours and survived for short periods, some of them beginning degeneration after five days. Large epithelial cells also appeared from the abdominal ganglion which survived for a week. From the subesophagal ganglion very slender cells appeared and survived for about 10 days. No cell migration occurred from the brain, the frontal ganglion, and the complex of corpus cardiacum and corpus allatum. Explants of circulatory organs (hearts and alary muscle) produced three types of cells, i.e., (i) very flat, epithelial-like cells which formed loose cell sheets and survived for about 30 days; (ii) very slender, fiber-like cells which survived for about 30 days; and (iii) very large, flat cells which were spherical, elliptical, or ovoid and survived for about 20 days. Epithelial cells migrated from midgut fragments, formed cell sheets, and survived for about 15 days.

Malpighian tubules are not tolerant to trypsinization in Rinaldini's salt solution lacking Ca^{2+} and Mg^{2+}. However, tubule tissues placed on

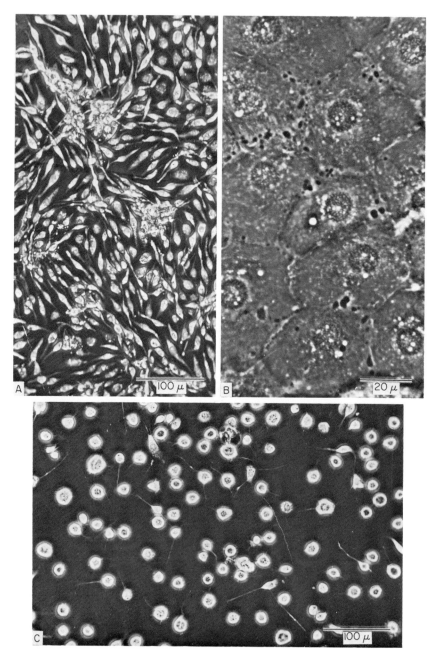

FIG. 1. Cells grown *in vitro* from the rice stem borer (*Chilo suppressalis*). (A) Fibroblast-like cells from pupal ovary. (B) Epithelial-like cells from pupal ovary. (C) Wandering cells from larval brain. (Courtesy of J. Mitsuhashi.)

the glass surface with the culture medium survived for about 10 days, and epithelial-like cells migrating from them survived for about five days. Large flat cells were liberated from fat body fragments, formed pseudopodia, and survived for about 15 days. Epithelial cells migrated from the silk glands, formed loose cell sheets, and survived for about 30 days.

No cell migrations were observed from salivary glands and prothoracic glands.

In the culture of testes, trypsinization was avoided since the spermatocysts were fragile, and three types of cells were observed, i.e., (i) small epithelial cells which migrated from the cluster of spermatocysts, formed small cell sheets, and survived for about 50 days; (ii) large phagocyte-like cells which came out from the cluster of spermatocysts and survived for about 20 days; and (iii) very large epithelial-like cells which migrated from the explants and survived for about 60 days.

Four types of cells were obtained from the ovariole tissues, i.e., (i) small epithelial cells which migrated from the cut opening of the explants within 24 hours, formed loose cell sheets, and were degenerated after a week; (ii) wandering cells which showed active amoeboid movement and survived for about 60 days (mitoses were sometimes seen); (iii) large epithelial cells which formed compact cell sheets and survived for about 90 days; and (iv) very large epithelial-like cells which formed cell sheets around the explants and survived for about 60 days. From these observations it appeared that the wandering cells and the large epithelial cells obtained from the explanted ovariole tissue were the most promising for subculturing and establishment of cell lines because they could survive for long periods and multiply by mitoses.

b. Hemocytes. Mitsuhashi (1966) cultivated larval hemocytes of the rice stem borer for long periods and established a cell line.

i. PRIMARY CULTURE. Hemolymph was dropped into a modified Ringer–Tyrode's salt solution (Carlson, 1946). Most of the hemocytes attached themselves to the glass surface within a few minutes. Some hemocytes aggregated to form masses while others became flat by sending out pseudopod-like cytoplasmic processes. After most of the hemocytes settled, they were washed by changing the salt solution several times. After the washing, the Ringer–Tyrode's solution was replaced with culture medium. Cultures were incubated at 25° under natural light, and the medium was changed every week.

Mitsuhashi (1966) classified seven types of hemocytes of *Chilo suppressalis* by their size, shape, staining property, and behavior, i.e., prohemocytes, plasmatocytes, granular hemocytes, spherule cells, oenocytoids, podocytes, and veriform cells. In the primary culture, plasmatocytes and granular hemocytes soon attached themselves to the glass surface and became flat by spreading their cytoplasm. The prohemocytes aggregated to form cell masses, and the spherule cells, oenocytoids, podocytes, and veriform cells did not attach themselves to the glass surface. Plasmatocytes and prohemocytes survived and multiplied by mitosis for long periods, but the granular hemocytes usually did not survive for more than two days. The plasmatocytes usually began mitosis within a week and often formed cell sheets. Sometimes multipolar mitoses were seen in the plasmatocytes, and very large plasmatocytes, probably polyploid, appeared. The prohemocytes began multiplication by mitosis within a week and were often seen on the plasmatocyte cell sheets. They formed tissue-like cell masses and sometimes networks. Mitoses were observed only after metaphase. The primary culture of the plasmatocytes and prohemocytes was maintained for more than 12 months, and the cells still multiplied by mitoses.

ii. SUBCULTURE. In the seven-month-old primary culture, the plasmatocytes formed cell sheets and the prohemocytes built up thick tissue-like cell masses. Small portions of the plasmatocyte cell sheets and prohemocyte masses were scratched with sterile needles, and the cells that separated from the glass surface were transferred into a new culture vessel. It was possible to detach cells from the glass surface, by trypsinization for 10 minutes at 25°, without deleterious effects. A small amount of the culture medium which was previously conditioned with cultivated hemocytes was added to the subcultured cells. Some plasmatocytes migrated from the explanted cell masses soon after the subculturing and then became flat on the glass surface, but the prohemocytes scarcely ever attached themselves to the glass surface. Mitoses usually became active two days after subculturing, and multipolar mitoses were also occasionally observed.

After the cells of primary culture multiplied to cover the whole area of the glass surface, a part of the secondary culture was again subcultured. Cells were successively subcultured for eight generations.

In this series of experiments, Mitsuhashi (1966) examined the effects of medium modifications and found that the addition of fetal bovine serum (20%) promoted cell multiplication and mitosis. Addition of *Chilo suppressalis* or *Bombyx mori* hemolymph (5%) did not promote cell multiplication.

Although Mitsuhashi establised a cell line from the hemocytes of diapausing larvae of *Chilo suppressalis*, all cultures were accidentally infected with *Chilo* irridescent virus (CIV) (Mitsuhashi, 1967). (See Fig. 2.) However, he did keep an infected cell line. Using this line, Mitsuhashi (1968) examined the effects of temperature and cold-storage

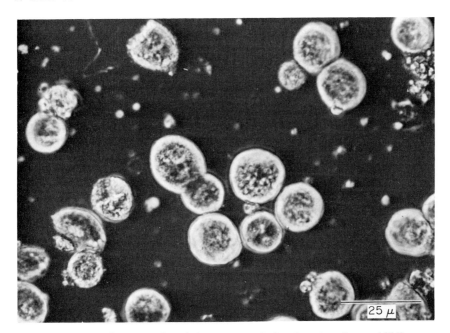

FIG. 2. A cell line from larval hemocytes of the rice stem borer (*Chilo suppressalis*). Cells are persistently infected with *Chilo* iridescent virus. (Courtesy of J. Mitsuhashi.)

on the multiplication of cells. The stock cell cultures had been maintained in 80-ml medicine bottles at 25°, and subculturing was carried out at one- to two-week intervals. The cells were centrifuged at 2000 rpm for 10 minutes, and half of the culture medium was renewed. Sedimented cells were separated by pipetting, and 1.5-ml portions of the cell suspension were distributed into 15- by 150-mm culture tubes and incubated at 20°, 22°, 25°, 28°, and 30°, respectively. The maximum cell multiplication was observed at 25°. The cells increased in number at 22°–28° but decreased in number at 20° or at 30°. The cells recovered their viability after preservation at 5° for 30–120 days, but the multiplication of cells was slightly inferior to the control.

3. Silkworm (*Bombyx mori*)

Grace (1967) established a cell line from the silkworm using the same method and medium as for the *Antherea eucalypti* cells (Grace, 1962). (See Fig. 3.)

Six whole ovaries and the dissociated cells from six ovaries were suspended in 3 ml of medium in petri dishes. In the cultures of dissociated

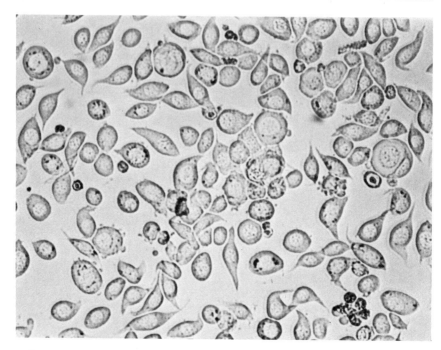

Fig. 3. A cell line from ovary of the silkworm (*Bombyx mori*). (Courtesy of T. D. C. Grace.)

cells, most cells attached themselves to the substrate within 12 hours. During the next four to five days, many cells died, but by the 10th day dividing cells were common and some cells formed sheets which attached to the substrate. Nine months later, cells in one of these cultures rapidly increased in number. The majority of the cells did not attach to the substrate, and two weeks later they were transferred to a new culture vessel. Subcultures were made at two- to three-week intervals for three months and then at six-day intervals.

The most common type of cell was spindle-shaped, 12 to 25 μ wide and 50 to 70 μ long. The only other type of cells formed small sheets on the surface of the culture vessel, were slightly spindle-shaped to round, and measured 18–30 μ in diameter.

After subculturing for two years, the generation time of the cells was 48 hours. The cells became adapted to a medium containing 1% bovine plasma albumin and 1% heat-treated hemolymph of *Antheraea pernyi*. The cells were viable after being kept for 10 months at $-180°$ in a medium containing 10% glycerol. Most cells contained over 100 chromosomes when examined 15 and 18 months after the line was established.

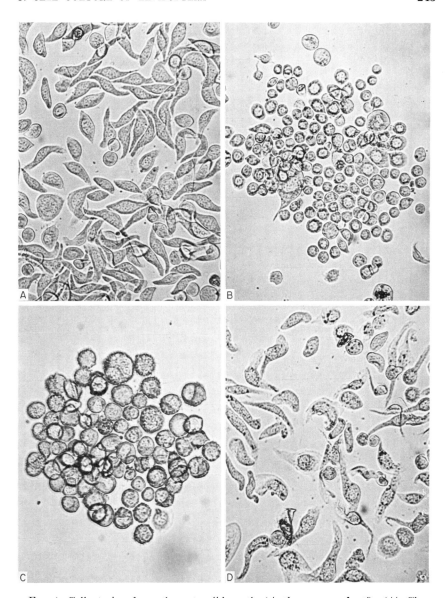

Fig. 4. Cell strains from the saturniid moth (*Antheraea eucalypti*). (A) Clone Ae C8; spindle-shaped cells. (B) Clone Ae C7; polygonal cells. (C) Clone Ae C6; round cells. (D) Clone Ae C4; cells very variable in shape and size. [From T. D. C. Grace, *Exp. Cell Res.* **52**, 453, 454 (1968); *In Vitro* **3**, 109 (1968), reproduced with permission of the Tissue Culture Association.]

C. Cloning of Cells

Grace (1968a,b) established 10 clones from the line of saturniid moth (*Antheraea eucalypti*) cells (See Fig. 4.) by the following technique. About 100 cells were placed in 3 ml of Grace's medium in a small test tube. Cells were thoroughly separated by pipetting and were transferred to a 2-in.-diameter glass petri dish. After seven days at 30°, each colony of cells that appeared morphologically distinct was sucked up in a micro-pipette and transferred to 0.5 ml of medium in a small glass ring sealed to a petri dish with Vaseline. When there were about 100 cells in the ring they were transferred to a 2-in. petri dish. This procedure of isolating cells was repeated three times. The 10 clones could be grouped into four cell types: (i) spindle-shaped cells (six clones), (ii) polygonal cells (two clones), (iii) round cells (one clone), and (iv) cells very variable in shape and size (one clone). There were differences in the growth rates of the clones.

REFERENCES

Aizawa, K., and Sato, F. (1963). *Ann. Epiphyt.* **14**, 125.
Aizawa, K., and Vago, C. (1959a). *C. R. Acad. Sci.* **249**, 928.
Aizawa, K., and Vago, C. (1959b). *Entomophaga* **4**, 249.
Aizawa, K., Sato, F., and Murakami, A. (1961). *J. Sericult. Sci. Jap.* **30**, 445.
Bellett, A. J. D. (1965a). *Virology* **26**, 127.
Bellett, A. J. D. (1965b). *Virology* **26**, 132.
Bellett, A. J. D., and Mercer, E. H. (1964). *Virology* **24**, 645.
Carlson, J. G. (1946). *Biol. Bull.* **90**, 109.
Clements, A. N., and Grace, T. D. C. (1967). *J. Insect Physiol.* **13**, 1327.
Day, M. F., and Grace, T. D. C. (1959). *Rev. Entomol.* **4**, 17.
Flandre, O., Vago, C., and Chastang, S. (1962). *C. R. Acad. Sci.* **255**, 1654.
Fosset, J., and Chastang, S. (1963). *Ann. Epiphyt.* **14**, 35.
Gaw, Z.-Y., Liu, N. T., and Zia, T. U. (1959). *Act. Virol.* (*Prague*), *Engl. Ed.* **3**, Suppl., 55.
Glaser, R. W. (1917). *Psyche* **24**, 1.
Goldschmidt, R. (1915). *Proc. Nat. Acad. Sci. U.S.* **1**, 220.
Grace, T. D. C. (1954). *Nature* (*London*) **174**, 187.
Grace, T. D. C. (1958a). *Aust. J. Biol. Sci.* **11**, 407.
Grace, T. D. C. (1958b). *J. Gen. Physiol.* **41**, 1027.
Grace, T. D. C. (1958c). *Science* **128**, 3318.
Grace, T. D. C. (1959). *Ann. N.Y. Acad. Sci.* **77**, 275.
Grace, T. D. C. (1962). *Nature* (*London*) **195**, 788.
Grace, T. D. C. (1967). *Nature* (*London*) **216**, 613.
Grace, T. D. C. (1968a). *Exp. Cell Res.* **52**, 451.
Grace, T. D. C. (1968b). *In Vitro* **3**, 104–117.
Grace, T. D. C., and Brzostowski, H. W. (1966). *J. Insect Physiol.* **12**, 625.

Hartzell, A. (1958). *Proc. Int. Congr. Entomol. 10th, 1956* Vol. 2, p. 319.
Hartzell, A. (1961). *Proc. Int. Congr. Entomol., 11th, 1960* Vol. 1, p. 350.
Hirumi, H., and Maramorosch, K. (1964). *Contrib. Boyce Thompson Inst.* **22,** 259.
Hukuhara, T. (1966). *J. Sericult. Sci., Jap.* **35,** 349.
Jones, B. M. (1962). *Biol. Rev.* **37,** 512.
Jones, B. M. (1966). *In* "Cells and Tissues in Culture" (E. N. Willmer, ed.), Vol. 3, pp. 397–457. Academic Press, New York.
Jones, B. M., and Cunningham, I. (1960). *Nature (London)* **187,** 1072.
Jones, B. M., and Cunningham, I. (1961). *Exp. Cell Res.,* **23,** 386.
Kamano, S. (1964). *Jap. J. Appl. Entomol. Zool.* **8,** 101.
Krause, G. (1962). *Ver. Deut. Zool. Ges. Vienna* pp. 190–197.
Krause, G., Krause, J., and Geisler, M. (1966). *Z. Zellforsch. Mikrosk. Anat.* **70,** 393.
Krejzová, R. (1966a). *Věstn. Česk. Společnosti Zool.* **30,** 107.
Krejzová, R. (1966b). *Věstn. Česk. Společnosti Zool.* **30,** 111.
Loeb, M. J.. and Schneiderman. H. A. (1956). *Ann. Entomol. Soc. Amer.* **49,** 493.
Maramorosch, K. (1962). *Proc. Int. Congr. Entomol. 11th, 1960* Vol. 2, p. 801.
Martignoni, M. E. (1960). *Experientia* **16,** 125.
Martignoni, M. E. (1962). *Proc. Biol. Colloq. [Oregon State Univ.]* **23,** 89–110.
Martignoni, M. E., and Scallion, R. J. (1961a). *Biol. Bull.* **121,** 507.
Martignoni, M. E., and Scallion, R. J. (1961b). *Nature (London)* **190,** 1133.
Martignoni, M. E., Zitcer, E. M., and Wagner, R. P. (1958). *Science* **128,** 360.
Medvedeva, N. B. (1959). *C. R. Acad. Sci. (Dopov.), Ukr.* **7,** 790.
Medvedeva, N. B. (1960). *Entomol. Obozr.* **39,** 49.
Mitsuhashi, J. (1965a). *Kontyû* **33,** 271.
Mitsuhashi, J. (1965b). *Jap. J. Appl. Entomol. Zool.* **9,** 217.
Mitsuhashi, J. (1966). *Appl. Entomol. Zool.* **1,** 5.
Mitsuhashi, J. (1967). *Nature (London)* **215,** 863.
Mitsuhashi, J. (1968). *Appl. Entomol. Zool.* **3,** 1.
Rahman, S. B., Perlman, D., and Ristich, S. S. (1966). *Proc. Soc. Exp. Biol. Med.* **123,** 711.
Sen Gupta, K. (1961). *Folia Biol. (Prague)* **7,** 400.
Sen Gupta, K. (1963). *Ann. Epiphyt.* **14,** 39.
Smith, K. M. (1967) "Insect Virology." Academic Press, New York.
Sohi, S. S. (1968). *Can. J. Zool.* **46,** 11.
Stanley, M. S. M., and Vaughn, J. L. (1967). *J. Insect Physiol.* **13,** 1613.
Suitor, E. C., Jr. (1966). *Virology* **30,** 143.
Thomson, J. A., and Grace, T. D. C. (1963). *Aust. J. Biol. Sci.* **16,** 869.
Trager, W. (1935). *J. Exp. Med.* **61,** 501.
Vago, C. (1958). *Mikroskopie* **13,** 246.
Vago, C. (1959). *Entomophaga* **4,** 23.
Vago, C. (1961). *Entomophaga* **6,** 265.
Vago, C. (1967). *Methods Virol.* **1,** 567–602.
Vago, C.. and Bergoin, M. (1963). *Entomophaga* **8,** 253.
Vago, C., and Chastang, S. (1958a). *Experientia* **14,** 110.
Vago, C., and Chastang, S. (1958b). *Experientia* **14,** 426.
Vago, C., and Chastang, S. (1960). *C. R. Acad. Sci.* **251,** 903.
Vago, C., and Chastang, S. (1962a). *Entomophaga* **7,** 175.
Vago, C., and Chastang, S. (1962b). *C. R. Acad. Sci.* **255,** 3226.
Vago, C., and Flandre, O. (1963). *Ann. Epiphyt.* **14,** 127.
Vago, C., Fosset, J., and Meynadier, G. (1961a). *C. R. Acad. Sci.* **252,** 2759.

Vago, C., Fosset, J., and Meynadier, G. (1961b). *Rev. Pathol. Végé. Entomol. Agr. France* **40**, 111.

Vaughn, J. L. (1968). *In* "Insect Viruses" (K. Maramorosch, ed.), pp. 108–128. Springer, Berlin.

White, J. F., and Sastrodihardjo, S. (1966). *Nature (London)* **212**, 314.

Wigglesworth. V. B. (1959). *Annu. Rev. Entomol.* **4**, 1.

Wyatt, G. R., Lougheed, T. C., and Wyatt, S. S. (1956). *J. Gen. Physiol.* **39**, 853.

Wyatt, S. S. (1956). *J. Gen. Physiol.* **39**, 841.

Yunker, C. E., Vaughn, J. L., and Cory, J. (1967). *Science* **155**, 1565.

7

CELL CULTURE OF DIPTERA

Silvana Dolfini

I. INTRODUCTION

Since the first attempts at *in vitro* culturing of invertebrate tissues, insect tissue cultures, especially those of Diptera, have aroused great interest and have been the object of numerous researches.

The development of these cultures was rather slow, many difficulties arose, and the results, at first, were very modest. The slow progress can be attributed to the scanty knowledge of the biochemistry and physiology of this order of insects, but the potential interest of such cultures induced researchers to persevere in this quest, and recently, at long last, several successes rewarded their efforts, i.e., cell lines have been established from different tissues of different Diptera (*Drosophila, Aedes,* and *Anopheles*).

According to a generally accepted definition (Martignoni, 1962; Fedoroff, 1967), we can distinguish two types of cultures.

1. Organ cultures: By this we mean maintenance *in vitro* of tissues, organ primordia, and the whole or parts of an organ in a way that preserves their architecture and/or function and that allows a differentiation and a growth of the cells in directions that would be expected *in vivo*.

2. Cell cultures: This term denotes the growing *in vitro*, by division, of cells no longer organized into tissues but isolated by migration from an explant or by dissociation from different tissues. Cell culture causes a cell dedifferentiation, that is, a shift towards a less specialized state.

Looking at the history of Diptera tissue cultures, we can roughly divide it into two phases which correspond practically to the distinctions mentioned above. As a matter of fact, the first authors applied themselves to the organ cultures and took an interest in problems of gametogenesis, differentiation, and morphogenesis.

The media used were mostly simple mixtures of salt solutions and hemolymph. Later on, organ cultures were used either to study the effect of some substances (hormones and agents as radiations) or to study the relationship between two different organs.

Only recently, however, have cell cultures been successfully tried. This is due to the possibility of devising synthetic or partially synthetic media, more complete than the previous ones and more similar in composition to Diptera fluids. These media allowed the survival and the division of isolated cells.

Two genera of the order of Diptera were the main sources of tissues for the cultures: *Drosophila* (especially *D. melanogaster* Meig., suborder Brachicera, family Drosophilidae) and *Aedes* (especially *A. aegypti* L., suborder Nematocera, family Culicidae).

The reasons which led to the attempt to obtain cultures of tissues of these two species are different and correspond practically to the two main directions followed by researchers occupied with Diptera tissue cultures.

Drosophila, one of the favorite organisms of geneticists, is the ideal material for studying somatic cell genetics chiefly because of (a) its low chromosome number, (b) clear-cut differences between pairs, and (c) a large choice of chromosomal markers.

Aedes and other species of the same family, on the contrary, are the vectors of the causal agents of many diseases that affect man and animals (i.e., malaria, yellow fever, and western equine encephalomyelitis). The culture *in vitro* of mosquito cells would permit a more intensive investigation of these agents.

As a conclusion, we can also briefly mention *Calliphora erythrocephala* L. (suborder Brachicera, family Larvevoridae) and *Musca domestica* L. (suborder Brachicera, family Muscidae). Several authors have studied the development *in vitro* and the differentiation of organs of these insects. In this review I shall deal separately with the results obtained by culturing cells from the different insects (*Drosophila, Aedes, Calliphora*, etc.), first giving a brief outline of the results of organ cultures.

II. CULTURES OF *Drosophila, Calliphora,* AND *Musca* TISSUES

A. Organ Cultures

The first culturists to attempt to grow Diptera tissues *in vitro* were Collier in 1920, who tried to culture the gut epithelium of *Musca domestica* and *Calliphora vomitoria*, and Frew (1928), who cultured entire larval imaginal discs from mature and immature larvae of the blow-fly (*Calliphora erythrocephala*) in different body fluids.

The very first attempts at culturing organs of *Drosophila melanogaster* aimed exclusively at obtaining *in vitro* a differentiation of imaginal discs (Gottschewski and Fischer, 1939; Fischer and Gottschewski, 1939) or testes (Stern, 1940) in very simple media.

After a long interval, the Japanese resumed research in this field. In fact, Kuroda (1954a,b) devised a synthetic medium, later partially modified (Kuroda, 1956), which allowed an approach to the problem of differentiation and its genetic control. The action of the genotype, the effect of the presence of the cephalic complex on the growth and differentiation of the eye-antennal and wing discs (Kuroda and Yamaguchi, 1956; Kuroda, 1959), the tryptophan metabolism, and the effect of the metamorphic hormone (Horikawa, 1956, 1957) were studied.

Kuroda and Tamura (1955, 1956a,b, 1957), in the same medium, K-6, cultured melanotic tumors and studied the effects of PTC (phenylthiocarbamide) and Cu^{2+} and Fe^{3+} on their growth.

In addition, the culture *in vitro* of such organs as imaginal discs, salivary glands, testes, etc., has proved to be a useful instrument for the investigation of the effects of radiation on the larvae of *Drosophila* (Horikawa, 1958; Horikawa and Sugahara, 1960a,b).

The problem of differentiation was also attacked by Demal and his group. The differentiation of imaginal discs, genital glands, aorta fragments, and salivary glands from *Drosophila melanogaster* and *Calliphora erythrocephala* (Demal, 1956; Demal and Leloup, 1963; Leloup and Demal, 1968) and the maintenance of neurosecretion *in vitro* (Leloup and Gianfelici, 1966; Gianfelici, 1968) were thoroughly analyzed.

The behavior *in vitro* of organs of *Drosophila* has also been investigated by Schneider (1963, 1964), who describes the development of eye-antennal discs (with attached cephalic complex) of larvae of *D. melanogaster* and *D. virilis*. The explants were cultured in hanging drops for periods ranging from 4 to 48 days, and a synthetic medium supplemented with various extracts was used. The differentiation is studied from the points of view of both the outward morphology and pigment deposition. In a subsequent paper (Schneider, 1966) a more detailed description is given of the histological development of these organs of *Drosophila* cultured *in vitro* for varying lengths of time.

Following a genetic trend, Castiglioni and Rezzonico Raimondi (1961a,b) produced hanging drop cultures of cephalic ganglia and lymph glands of different wild stocks of *Drosophila* in various nonsynthetic media. Ganglia survival for over a month together with cell migrations and infrequent mitoses during the second and third week were revealed. Lymph glands, on the contrary, remained alive for only 10–13 days.

Then Castiglioni and Rezzonico Raimondi (1963a,b) and Rezzonico Raimondi *et al.* (1964), in order to analyze the action of the genotype upon the behavior of cultured somatic cells and following the same technique, cultured in K-6 medium organs of three wild stocks and their F_1 hybrids. They were able to detect some stock specific differences.

The most recent contribution to the study of maintaining *in vitro* organs of *D. melanogaster* was made by Robb (1969). Using a system of cells developmentally determined and relatively homogeneous (i.e., imaginal discs) he succeeded in determining the composition of a chemically defined synthetic medium (R14). This medium permits linear total RNA and acid-insoluble protein synthesis for more than 48 hours, DNA synthesis for several hours, and normal differentiation after 74 hours.

B. Cell Cultures

The first successful attempt at growing *in vitro* single cells of *Drosophila* was performed by Horikawa and Kuroda (1959). They cultured blood cells from sterile larvae in a synthetic medium that was a modification of K-6 (Kuroda, 1956). Fischer and Gottschweski (1939) had already tried to culture hemolymph cells and reported a blackening of these cells *in vitro* and the formation of pseudoepithelia.

The improvements in the composition of the medium introduced by Horikawa and Kuroda were the following: The series of amino acids replaced the casein hydrolysate; cholesterol was introduced; and the pH was adjusted to 6.4 instead of 7.2. The blood cells, collected by stabbing the larvae, were cultured in roller tubes (12 rph) at the concentration of 500–1000 cells/ml at 25°. The authors observed mitoses up to the 75th day of culture and, also, a difference in the mitotic activity of cells deriving from different stocks.

These may be regarded as the first long-term cultures of *Drosophila* cells; however, it is not possible to consider them as a cell line because no attempt has been made to obtain subcultures. We must also emphasize that this is the first attempt at genetic analysis, which permits an absolutely new description of the phenotype.

Maintenance *in vitro* of *Drosophila* cells for a certain period has been achieved by Cunningham (1961) and by Hanly (1961). The former succeeded in separating the nurse cells and ova and maintaining them *in vitro;* the latter observed several mitotic cycles in explants made from either early embryos or larval cephalic ganglia and maintained *in vitro* for over two months.

Schneider (1963) also reports ovarian tissues from *D. melanogaster* at various stages of development cultured in hanging drops. Large numbers of cells from preadult stages attached to the coverslip, and mitotic divisions were seen up to the 12th day.

The main problem to solve has always been that of the choice of the source of the tissues to culture. It is well known that it is more difficult to promote the growth of adult tissues than that of undifferentiated tissues. Therefore, the embryo should be an ideal organism from which to obtain tissues for culturing *in vitro*. It is in a state of active growth, and it contains within itself or in the yolk all the hormones and growth factors. For that reason Kuroda (1963) chose the embryos of *Drosophila* at the blastodermal stage as the source of tissues from which to dissociate single cells to culture in a synthetic medium. The eggs (Oregon-R) are dechorionated by immersion in 3% NaClO for six minutes, sterilized in 70% alcohol for 10 minutes, and rinsed in sterile Carlson's salt solution. The dissociation is achieved by pressing slightly on a coverslip placed over the embryos and by flushing the fragments through the tip of a pipette. After four days of culture at 25°, in Carlson's solution containing 6 gm of lactalbumin hydrolysate and 800 mg of yeast extract/100 ml of medium at pH 7.8, the number of cell nuclei increased fourfold.

Nearly analogous results, from the standpoint of survival, were obtained by Lesseps (1965), who made use of a system of single embryonic cells cultured *in vitro* to study a very important problem in relation to differentiation: How do dissociated cells interact *in vitro* to form aggregates, and how do they sort out and differentiate within the aggregates? Following a similar technique (removal of the chorions in 2.5% NaClO, slitting of the vitelline membrane with tungsten needles, and dissociation into single cells by incubating the embryos for 15 minutes in a calcium- and magnesium-free salt solution containing 0.12% EDTA and 0.15% trypsin) he succeeded in isolating cells and culturing them, at 25° in a medium similar to that devised by Schneider (1964) and supplemented with 10% fetal bovine serum, for a period ranging from five to seven days. The author describes the formation of aggregates, their contractions, and the characteristic positions of the different cell types within the aggregates. He does not, however, observe differences between the behavior of wild embryos and embryos of the mutant strain X2.

A remarkable step forward was made by Horikawa and Fox (1964), who established a technique for growing embryonic single cells, even for long periods of time, thus clearing the way for a series of cytogenetic, genetic, and biochemical researches.

The various stages of this method, which practically recalls Kuroda's (1963), are as follows: removal of the chorion in 3% NaClO for two minutes, sterilization for 15 minutes in 0.05% $HgCl_2$ and 70% ethyl alcohol, dissociation in a small glass homogenizer, filtration, and suspension of the cells in a synthetic medium (H-5) at pH 6.5 and supplemented with 10% newborn calf serum. The addition of the serum to culture media, performed years ago with mammalian cell cultures, is shown to be necessary also for insect cell growth. Fisher *et al.* (1958, 1959) proved that the serum is essential because of the presence of two proteins: (a) serum albumin and (b) an α-globulin. The first functions as a carrier of small molecules; the second is necessary for the attachment and spreading of cells on a glass surface.

Horikawa and Fox measured the growth *in vitro* by cell countings on subsequent days, examining different hours of embryonic development and different stocks. At the optimum temperature (30°) the greatest growth (the initial cell number increased four times) occurred using wild embryos six hours after fertilization. The chromosome number seemed to remain constant at the diploid number in these primary cultures.

These cells have been maintained in culture for 520 days (Horikawa *et al.*, 1966), by subsequent subcultures. At the time of the transfer the cells are collected, centrifuged, and resuspended in fresh medium; after the first transfers the H-5 medium is replaced by a more diluted one

(H-6). The cells, both the large (20–35 μ in diameter) and the small (5–10 μ), retain their embryonic appearance. The mean generation time of the small cells is, at the beginning of the culture, 30 hours, but it gradually increases as the culture ages.

As to the chromosome number, for up to 160 days of culture the modal class remains that with eight chromosomes. After 60 days a new cell type appears, that is, large cells (15–30 μ in diameter) with a clear cytoplasm, which seem to divide by budding; but unfortunately, the authors didn't count the chromosome number in these new cells.

To conclude, we may consider this kind of culture as the first example of a cell line of *Drosophila* but not as an established line; the appearance of a new cell type could perhaps be the emergence of a permanent line. This system was devised by the authors also out of a concern with the problems of differentiation and its genetic control. Following this trend and in order to elucidate the mechanisms responsible for the initiation of the synthesis of specific, gene-controlled proteins at particular times during development, the effect of the substrate on the level of three enzymes present at low level in embryonic cells of *Drosophila* was analyzed. The results show that each enzyme responds in a different way to the presence of its substrate (Horikawa *et al.*, 1967). The second step was the analysis of the problem of the mechanisms of cell–cell interactions during development (Fox *et al.*, 1968), i.e., the formation by rotation of aggregates of embryonic cells, the types of aggregates, the factors affecting this process, the influence of puromycin and actinomycin D led to the hypothesis that a protein component of the cell surface is responsible for the specificity of the aggregation phenomenon. The problem of aggregation patterns has also been investigated by Kuroda (1968, 1969), who, culturing (in the K-10 medium) single cells isolated from larval organs by trypsinization and rotating them on a giratory shaker, observed characteristic aggregation patterns according to the different imaginal discs and the different strains used. Horikawa and Fox's technique was also followed by Seecof and Unanue (1968), who grew cells from three- to seven-hours old embryos of *Drosophila melanogaster* in Schneider's medium for 30 days. They observed fixation of the cells to surfaces and a differentiation of pulsatile-like muscle cells and neuron-like cells.

Horikawa and Fox's technique allows primary cultures of *Drosophila* embryonic cells to be obtained in a simple way and, therefore, makes possible many investigations and, also, a first approach to somatic cell genetics owing to the unique genetic potentialities of this cellular material, at least during the first period of culture when the cells are actively multiplying. A unique peculiarity of this material is the low chromosome number ($2n = 8$) and the easily recognizable pairs. These advantageous conditions have helped to clarify the origin of the general phenomenon of heteroploidy in cultured cells.

The research has been interested in both the mechanism itself and the environmental conditions which cause it. Dolfini and Gottardi (1966) proved that the heteroploidy is present very early in the primary cultures and that the more probable mechanism of origin is nondisjunction or other mitotic errors. Moreover, in certain culture conditions a selection of a genotype can occur, i.e., the one with seven chromosomes. The numerical variations, in the majority of cases, would involve the first and the fourth pair of chromosomes. Later on, Ottaviano Gottardi (1968) thoroughly examined the phenomenon, making clear that the distribution of chromosome numbers, as well as the cell growth, are controlled by the initial cell concentration. At a low initial cell concentration the diploid karyotype remains nearly constant. At a high initial cell concentration, that is, under limiting conditions, a new karyotype would be selected. This finding could also explain the discrepancy between the data of Horikawa and Fox (1964), who observed a constant diploid number in their cultured cells, and the data of Dolfini and Gottardi (1966).

However, Kakpakov and Gvosdev (1968) recently reported on the maintenance of the diploid number in embryonic cells of *Drosophila melanogaster* cultured for 40 days in a different medium (C-12).

Furthermore, the possibility, offered by *Drosophila* cells, of clearly distinguishing the different chromosome pairs led to another investigation: By means of the Horikawa and Fox method of culturing single cells and the autoradiographic technique, the replication pattern of the chromosomal DNA was studied (Barigozzi *et al.*, 1966, 1967). Continuous labeling experiments (the cell were exposed to ^{3}H-thymidine at a concentration of 0.5 μCi/ml of medium for $3\frac{1}{2}$, 4, and 6 hours and then autoradiographed) showed a clear asynchrony in the replication pattern of the chromosomal DNA. The following chromosomes, or chromosomal sections, are late duplicating: the whole Y chromosome, the proximal portion of the X, and the centrometric sections of II and III autosomes. The fourth pair seems to be late duplicating along its entire length (Fig. 1). This distribution of the asynchronous portions corresponds to that of the heterochromatin, defined according to both cytological and genetic data.

The recent work of Halfer *et al.* (1969) represents an extension of this investigation. Using the same system of short-term cultures, the chronology of DNA replication of the Y chromosome of three stocks of *D. melanogaster* carrying translocations between the Y and the X, II and III autosome, respectively, was studied. The portions in which the

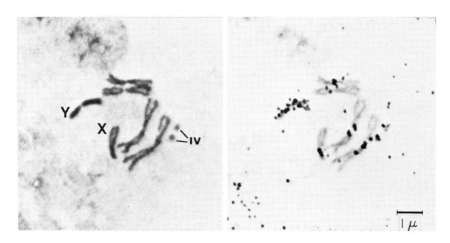

Fig. 1. Autoradiograph of a *Drosophila melanogaster* male cell in metaphase after a four-hour contact with ^{3}H-thymidine. To the right, the cell showing the grains on the heterochromatic sections. To the left, the same cell after removal of the grains. Magnification: ×2700. (Courtesy of Carlotta Halfer.)

Y is split are differently located, either as an independent centric fragment and/or as segments variously translocated on hetero- and euchromatin of other chromosomes. The authors observe that the timing of replication of the different Y-chromosome segments (always replicating later than the euchromatin) varies independently of the eu- or heterochromatic nature of the adjoining chromosome sections and suppose a position effect without spreading effect.

The problem of the genotypical control of the behavior *in vitro* of genetically different stocks has been studied by Horikawa and Fox (1964), who found different growth of the stocks Oregon-R-EL2 (wild type) and rosy-2 and maroon-like (mutants). Rezzonico Raimondi and Gottardi (1967), following the earlier studies of Castiglioni and Rezzonico Raimondi (1963a,b), cultured, by the Horikawa and Fox method, cells from three inbred stocks and described their differing development *in vitro*.

A further remarkable step forward in the development of insect cell culturing was made, a few months after Horikawa and Fox's paper, by Echalier *et al.* (1965), who, in France, devised a technique for culturing embryonic tissues of *Drosophila*. The main difference between the two methods is that in the case of the second, tissues fragments adhering to a coverslip are cultured rather than single cells in suspension. Moreover, the composition of the medium is different and is as similar to larval hemolymph as possible. The pH is 6.6 and the temperature

26°. The appearance of these cultures is peculiar. From the fragments
adhering to the glass surface an outgrowth of polygonal or spindle-
shaped cells occurs after 48 hours. Then, after two weeks, a "secondary
migration" of fibroblast-like cells actively multiplying follows. These
primary cultures have been maintained for six weeks; then subcultures
in microdrops under paraffin oil were obtained and infected with σ virus
(carbon dioxide sensitivity virus). As a matter of fact, all these attempts
to culture the *Drosophila* cells were made with this virological purpose,
that is, to explain the relationships between the virus and its host at
cellular level. In fact, a multiplication of σ in these cultures in microdrops is revealed (from 4×10^3 infecting unities to 6×10^5 after two
months) (Ohanessian and Echalier, 1967). Unexpectedly, on one occasion, a small group of cells, quite distinct from the rest by reason of
their great size, their peculiar morphology, and high mitotic activity,
was noted in these primary cultures. These cells, round or spindle-shaped
and isolated and maintained by weekly subcultures, gave rise to an
established line, highly heteroploid and the first in the history of *Drosophila* cell cultures. This line is named CED ("cellules embryonnaires de

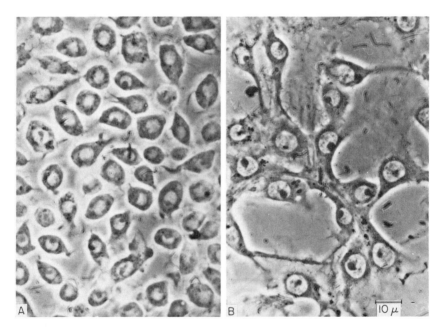

Fig. 2. Phase contrast photographs of the cells of two established lines of *Drosophila melanogaster*. (A) K line, the cells are at the 67th passage. (B) C line, the
cells are at the 56th passage. Magnification: ×700. (Courtesy of Guy Echalier.)

Drosophile") (Echalier and Ohanessian, 1968). Ohanessian and Echalier (1968) tried to obtain multiplication of the σ virus in these cells, as in the primary cultures, but the results were different. The viral titer rose to a high level a few hours after infection, but then dropped to zero.

The subsequent (and independent from the above-mentioned) isolation by Echalier and Ohanessian (1969) of eight established cell lines (always from primary cultures of embryonic cells of *Drosophila melanogaster*) may be considered the latest and the most important achievement in this field. The cells from which the lines originated appeared in the primary cultures at the fifth month. The lines are now (April 1971) at the 37th month of culture (personal communication). The cells are small, spindle-shaped, and similar to those of the primary cultures, but every line has a distinct morphology, as far as the degree of independence of the cells and the capacity of adhesion to the glass are concerned (Fig. 2). The duration of the cell cycle and its phases of one of these lines (named K_C) has been determined: G_1, S, G_2, and G_T last on the average 1.8, 10.0, 7.2, and 18.8 hours, respectively (Dolfini *et al.*, 1970). As to the chromosome number, the major part of the cells are nearly diploid, while between 5–10% are tetraploid. Aneuploidy and structural rearrangements are present and consist mainly of (a) loss of one of the

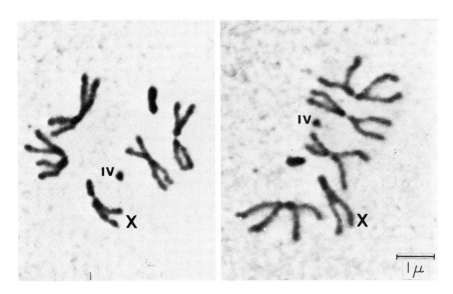

Fig. 3. Metaphases of cells of the K_C line of *Drosophila melanogaster* showing the presence of a heterochromatic fragment (presumably a part of the Y) and the loss of a chromosome of the IV pair. Magnification: ×3200.

chromosomes of the IV pair, (b) splitting of the Y chromosome into two portions, one acentric, presumably translocated onto the heterochromatic segment of the X chromosome, and one centric, and (c) deletion of a segment of one of the two large autosomes (Dolfini, 1971) (Fig. 3). This situation characterizes the cell line with a clear chromosomal marker.*

Recently, cultures of cells from a different source, i.e., from *Musca domestica* L. and *Musca sorbens* Wied., have been tried (Greenberg and Archetti, 1969). Embryonic cells and cells from larvae, pupae, and adults were cultured at 24° in Schneider's medium. The best results were obtained from embryonic cells. Outgrowths from the early egg stage were most frequent and produced a greater variety of cell types than the other fly stages. These cultures have been kept until the sixth week. This is the first report concerning either of these common medically important Diptera.

III. CULTURES OF *Aedes, Culex, Glossina,* AND *Anopheles* TISSUES

A. Organ Cultures

Many researchers have tried to culture mosquito organs in order to prove a multiplication of agents (protozoa, viruses) of diseases transmitted by Diptera in the cultured tissues of the host insect and to ascertain in which tissues and how this multiplication really occurs.

After the pioneering work of Kohring (1930), the first true contribution was made by Trager (1938), who successfully cultured midgut fragments of larvae and ovaries of adult *Aedes aegypti* and found variability in the survival of the different explants, but survival of the virus of western equine encephalomyelitis in both cases. On the other hand, a real multiplication of the virus occurred in cultures of larval thoracic tissue and pupal head. Later, much work was done in this direction, the results of which I shall briefly summarize. Salivary glands of *Anopheles maculipennis* and *Stegomyia fasciata* (Gavrilov and Gowez, 1941), gut tissues from adult mosquitoes (Ball, 1954), and tissues from pupae or

---

* *Note added in proof:* Recently two important papers reporting on the establishment of *Drosophila* cell lines appeared: Echalier, G., and Ohanessian, A. (1970). *In Vitro* **6**, 162; Kakpakov, V. T., Gvozdev, V. A., Platova, T. P., and Polukarova, L. G. (1969). *Genetika (USSR)* **5**, 67.

adults of *Glossina palpalis* (Trager, 1959a,b) gave cellular outgrowth and mitoses.

The behavior of Japanese B virus (arthropod-borne virus) (Price, 1956), of oocysts of *Plasmodium relictum* (Ball, 1954; Ball and Chao, 1957, 1960), of *Trypanosoma vivax* (Trager, 1959a,b), and of West Nile virus (Peleg and Trager, 1963a,b) in different mosquito tissues has been studied and growth has often been successfully achieved.

Since that time researchers have increasingly concentrated their efforts on improving the culture techniques and media in order to permit a better growth and to obtain more satisfactory results from virological research. Vago and Flandre (1963), for instance, tried to culture explants of ovaries and imaginal discs from *Aedes aegypti* in a different way, that is, in a semisolid plasma clot. They observed an outgrowth of fibroblasts and the presence of mitoses for a certain time.

Kitamura (1964) carried out several experiments to improve, and possibly simplify, the media devised up to that time. He cultured fragments of ovaries removed from adult *Culex pipiens* var. *molestus* at 24° in a rather simple medium supplemented with 10% chicken plasma. The explants were kept twitching for over three weeks; the cells, spindle-shaped, began to migrate after 20 hours, spreading over the surface of the glass. Actively dividing cells were observed for more than three weeks.

It must be noted, however, that this medium was not suitable for other species of mosquitoes; nevertheless, *Culex* ovarian tissues showed relatively high adaptative potential for osmotic pressure of surrounding fluid and should be considered the best source of tissue to culture *in vitro*.

In his next paper Kitamura (1965) reported an improvement of his medium. Subsequently, Peleg (1965) made further progress, devising a new culture medium (Trager's medium modified with 20% calf serum and 1% chick embryo extract). The tissues for culturing were fragments obtained by cutting whole, newly hatched *Aedes aegypti* larvae into small pieces. The first appearance of cells outside the explants was observed only after 8–10 days. The number of cells then slowly increased and mitotic figures were observed even in five-month-old cultures, but the extent of growth was generally small and limited to the vicinity of the explant.

Only Beckel (1956) was interested in differentiation problems. He cultured ovaries removed from adult females of three different species (*Aedes hexodontus, A. aegypti,* and *A. communis*), in the medium M 199 partially modified, to see whether a development of isolated ovaries could be induced or continued. Muscle tissue of the ovaries of *A. hexo-dontus* and *A. communis* showed contraction for seven days, that of *A. aegypti* for 60 days, but no egg development occurred in any case.

B. Cell Cultures

A technique similar to that devised for culturing *Drosophila* cells was used, with appropriate modifications, by Peleg (1966) to grow *in vitro* cells of *Aedes aegypti*. Embryos at different developmental stages are sterilized and lightly homogenized; after centrifugation of the tissue pulp and a further centrifugation of the supernatant, the isolated cells are seeded either in Leighton tubes or in Porter flasks. With regard to the medium, the best results have been obtained with the Trager's modified medium (1959a) or with Kitamura's medium (1965), both supplemented with 10% chick embryo extract. New transparent cells appeared on the third or fourth day and then multiplied actively, sup-porting the proliferation of WN virus. Cultures were maintained for over three weeks.

The best result, however, was achieved shortly afterwards by Grace (1966), who established the first *in vitro* cell line of *Aedes aegypti*. He cultured bodies and alimentary canals obtained from axenical grown larvae at 30° in the same medium used for the growth of the cell lines of *Antheraea eucalypti* (Grace, 1962) supplemented with 10% of hemo-lymph from *A. eucalypti*. The cells migrated from the explants and actively divided. The first subculture was made after four weeks, and since then, subcultures have been made every week. The two most com-mon cell types in the cultures are spindle-shaped cells (40 to 50 μ long and 8 to 10 μ wide) and round cells (20 μ in diameter). Chromosome countings revealed a remarkable polyploidy. Most of the cells had 96 chromosomes (32n); the next most frequent number was 48 (16n). Serological and virological tests and chromosome countings support the view that the cells are of mosquito origin.

Suitor *et al.* (1966) succeeded in cloning one of these cell types (the spindle-shaped) using Grace's medium supplemented with 10% fetal bovine serum with 0.5% *Philosamia cynthia* (Lepidopter) hemolymph. In the clone, the spindle-shaped cells were predominant, but the round cells were also present. Initially, the authors believed that the clone was not pure, but they later realized that the round cells were develop-mental stages of the spindle-shaped ones; in fact, a spindle-shaped cell, dividing into two, assumes a round form, and so on, but on reaching greater numbers the older cells revert to a more elongated spindle shape. The number of chromosomes in the cells of the clone ($\approx$100) corresponds to that found by Grace. This stable mosquito cell line derived by Grace (1966) from *Aedes aegypti* became a new substrate for the cultivation of different microorganisms and for solving many problems in virology and in parasitology.

To give an example, Rehacek (1968) studied the sensitivity of these cells to different arboviruses and found that the MVE, JBE, West Nile, and Kunjin viruses multiplied in the cultures.

Schneider (1968) tried to culture the seven-, eight-, and nine-day *Plasmodium gallinaceum*, but the results were less successful with regard to growth and development. This fact may be due to changes in the cell morphology and properties occurring during the process of adaptation.

The work of Grace (1966) demonstrated the feasibility of establishing continuous cell lines of mosquito origin. Following his lead, other people successfully obtained new cell lines.

Singh (1967) reports the establishment of three cell lines of *Aedes albopictus* and two of *A. aegypti*. Freshly hatched larvae, from eggs which have been sterilized and washed several times, provide the tissue. These larvae are immersed in a 0.25% trypsin solution, cut into small pieces and immersed again in trypsin for 10 minutes at 37°, and pipetted and centrifuged at 1000 rpm. The sediment is then washed, suspended in the medium, and incubated at 28°. The medium is that of Mitsuhashi and Maramorosch (1964) supplemented with 10% fetal bovine serum at pH 7.0. In the cultures of *A. albopictus*, the cells of three types attached to the glass surface multiplied and were subcultured several times. The cells were round (6–20 μ in diameter), spindle-shaped (7 to 10 μ wide and 15 to 90 μ long), and round binucleated. The cultures of *A. aegypti* cells behaved in a different way; the cells attached themselves to the surface only after a certain time and were then subcultured.

At the time of publishing his paper, the cell lines of *A. albopictus* were in their 30th, 25th, and 21st passages and those of *A. aegypti* were in their 30th and 15th passages. As to the number of chromosomes, the author does not go into this matter in detail and refers only to diploid and polyploid cells (Fig. 4).

Another cell line has been established by Peleg (1968), who started from embryonic tissues of *Aedes aegypti*. Floating cells, appearing after four to six months in the primary cultures, were the beginning of the line. The medium was based on that of Kitamura (1965) but without insect hemolymph. The cells attached loosely to the glass surface. The growth of three arboviruses was followed until the 70th day.

Furthermore, Varma and Pudney (1969) established two cell lines and one cell strain from larval tissues of *Aedes aegypti* in different media. These cells grow adhering to the glass surface, and every line

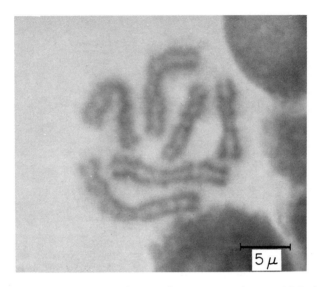

Fig. 4. Chromosomes of the *Aedes albopictus* cell line established by Singh, analyzed by T. Stevens. Monolayer cultures in their 50th passage. The photograph shows the six chromosomes typical of these cells at this level of passage. Twelve chromosomes were observed in about 25% of figures. Magnification: ×2700. (Courtesy of Thomas M. Stevens.)

shows a peculiar appearance. In the cell line Mos. 29, fibroblast-type cells are predominant (the chromosome number remains diploid: 2n = 6); the cell line Mos. 20 consists of closely packed fibroblast-type cells; and the cell strain Mos. 20(A), on the contrary, consists of epithelial-type cells regularly arranged.

A different source of tissues was chosen by Schneider (1969). The establishment of three cell lines originating from larval tissues of the mosquito *Anopheles stephensi* L. represents the latest advance in this field. The primary cultures consisted of minced tissues from early first instar larvae in a modified Wyatt–Grace medium. Trypsinized cells from such cultures readily grew when transferred to new flasks. Since these initial transfers, each of the cell lines has been cultured a minimum of 30 times. The appearance of these cells is epithelial, and the main feature of these lines is the maintenance of the diploid number (2n = 6).

IV. CONCLUSION

In the last few years many advances have been made; cell cultures of Diptera have passed through the pioneering stage and are now a precise reality. The great efforts made in this direction were recently rewarded by the establishment of permanent cell lines.

As to *Drosophila* cells, this system offers unique potentialities. The large choice of cytological and genetical markers and the low chromosome number joined with the technical possibility to establish now, rather easily, cell lines make possible the study of somatic cell genetics. Much work, of course, still has to be done. We need to obtain cellular clones, to select proper markers (chromosomal, morphological, and nutritional markers), and to realize cell fusion followed by somatic recombination (which is known to occur in *Drosophila*).

Moreover, among the most interesting future lines of research for which *Drosophila* cell lines are the more suitable material we may cite the analysis of DNA replication and various structural problems of the chromosomes, the study of gene action, and the study of differentiation.

With regard to *Aedes* and *Anopheles*, the possibility of disposing of permanent lines of these organisms will serve as a boost to virological and parasitological research.

To conclude, the latest encouraging achievements suggest that brilliant results could be obtained in this field in the future.

REFERENCES

Ball, G. H. (1954). *J. Exp. Parasitol.* 3, 358.

Ball, G. H., and Chao, J. (1957). *J. Parasitol.* 43, 409.

Ball, G. H., and Chao, J. (1960). *J. Exp. Parasitol.* 9, 47.

Barigozzi, C., Dolfini, S., Fraccaro, M., Rezzonico Raimondi, G., and Tiepolo, L. (1966). *Exp. Cell Res.* 43, 231.

Barigozzi, C., Dolfini, S., Fraccaro, M., Halfer, C., Rezzonico Raimondi, G., and Tiepolo, L. (1967). *Atti Ass. Genet. Ital.* 12, 291.

Beckel, W. E. (1956). *Nature (London)* 177, 534.

Castiglioni, M. C., and Rezzonico Raimondi, G. (1961a). *Experientia* 17, 88.

Castiglioni, M. C., and Rezzonico Raimondi, G. (1961b). *Atti Ass. Genet. Ital.* 6, 139.

Castiglioni, M. C., and Rezzonico Raimondi, G. (1963a). *Experientia* 19, 527.

Castiglioni, M. C., and Rezzonico Raimondi, G. (1963b). *Rend. Ist. Lomb. Sci. Lett.* 97, 117.

Collier, W. A. (1920). *Wiss. Insektenbiol.* 16, 1.

Cunningham, I. (1961). M.Sc. Thesis, University of Edinburgh.

Demal, J. (1956). *Ann. Sci. Nat. Zool. Biol. Anim.* [11] 18, 155.

Demal, J., and Leloup, A. M. (1963). *Ann. Epiphyt.* 14, 91.

Dolfini, S., and Gottardi, A. (1966). *Experientia* 22, 144.

Dolfini, S., Courgeon, A. M., and Tiepolo, L. (1970). *Experientia* 26, 1020.

Dolfini, S. (1971). *Chromosoma (Berl.)* 33, 196.

Echalier, G., and Ohanessian, A. (1968). *Proc. Int. Colloq. Invertebr. Tissue Cult., 2nd, 1967* p. 174.

Echalier, G., and Ohanessian, A. (1969). C. R. Acad. Sci. 268, 1771.

Echalier, G., Ohanessian, A., and Brun, G. (1965). C. R. Acad. Sci. 261, 3211.

Federoff, S. (1967). Hereditas 57, 86.

Fischer, I., and Gottschewski, G. (1939). Naturwissenschaften 27, 391.

Fisher, H. W., Puck, T. T., and Sato, G. (1958). Proc. Nat. Acad. Sci. U. S. 44, 4.

Fisher, H. W., Puck, T. T., and Sato, G. (1959). J. Exp. Med. 109, 649.

Fox, A. S., Horikawa, M., and Ling, L. N. (1968). In Vitro 3, 65.

Frew, J. G. H. (1928). J. Exp. Biol. 6, 1.

Gavrilov, M., and Gowez, S. (1941). Ann. Parasitol. Hum. Comp. 18, 180.

Gianfelici, E. (1968). Proc. Int. Colloq. Invertebr. Tissue Cult., 2nd, 1967 p. 155.

Gottschewski, G., and Fischer, I. (1939). Naturwissenschaften 27, 584.

Grace, T. D. C. (1962). Nature (London) 195, 788.

Grace, T. D. C. (1966). Nature (London) 211, 366.

Greenberg, B., and Archetti, I. (1969). Exp. Cell Res. 54, 284.

Halfer, C., Tiepolo, L., Barigozzi, C., and Fraccaro, M. (1969). Chromosoma 27, 395.

Hanly, E. W. (1961). Diss. Abstr. 22, 980.

Horikawa, M. (1956). Drosophila Inform. Serv. 30, 122.

Horikawa, M. (1957). Drosophila Inform. Serv. 31, 124.

Horikawa, M. (1958). Drosophila Inform. Serv. 32, 126.

Horikawa, M., and Fox, A. S. (1964). Science 145, 1437.

Horikawa, M., and Kuroda, Y. (1959). Nature (London) 184, 2017.

Horikawa, M., and Sugahara, T. (1960a). Radiat. Res. 12, 266.

Horikawa, M., and Sugahara, T. (1960b). Radiat. Res. 13, 825.

Horikawa, M., Ling, L. N., and Fox, A. S. (1966). Nature (London) 210, 183.

Horikawa, M., Ling, L. N., and Fox, A. S. (1967). Genetics 55, 569.

Kakpakov, V. T., and Gvosdev, V. A. (1968). Drosophila Inform. Serv. 43, 142.

Kitamura, S. (1964). Kobe J. Med. Sci. 10, 85.

Kitamura, S. (1965). Kobe J. Med. Sci. 11, 23.

Kohring, V. (1930). J. Morphol. 49, 45.

Kuroda, Y. (1954a). Drosophila Inform. Serv. 28, 127.

Kuroda, Y. (1954b). Drosophila Inform. Serv. 28, 127.

Kuroda, Y. (1956). Drosophila Inform. Serv. 30, 161.

Kuroda, Y. (1959). Med. J. Osaka Univ. 10, 1.

Kuroda, Y. (1963). Drosophila Inform. Serv. 38, 89.

Kuroda, Y. (1968). Proc. Int. Congr. Genet., 12th, 1968 Vol. 2, p. 100.

Kuroda, Y. (1969). Drosophila Inform. Serv. 44, 109.

Kuroda, Y., and Tamura, S. (1955). Zool. Mag. 65, 35.

Kuroda, Y., and Tamura, S. (1956a). Zool. Mag. 65, 11.

Kuroda, Y., and Tamura, S. (1956b). Med. J. Osaka Univ. 7, 137.

Kuroda, Y., and Tamura, S. (1957). Zool. Mag. 66, 6.

Kuroda, Y., and Yamaguchi, K. (1956). Jap. J. Genet. 31, 98.

Leloup, A. M., and Demal, J. (1968). Proc. Int. Colloq. Invertebr. Tissue Cult., 2nd, 1967 p. 126.

Leloup, A. M., and Gianfelici, E. (1966). Ann. Endocrinol. 27, 506.

Lesseps, R. J. (1965). Science 148, 502.

Martignoni, M. E. (1962). Proc. Annu. Biol. Colloq. [Oregon State Univ.] 23, 89.

Mitsuhashi, Y., and Maramorosch, K. (1964). Contrib. Boyce Thompson Inst. 22, 435.

Ohanessian, A., and Echalier, G. (1967). Nature (London) 213, 1049.

Ohanessian, A., and Echalier, G. (1968). *Proc. Int. Colloq. Invertebr. Tissue Cult.,* *2nd, 1967* p. 227.
Ottaviano Gottardi, A. (1968). *Proc. Int. Colloq. Invertebr. Tissue Cult., 2nd, 1967* p. 189.
Peleg, J. (1965). *Nature (London)* **206,** 427.
Peleg, J. (1966). *Experientia* **22,** 555.
Peleg, J. (1968). *Virology* **35,** 617.
Peleg, J., and Trager, W. (1963a). *Ann. J. Trop. Med. Hyg.* **12,** 820.
Peleg, J., and Trager, W. (1963b). *Ann. Epiphyt.* **14,** 211.
Price, W. H. (1956). *Publ. Health Rep.* **71,** 125.
Rehacek, J. (1968). *Proc. Int. Colloq. Invertebr. Tissue Cult., 2nd, 1967* p. 241.
Rezzonico Raimondi, G., and Gottardi, A. (1967). *J. Insect Physiol.* **13,** 523.
Rezzonico Raimondi, G., Ghini, C., and Dolfini, S. (1964). *Experientia* **20,** 440.
Robb, J. A. (1969). *J. Cell Biol.* **41,** 876.
Schneider, I. (1963). *Genetics* **48,** 908.
Schneider, I. (1964). *J. Exp. Zool.* **156,** 91.
Schneider, I. (1966). *J. Embryol. Exp. Morphol.* **15,** 271.
Schneider, I. (1968). *Proc. Int. Colloq. Invertebr. Tissue Cult., 2nd, 1967* p. 247.
Schneider, I. (1969). *J. Cell Biol.* **42,** 603.
Seecof, R. L., and Unanue, R. L. (1968). *Exp. Cell Res.* **50,** 654.
Singh, K. R. P. (1967). *Curr. Sci.* **36,** 506.
Stern, C. (1940). *Growth* **4,** 377.
Suitor, E. C., Chang, L. L., and Liu, H. H. (1966). *Exp. Cell Res.* **44,** 572.
Trager, W. (1938). *Ann. J. Trop. Med.* **18,** 387.
Trager, W. (1959a). *Nature (London)* **184,** 30.
Trager, W. (1959b). *Ann. Trop. Med. Parasitol.* **53,** 473.
Vago, C., and Flandre, O. (1963). *Ann. Epiphyt.* **14,** 127.
Varma, M. G. R., and Pudney, M. (1969). *J. Med. Entomol.* **6,** 432.

8

CELL CULTURE OF COLEOPTERA, ORTHOPTERA, AND DICTYOPTERA

J. M. Quiot

I. INTRODUCTION

A survey of the amount of work carried out on cell culture of different groups of insects shows that these studies have been confined to a few

267

types. Besides the Lepidoptera, on which the majority of work on cell culture has been done, and besides the Diptera or the Homoptera, on which rapid progress has recently been made, information is based on a relatively limited number of investigations.

Concerning the Coleoptera, Orthoptera, and Dictyoptera, it is difficult to understand the relative lack of interest in these groups. While the Dictyoptera have a little value from a practical or economic point of view, the Orthoptera (especially the locusts) as well as the Coleoptera are often responsible for damage to crops, damage which equals or sometimes even exceeds that done by Lepidoptera.

The lag of research on tissue culture in these orders is probably directly related to the intensity of work on the physiology and composition of the hemolymph of each of these groups. Information on physiological and biological aspects is more extensive for the Lepidoptera than for other groups, almost certainly because of the ease with which they can be raised and because of the tradition in histology of using *Bombyx* as "guinea pig."

However, the gap in the amount of work on cell culture of different insect groups is now being narrowed. In particular, tissue culture of Coleoptera, Orthoptera, and Dictyoptera has made progress, and the early research on Dictyoptera has now been followed by up-to-date research on a level comparable to that on Lepidoptera and Diptera.

This increased interest is justified for different reasons. Among the Coleoptera, numerous viral, rickettsial, and mycoplasmic diseases have been described in the last few years, and cell culture becomes a necessity for pathological studies.

For the Orthoptera, in addition to the above reasons, the *in vitro* study of intestinal tumors is becoming important. The Dictyoptera are particularly interesting animals from the point of view of physiology and cytology because they represent a group of phylogenetically older insects and for this reason have often been used to study the phenomena of cellular regeneration and differentiation.

II. CELL CULTURE OF COLEOPTERA

A. Preliminary Attempts

The Coleoptera constitute a very important order because of the number of families and species and because of the economic importance of their damage to plants. However, they probably represent the insect group least studied *in vitro*. Indeed, until the last few years, only experiments with organ and hemocyte survival had taken place. A long time ago, Lazarenko (1925) obtained the formation of syncytia with the amoebocytes of *Oryctes nasicornis* as well as several mitoses from a suspension of hemocytes in larval hemolymph.

Later, Butz (1957) studied the tolerance of insects to different concentrations of Na^+, K^+, and Ca^{2+} and to changes of osmotic pressure. His experiments were made with the isolated heart of the holometabolic insect *Tenebrio molitor* at larval, pupal, and adult stages. The dissected hearts were placed in solutions of different concentrations of Na^+, K^+, and Ca^{2+}, and the beats were observed at the microscope every five minutes.

The first, and probably the only, true cell cultures of Coleoptera were obtained from Scarabaeids *Oryctes nasicornis*, *Cetonia aurata*, *Dorcus parallelipipedus*, and *Melolontha melolontha* (Vago *et al.*, 1968; Vago and Quiot, 1969; Charpentier, 1971). The study *in vitro* of cells of *Melolontha* is particularly interesting because this insect is sensitive to many viral (spheroidosis, lethargy) and rickettsial (*Rickettsiella melolonthae*) diseases.

B. Tissues Used and Culture Techniques

The studies have essentially concerned larvae of *Oryctes nasicornis*, *Cetonia aurata*, and *Melolontha melolontha* at different stages of their development and embryos and nymphs of *Dorcus parallelipipedus*.

Tissues used for cultures come from the dorsal vessel (Vago *et al.*, 1968) and from the embryonic and intestinal tissues (Charpentier, 1971). Larvae of *O. nasicornis*, *C. aurata*, and *M. melolontha* anesthetized with ether are held by the ventral side and disinfected superficially. If the larva is not anesthetized, intestinal contractions are so severe that this organ will extrude through the smallest opening in the tegument and will spoil the aseptic dissection.

A horseshoe-shaped incision is made in the dorsal tegument and the flap is folded to the rear (Fig. 1). In order to excise the dorsal vessel, it is necessary to first remove the adipose tissue and alary muscles which keep it in place on the tegument. The organ is placed in a sterile medium and the rest of the adipose tissue and muscles are removed completely under the binocular dissecting microscope. It is then cut into small pieces, which must be rinsed many times with sterile medium in order to eliminate the blood cells. These sometimes adhere so strongly to the organ that they must be kept in the medium for a long period before the culture is set up.

FIG. 1. Simplified dissection of *Melolontha melolontha* (Coleoptera) larva for removing the dorsal vessel (v).

The intestines of larvae L3 of *D. parallelipipedus* are taken from insects raised aseptically (Charpentier, 1968). The dorsal tegument, incised in front and on the sides, is folded towards the front. The mesenteron is thus well visible and can be easily removed. In young nymphs the intestine is the only organ visible and can be conveniently isolated directly in the culture medium.

Embryos are placed in culture after being dechorionated. The surface of the chorion is first disinfected with a 4% solution of sodium hypochlorite for five minutes (Charpentier, 1968) or with White's solution for 20 minutes (Sen Gupta, 1961).

Various culture techniques are used. After the first trials were performed in hanging drops and in sitting drops, most cultures were carried out in Vago-type inversible vials (Fig. 2), in flat flasks made of glass or plastic (Falcon), or in tissue culture tubes of the Leigthton type.

FIG. 2. Schema of Vago–Flandre reversible tissue culture flask.

TABLE I

INORGANIC COMPOSITION OF HEMOLYMPH OF SOME COLEOPTERA

Species	meq/liter				References
	Na	K	Ca	Mg	
Melolontha melolontha (adult)	113.0	5.8	15.3	41.3	Duchateau *et al.* (1953)
Cetonia aurata (larva)	51.3	18.6	22.8	80.0	Duchateau *et al.* (1953)
Tenebrio molitor (larva)	77.0	32.0	—	—	Ramsay (1953)
Geotrupes stercorosus (adult)	119.1	16.0	17.8	49.8	Duchateau *et al.* (1953)
Dytiscus marginalis (adult)	165.1	6.4	22.5	37.5	Duchateau *et al.* (1953)

C. Culture Media

By analysis of the hemolymph, it was found that Coleoptera are part of an insect group in which the Na/K ratio is higher than 1 (Table I). Using these facts and in the frame of studies done by Vago and Quiot (1969) on the standardization of culture media of invertebrate cells, the media are based on formula of TC 199 (Morgan *et al.*, 1950) or on Eagle's (1955). The pH values are adjusted to 6.6 with sodium bicarbonate. The media are finally completed by addition of 10 or 15% sterile fetal calf serum. Δt ranges from $-0.50°$ to $-0.55°$ (Table II).

In cultures maintained at 24°, the medium is renewed every 7–10

TABLE II

CULTURE MEDIUM OF STANDARD FRACTIONS FOR COLEOPTERA, ORTHOPTERA, AND DICTYOPTERA: MEDIUM 72[a]

Constituents	gm/liter
1. B.S.S. of TC 199 (dried)	8.89
or B.S.S. of M.E.M. Eagle (dried)[b]	7.725
2. Organic fraction of TC 199 (dried)	1.19
or organic fraction of M.E.M. Eagle (dried)	0.853
3. (a) Lactalbumin hydrolysate in sufficient quantity to obtain the desired osmotic pressure	
(b) Glucose	1.00
4. NaHCO₃ to obtain pH 6.6 for Orthoptera	
6.8–7 for Coleoptera	
7.2 for Dictyoptera	

[a] Vago *et al.*, 1968; Vago and Quiot, 1969.
[b] B.S.S. = balanced salt solution; M.E.M. = minimum essential medium.

days. In spite of the rinsings, numerous blood cells rapidly invade the medium, extending pseudopodia or remaining in suspension. They will be eliminated gradually during the different changes of medium. The explants preserve the ability to contract for an extended period.

D. Development of the Cultures

In the dorsal vessel cultures of *Melolontha melolontha* (Vago *et al.*, 1968) (Fig. 3), about three days after the culture was set up, the cells migrate, either by detaching themselves one after another or in different explant sites by the formation of large buds of parked cells. Migration of the first type occurs especially in explants from anterior and posterior parts of the dorsal vessel, while the buds appear more frequently on those originating in the central part.

The cells are of a fibroblast type coming, very likely, from the connective sheaths surrounding the dorsal vessel. They generally present a large size (sometimes up to 80 μ), are spread out, and strongly fix themselves on the surface of the recipient. They emit along thin pseudopodia or a slender and wavy folded membrane. Their cytoplasm is clear, transparent, and nonvacuolated and contains numerous granula-

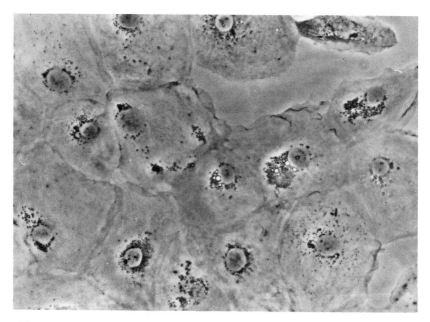

Fig. 3. Cultured larval vessel cells of *Melolontha melolontha* (Coleoptera). Phase contrast, ×350.

tions localized around the nucleus, sometimes in a regular pattern. The nucleus, showing one, two, or three nucleoli, is round and of medium size, more refractive and more dense than the cytoplasm.

After about 10 days most of the cells, which are pressed one against the other, form broad sheets around the explants in the interior of which, because of the packing, they present the appearance of epithelial cells in some cases.

Such cultures of dorsal vessels of *M. melolontha* were maintained more than eight months with regular and continuing mitotic activity in culture flasks.

The dorsal vessels of *Oryctes nasicornis* and *Cetonia aurata* show fibroblast-type cell sheets, the cells appearing less wide than those of *M. melolontha* but equally characterized by large size and numerous perinuclear cytoplasmic granulations (Vago et al., 1968).

From the intestinal tissues of *Dorcus parallelipipedus*, fibroblast-type cell layers adhering to the culture vessel walls are observed, as well as numerous cells in suspension which may be maintained for 15 weeks. The adherent cells have, however, degenerated after four or five weeks. Another type of flat cell, from 40 to 50 μ in diameter and angular and with a small nucleus, is also found. These cells could be considered as epithelial cells.

The embryonic tissue of *D. parallelipipedus*, after a migration of spherical cells of varied size (the largest having a 40-μ diameter; the smallest, 15-μ) which disappear after 7–18 days of culture, fibroblast-type cells appear (40–60 μ in diameter) and can be maintained for several weeks.

E. Utilization of the Cultures

Most of the attempts at Coleoptera cell cultures were done for pathological studies. Thus, in the resulting cultures, the *Rickettsiella* of *Melolontha melolontha* were grown as well as the recently discovered virus of the spheroidosis (Vago, 1963) of the same insect. The same virus was studied on the tissues cultured from already infected larvae (Vol. II, Chapter 7).

III. CELL CULTURE OF ORTHOPTERA

In spite of numerous attempts, utilizing various media, to maintain living tissues of Orthoptera, true cell cultures of long duration presenting mitotic activity are relatively rare.

TABLE III
LEWIS MEDIUM FOR GRASSHOPPER TESTICLES

Substances	Amount
Seawater	30 cm³
Distilled water	50 cm³
Broth of grasshoppers	20 cm³
NaHCO₃	0.02%
Dextrose	0.25%

Attempts *in vitro* have already been done by Lewis (1916) from grasshopper testicles in a medium based on seawater (Table III). This medium is, in fact, a modification of Locke's medium using diluted seawater as a mineral solution. Lewis determined that in such a medium germinating cells maintain themselves for a while and show several mitoses.

Lewis and Robertson (1916) and Murray (1926) took the same medium and replaced the locust broth with 0.1 gm of peptone. Into this medium Lewis and Robertson (1916) put the testicles of *Chorthippus curtipennis* to study the cytoplasmic structures of germinating cells and, in particular, the mitochondria.

In order to carry out cytological and physiological studies, Murray (1926) kept the ovaries of *Gryllus abbreviatus* and *Nemobius fasciatus* (and also the follicular cells) alive 48–72 hours.

About the same time, Chambers (1925) put follicles excised from testicles of the grasshopper *Dissosteira carolina* in a drop of lymph in order to carry out microdissection of mitochondrial and nuclear structures of the male germinal cells. These were extracted directly from the insects after an incision of the leg at the level of the basal joint. The thin follicular envelope was then torn and the coverglass inverted in a

TABLE IV
INORGANIC COMPOSITION OF HEMOLYMPH OF SOME ORTHOPTERA

Species	meq/liter				References
	Na	K	Ca	Mg	
Locusta migratoria (larva)	60.0	12.0	17.2	24.8	Duchateau et al. (1953)
Schistocerca gregaria (larva)	81.3	5.3	17.8	34.6	Duchateau et al. (1953)
Anabrus simplex (adult)	21.9	15.4	3.0	1.4	Pepper et al. (1941)
Chortophaga viridifasciata (adult)	108.9	3.4	2.8	21	Barsa (1954)
Tettigonia viridissima (adult)	83.0	51.0	—	—	Boné (1944)

moist chamber. The spermatocytes isolated from the lymph were maintained alive for many hours, and several phases of division were observed.

Later, the workers utilized as media physiological solutions corresponding more or less to the chemical data given by analysis of the hemolymph (Table IV).

The main media are a Carlson medium (1946) (Table V) and another Carlson medium (1950) modified by Gaulden and Carlson (1951) (Table V); a Shaw medium (Table VI) also modified by Gaulden and Perry (1958), Carlson (1961) and Bergerard and Morio (1963); and the medium of Vago et al. (1968).

It is interesting to note that most of the in vitro studies on Orthoptera were based on the neuroblasts of embryos of a unique species, Chorthophaga viridifasciata (Carlson and Hollaender, 1944, 1945, 1948; Carlson, 1946, 1950, 1961; Gaulden and Carlson, 1947, 1951; Gaulden and Kokomoor, 1955; Carlson et al., 1953; Gaulden and Perry, 1958; St. Aman and Tipton, 1954; Roberts, 1955; Shaw, 1956).

In addition, in vitro cultures were used especially for studies of the effects of uv radiation, at different intensities, on the mitotic activity of these same neuroblasts of C. viridifasciata (Carlson, 1946, 1950, 1961; Carlson and Hollaender, 1945, 1948; Carlson et al., 1953; Gaulden and Kokomoor, 1955; Gaulden and Perry, 1958).

Other species of Orthoptera as well as other organs or tissues were also used. For example, the spermatocytes of C. viridifasciata, Dissosteina carolina, Melanoplus femurrubrum, Arphia xantroptera, and Hippicus sp. (Ris, 1949) and the embryos of Melanoplus differentialis

TABLE V

CARLSON MEDIUM AND MODIFICATION BY GAULDEN AND CARLSON

Substances[a]	Carlson (1946) (mg/100 cm³)	Gaulden and Carlson (1951) (mg/100 cm³)
NaCl	700	680
KCl	20	20
CaCl	20	20
MgCl₂	10	10
NaH₂PO₄	20	20
NaHCO₃	5	12
Glucose	800	770
pH	6.5	

[a] A small amount of yolk is added to each hanging drop to provide nitrogenous food materials for the cells.

TABLE VI
CULTURE MEDIUM G.G.[a]

Substances	Amount
Solution A	
Glutamic acid	7.35 gm
Glycine	3.75 gm
Concentrated KOH free of bicarbonate, pH	7.30 gm
Pyrex distilled water	100 ml
Solution B	
Glutamic acid	7.35 gm
Glycine	3.75 gm
NaOH (for analysis), pH	7.30 gm
Pyrex distilled water	100 ml
Solution C	
$CaCl_2 \cdot 2H_2O$	0.2 gm
$MgCl_2 \cdot 6H_2O$	0.1 gm
Pyrex distilled water	100 ml
Solution D	
NaH_2PO_4	0.8 gm
NaH_2CO_3	0.5 gm
Pyrex distilled water	100 ml
Solution E	
Anhydrous glucose	7.0 gm
(or glucose + H_2O)	7.7 gm
Pyrex distilled water	100 ml
Complete medium	
Solution A	0.75 ml
Solution B	1.25 ml
Solution C	1.00 ml
Solution D	1.00 ml
Solution E	1.00 ml
Pyrex distilled water approximately (the exact quantity depending on the toxicity desired)	3.0–5.0 ml
Supplement: homologous egg yolk	

[a] From Shaw, 1956.

(Bucklin, 1953) and *Locusta migratoria* (Bergerard and Morio, 1963).

The culture techniques are, in every case, those of the hanging drop, except in the works of Bergerard and Morio (1963) and those of Vago *et al.* (1968). The first author used 22-cm³ "salières," where the embryo is immersed in the medium, or the technique of putting the embryo (cleared of its vitellus) in suspension in paraffin oil inside a small drop of the medium.

Vago *et al.* (1968), during most of their culture work, used Vago–Hirumi reversible flasks and tissue culture plastic (Falcon) flasks. Cultures were carried out using many methods, including the following:

1. Explants from organs such as the ovaries of *Gryllus abbreviatus* and *Nemobius fasciatus* (Murray, 1926) and pieces of the dorsal vessel of *Gryllus bimaculatus, Schistocerca gregaria,* and *Locusta migratoria* (Vago et al., 1968)

2. Explants from embryos (Gaulden and Carlson, 1951)

3. Entire embryos (Carlson, 1946, 1950, 1961; Carlson and Hollaender, 1944, 1945, 1948; Carlson et al., 1953; Bucklin, 1953; Shaw, 1956)

4. Cells isolated mechanically (for spermatocyte studies) (Chambers, 1925; Ris, 1949) or enzymatically

Several attempts at suspending cells isolated by enzymatic methods were made by St. Aman and Tipton (1954) using a solution of 7.5 mg of trypsin and 7.5 mg of hyaluronidase in 10 ml of calcium-free medium. Embryos without chorions are treated with the trypsin–hyaluronidase mixture for an hour at 38°. A protein solution (5 mg of bovine albumin in 0.5 of calcium-free medium) is then added to the suspension. After centrifugation at 158 rpm for 15 minutes, the pellet is resuspended in a fresh medium. This method was modified by Roberts (1955) and Gaulden and Perry (1958) for the time of digestion (30 minutes instead of one hour) and the choice of the medium.

Roberts uses the Gaulden medium free of $CaCl_2$ and an increase in NaCl from 6.8 to 6.905 gm/100 ml of water. Gaulden and Perry chose the Shaw medium without calcium ions.

All the results obtained have no real value for cell culture because neither cellular migration nor even vesicular formation took place. The results were limited to more or less prolonged survival of tissues which permitted, however, morphological, cytological, and physiological studies.

Long-term cellular cultures were obtained by Vago et al. (1968) from larval dorsal vessels of *G. bimaculatus, S. gregaria* (Fig. 4) and *L. migratoria*. From the results of the analyses (Table IV) these insects apparently have a Na/K ratio greater than 1, and the authors chose the medium TC 199 (Morgan et al., 1950) as base. The pH was adjusted at 6.6 and the osmotic pressure maintained at a Δt of $-0.58°$ Finally, the medium was completed by 10% fetal calf serum.

After surface disinfection of the larvae, dissection and removal of the dorsal vessels are carried out according to the method outlined for Dictyoptera and Coleoptera. Culture was set up in hanging drops or in different types of flasks: Vago–Hirumi reversible or Falcon plastic flasks.

The first cells visible were blood cells, the majority of which remained in suspension around the explants. After three or four days, fibroblast-type cells started to migrate and to spread around the fragments of the dorsal vessels. They had the same characteristics as the cardiac cells

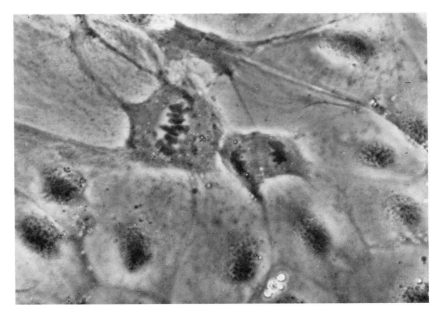

FIG. 4. Culture of heart cells of *Schistocerca gregaria* (Orthoptera). Two cells in different stages of mitosis: Phase contrast, ×530.

of Dictyoptera and Coleoptera, numerous cytoplasmic granulations around the nuclei, a clear and nonvacuolated cytoplasm, and a rather large nucleus well, refractive in phase contrast and which encloses one or many nucleoli. However, as a whole, the cells were smaller and, in some cases, much less tapered than the cells of cockroaches or Coleoptera. In the interior of the cell sheet, mitoses are frequently observed from the eighth day of culture. Such cultures can be maintained fully active for more than one year.

They were used for pathological studies and, in particular, for the study of a rickettsiosis causing paralysis of *G. bimaculatus* (Meynadier et al., 1968).

IV. CELL CULTURE OF DICTYOPTERA

A. Preliminary Attempts

Until the last few years, work accomplished *in vitro* with Dictyoptera was limited to attempts to maintain organs or tissues alive in different physiological solutions or in the hemolymph of the insect studied. Thus, Lazarenko (1925) observed formation of syncytia from amoebocytes of *Periplaneta americana* maintained in homologous hemolymph. Roeder (1948) made experiments on the effects of Na^+ and K^+ on the nervous system of *P. americana*. It was placed every minute in a physiological solution of 2.7 mM of K^+ and 2 mM of Ca^{2+}. Spontaneous electrical activity was registered when the slide was out of the physiological solution.

In 1963 Larsen maintained alive pieces of the dorsal vessel of *Blabera fusca* = *Blaberus craniifer* embryos during 260 days in TC 199 medium (Morgan et al., 1950) containing 2% Bacto-peptone. The Malpighian tubules continued to contract during 30 days and pieces of the posterior intestine maintained their peristaltic movements for 67 days. An isolated head of a 40-day-old embryo exhibited contractions in the dilator muscles of the clypeus for 68 days. An entire 28-day-old embryo freed of its vitellus and embryonic membranes was maintained alive for 150 days. These experiments, as in the organ cultures (see chapters on organ culture) of ovarioles and embryos of *P. americana* attempted by Duveau-Hagège (1963, 1964) and Lender and Fisher (1965), though not dealing with cell cultures, contributed to the knowledge of the nutritional requirements of tissues of Dictyoptera.

The studies on cell culture of Dictyoptera are limited to recent assays on a few species of cockroaches, i.e., *B. fusca* (Larsen, 1964, 1967; Landureau, 1965, 1966, 1968; Vago et al., 1968), *Leucophaea maderae* (Marks and Reinecke, 1964, 1965a; Vago et al., 1968), *P. americana* (Landureau, 1965, 1966, 1968, 1969; Landureau and Jollés, 1969; Vago et al., 1968) and *Blattella germanica* (Ting and Brooks, 1965; Landureau, 1965, 1966). The tissues used were the dorsal vessel, the regenerating cells of the legs, the sheaths of ovarioles, different pieces of embryos, and the hemocytes.

Often, the cultures are restricted to migrations of cells with limited survival. In other cases, dynamic cultures with mitoses are maintained during many months. Finally, in several cases cell strains are constituted with numerous subcultures.

B. Tissue Removal and Culture Techniques

With the Dictyoptera, disinfection of the animals before dissection is more important and perhaps more difficult than with the other insects because of the permanent contact of the cockroaches with a medium rich in germs of all kinds. For culture of embryonic cells, the septic nature of the oothecae presents a rather difficult problem.

Before removing the ootheca of *B. fusca* from the brood pouch, Larsen (1964) anesthetizes the female, then sterilizes the epidermis by immersion in a solution of 0.05% mercuric bichloride in 50% ethyl alcohol for two minutes. The surface of the ootheca is also sterilized in the same way and rinsed in distilled water before dissection in sterile Ringer solution. Ting and Brooks (1965) treat the surface of *B. germanica* with an aqueous solution of 0.2% Hyamine 1622, while Vago *et al.* (1968) rinse the larvae of *B. fusca, P. americana*, and *L. maderae* in a solution of 3% sodium hypochlorite, then in distilled water, and finally in 70% alcohol.

The aseptic removal of embryos appears easier with the ovoviviparous cockroaches since the embryos, at the same developmental stage, are contained in a brood pouch which may be removed aseptically. It is sufficient to carefully disinfect the surface of the female by a 20-minute bath in sublimated alcohol (Landureau, 1965). The age of the embryos is then determined, and only those with functional vessels are kept.

For the cockroaches with ootheca, the problem of asepsis is more complicated because the contamination is frequently found inside the ootheca, hence, the necessity of a double disinfection at the same time, i.e., of their surface and of the embryos, by a 10-minute immersion in sodium hypochlorite.

The removal of the dorsal vessel of cockroaches *B. fusca* (Fig. 5), *L. maderae*, or *P. americana* can be done in a few movements (Vago *et al.*, 1968). After fixing the insects ventrally on a dissection tray and disinfecting their tegument, a horseshoe-shaped incision is made on the dorsal tegument and the flap is folded to the rear. The dorsal vessel remains fixed on the underside of the tegument by the alary muscles and adipose tissue. With a pair of curved scissors, the muscles are sectioned and the adipose tissue taken away. The dorsal vessel is then taken out, put in a petri dish containing the medium, cleared of the remaining muscles and adipose tissue under a binocular dissecting microscope, and then cut into fragments. Repeated rinsings permit the elimination of most of the blood cells.

Various culture methods are employed. Hanging and sitting drops are often used in culture attempts, and Vago–Flandre or Vago–Hirumi flasks were very useful for the first assays of tissue cultures. Finally, plastic flasks served for many explant cultures and cell cultures treated by enzymes.

Marks and Reinecke's cultures (1964, 1965a,b) were often set up in Rose *et al.* (1958) culture chambers. The explants are placed under dialysis membranes. These latter maintain the tissues in position and give the cells the possibility to migrate and to attach themselves on two

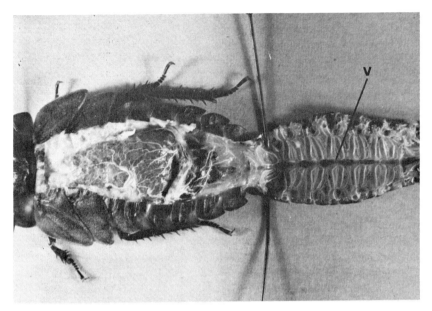

FIG. 5. Simplified dissection of *Blabera fusca* (Dictyoptera) for removing the dorsal vessel (v).

surfaces. About a third of the volume of these culture chambers is filled by culture medium.

Vago *et al.* (1968) start explant cultures of the dorsal vessel of *L. maderae, P. americana,* and *B. fusca* under a very thin film of medium to permit a better fixation of the explants, the normal quantity of the medium being added progressively.

The enzymatic dissociation of tissues by trypsin was obtained by Vago *et al.* (1968) for the dorsal vessel of *B. fusca, L. maderae,* and *P. americana* and by Landureau (1965, 1966, 1968) for embryos of the ovoviviparous *B. fusca* and for two oothecal species, *B. germanica* and *P. americana.* After aseptic removal, lots of 10 or 20 embryos, depending on the species studied, are placed in a centrifuge tube before being treated with trypsin and mechanically fragmented with Dowell straight scissors. The fragments are then placed in trypsin solution in an isotonic buffered medium, without Mg^{2+} and Ca^{2+} ions, at a concentration of 0.5% for viviparous cockroaches and 0.1% for the two others. The trypsin solution is renewed five minutes later and kept for 15 to 20 minutes at 37°. A slow centrifuging is sufficient to obtain a cell pellet which is divided into equal parts and placed in suspension in the culture medium.

In most cases, the cultures are incubated at temperatures ranging from 25° to 28°. (Dictyoptera often live in relatively elevated temperatures.)

C. Culture Media

Analyses of hemolymph of Dictyoptera generally show a positive Na/K ratio (Table VII). This fact has enabled most investigators who attempted cell cultures of species belonging to this group to base their media on formulas employed for vertebrate tissues.

Thus, Larsen (1964) used TC 199 medium, complemented with lactalbumin hydrolysate and yeast extract, to attempt culture of the cells of the dorsal vessel and embryo of *B. fusca*. Vago *et al.* (1968) chose for cultures of cardiac cells of *B. fusca*, *L. maderae*, and *P. americana* combinations of standard and variable fractions (Vago and Quiot, 1969) based on TC 199 or Eagle media. As for the cell cultures of Orthoptera and Coleoptera, these media were complemented with 10% fetal calf serum but adjusted to pH 7.2.

For the culture of regenerating cells of the legs, muscles, ovarioles, and adipose tissues of *L. maderae*, Marks and Reinecke (1964, 1965a,b) used, in some cases, a modification of Grace's medium (1962) with the amounts of ions indicated by Ludwig *et al.* (1957). In addition, the heat-treated hemolymph of the homologous insect was replaced by 1% Bactopeptone. In most cases, two new media were used: M.IV at a pH of 6.5 and M.V (modification of M.IV) at a pH of 6.7–6.8 (Table VIII). The Δt was −0.45°.

After studies on the value of the Na/K ratio in culture media of insect tissues, Ting and Brooks (1965) also determined a culture medium for cockroach tissue (Table IX) permitting the migration and a certain multiplication of cells of *B. germanica* while Landureau (1966, 1968, 1969) and Landureau and Jollès (1969) use a medium the composition

TABLE VII
INORGANIC COMPOSITION OF HEMOLYMPH OF SOME DICTYOPTERA

Species	meq/liter				References
	Na	K	Ca	Mg	
Periplaneta americana (adult)	157	7.6	4.2	5.4	Van Asperen and Van Esch (1956)
Periplaneta americana (larva)	100	15.4	3.3	—	Tobias (1948)
Blabera fusca (larva)	—	—	20.2	15.7	Van Asperen and Van Esch (1954)

TABLE VIII

NUTRIENT MEDIA M.IV AND M.V FOR DICTYOPTERA (*Leucophaea maderae*)[a]

Substances	Concentration (mg/100 ml)	
	M.IV	M.V
Solution A: Amino acids		
L-Lysine–HCl	40	30
L-Histidine–HCl	100	60
L-Arginine–HCl	30	40
L-Aspartic acid	10	10
L-Threonine	20	10
L-Asparagine	15	10
DL-Serine	70	30
L-Proline	40	40
Glycine	60	60
L-Alanine	25	10
β-Alanine	10	10
L-Valine	25	20
L-Methionine	5	10
L-Isoleucine	10	10
L-Leucine	15	10
L-Tyrosine–HCl	10	10
L-Phenylalanine	10	10
L-Tryptophan	5	10
L-Taurine	5	5
Solution B: Cations		
$CaCl_2$ (anhydrous)	30	50
KCl	45	40
$MgCl_2 \cdot 7H_2O$	10	20
NaCl	20	100
Solution C: Organic acid	(ml/100 ml)	
Malic acid	60	60
L-Ketoglutaric acid	60	40
Succinic acid	5	10
Fumaric acid	5	10
Citric acid	15	10
Glutamic acid	800	400
Add NaOH (dilute) until acids go into solution completely		
Solution D: Anions	(mg/100 ml)	
Na_2SO_4	10	20
NaH_2PO_4	30	50
$NaHCO_3$	20	20
Solution E: Sugars		
Fructose	200	200
Glucose	400	400
Sucrose	—	600
Solution F: Vitamins		
Thymine–HCl	002	002

TABLE VIII (*Continued*)

Substances	Concentration (mg/100 ml)	
	M.IV	M.V
Riboflavin	002	002
Calcium pentothenate	002	002
Pyridoxine–HCl	002	002
Paraaminobenzoic acid	002	002
Folic Acid	002	002
Biotin	002	002
Choline–HCl	002	002
Isoinositol	002	002
Carnitine	001	001
Solution G: Reductants		
Glutamine	100	200
Glutathion	—	10
Ascorbic acid	—	10
Solution H: Antibiotics		
Streptomycin (SO₄)	50	50
Penicillin (K⁺)	30	30
The pH should be adjusted to pH 6.75 and the medium sterilized by filtration before use		

[a] From Marks and Reinecke, 1965a.

of which is calculated through recent analyses of hemolymph of Dictyoptera (Table X).

Larsen's experiments (1963, 1964) confirm the statements made on other invertebrates (Vago and Chastang, 1958) concerning the importance of protein hydrolysates as growth stimulators. Explants cultured in the medium TC 199 complemented with 2% Bacto-peptone continued to contract for 16 months without proliferating. If lactalbumin hydrolysate and yeastolate are added, a certain cellular proliferation is observed after five months.

The osmotic pressure has a large influence on the adherence of cells to the recipient walls. Accordingly, the cells and the embryo fragments of *B. fusca*, treated with trypsin, adhere immediately after being placed in culture if the Δt is controlled and is consistently held at −0.82° But it must be maintained at −0.79° for *P. americana* and −0.76° for *B. germanica* in a dilution of the original medium is a better adherence of cells is desired (Landureau, 1966).

The replacement of chicken and bovine serum by homologous insect plasma or by that of the crayfish *Astacus nigrescens* did not bring noticeable improvement for cell cultures of a variety of organs of *B. germanica* in Ting and Brooks' medium (1965).

TABLE IX

CULTURE MEDIUM FOR DICTYOPTERA[a]

Substances	Concentration (mg/100 ml)
Solution A	
Inorganic salts	
NaCl	1100
KCl	140
CaCl$_2$	110
NaH$_2$PO$_4$	6
Organic acids	
Malic acid	50
Ketoglutaric acid	25
Succinic acid	5
Sodium citrate	5
Sugars	
Dextrose	80
Trehalose	50
Sucrose	20
Amino acids	
Lactalbumin hydrolysate	1000
Vitamins	
Yeast extract	200
pH adjusted to 6.6 with 10% KOH	
Solution B	
Reduced glutathione	50
Ascorbic acid	50
Glass distilled water	10 ml
Final culture medium	
Solution A	8 ml
Solution B	0.5 ml
Chicken or bovine serum	2 ml
Phenol red	0.2 ml

[a] From Ting and Brooks, 1965.

D. Cultures Obtained and Observations

While a large number of the attempted cultures resulted in cell migrations with a more or less long survival, some prolonged cultures, showing mitotic activity and the possibility of subcultures were recently obtained.

Cell migrations and proliferations were noted in cultures obtained by Larsen (1964) from fragments of the dorsal vessel, from head sections, from Malpighian tubules, and from the embryonic intestinal tract of *B. fusca* in a TC 199 medium complemented by lactalbumin hydrolysate.

TABLE X
CULTURE MEDIUM S19 FOR COCKROACHES[a]

Substances	Concentration (mg/100 ml)
Inorganic	
$CaCl_2$	49
KCl	105
$MgSO_4 \cdot 7H_2O$	126
$MnSO_4 \cdot H_2O$	6.5
NaCl	850
$NaHCO_3$	36
PO_3H_3	90
Sugars	
Glucose	300
Vitamins	
Folic Acid	0.001
D-Biotin	0.001
Choline–HCl	0.04
Inositol	0.005
Niacinamide	0.003
Calcium Pantothenate	0.01
Pyridoxine–HCl	0.003
Riboflavin	0.005
Thiamine–HCl	0.001
Amino acids	
L-Aspartic acid	25
L-Glutamic acid	150
L-Alanine	12
L-Arginine–HCl	80
L-Cysteine–HCl	26
L-Glutamine	30
Glycine	75
L-Histidine	30
L-Isoleucine	12
L-Leucine	25
L-Lysine	16
L-Methionine	50
L-Phenylalanine	20
L-Proline	75
L-Serine	8
L-Threonine	20
L-Tryptophan	20
L-Tyrosine	18
L-Valine	15
Blood human proteins	
Fraction V of Cohn	400
α_2-Macroglobulin	5
pH	7.4
Osmolarity	440 mOsM/liter

[a] From Landureau and Jollès, 1969.

Cellular migrations were also obtained by the same author (Larsen, 1967) from the cockroach *Blaberus discoidalis*. He started cultures using TC 199 medium with fragments of heart, intestines, and Malpighian tubules of embryos removed from gravid females. The organ fragments were put in culture together with ganglions or prothoracic glands excised from larvae 10 days after their fifth molt. The first cell migration occurred about one week later and a continued gradual growth for two to six months produced some cell sheets. At first, the fibroblasts migrated, forming a network in the center of which individual cell fibers became long and narrow and, in certain cases, exhibited rythmic vibrating movements. Then, sheets of epithelial round cells appeared. Finally, on the periphery of the explants, flask-shaped cells were noted.

With their medium, Ting and Brooks (1965) tried to establish cell cultures from Malpighian tubules, from an unidentified tissue adhering to them, from adipose tissue, and from ovarioles and oviducts of nymphs at the sixth stage of *B. germanica*. The Malpighian tubules exhibit contractions but do not show any cell migration. However, the unidentified tissue which adhered to them emitted, five hours later, numerous polygonal cells, rather flat and presenting small cytoplasmic granulations and a large nucleus. The cells survived two to nine days, then became round and fell into the medium.

The only part of the ovary showing cellular growth was the oviduct. Twenty-four hours after the start of the culture, two types of cells appeared and continued to migrate for 156 days in one culture and 84 days in another. One of these types was composed of flattened, polygon-shaped cells; the other, of long and spindle-shaped fibroblasts, in some cases, able to contract. Cell migrations were always accompanied by explant contractions.

Marks and Reinecke (1964, 1965a,b) described cell cultures from regenerating cells of legs of nymphal *L. maderae*. The mesothoracic legs of fifth stage nymphs were detached at the level of the trochanter–femural joint two days after the molt, and the regenerating tissues were removed from the stumps 10 to 20 days after the operation. The migration of three types of cells was observed: first, plasmatocytes of various forms, i.e., round, spindle-shaped, and even stellate configurations, which phagocytosed the dead blood cells. Several became round, detached themselves from the glass, and floated in the medium. Others migrated using pseudopodia. Cells of the second type coming from the subepithelial cellular reticulum were tapered, and they exhibited branched pseudopodia. They remained on the surface of the glass. The cells of the third type were of "signet ring" configurations.

It is interesting to note that attempts of nervous system culture (rare with invertebrates) has been tried with Dictyoptera. From the excised end of the fifth mesothoracic nerve of the nymphs of *L. maderae,* fibroid cells with branched pseudopodia proliferated while spreading along the substratum (Marks and Reinecke, 1964, 1965a,b).

Whole hemolymph was also cultured from lymphs of *L. maderae* by Marks and Reinecke (1964, 1965a,b) in the M.IV medium. Many cells detached from the blood clot and were maintained in good condition for 10–12 days in hanging drops.

Cell cultures from *B. fusca, P. americana,* and *B. germanica,* produced by digestion with trypsin (Landureau, 1965, 1966), are characterized by two migration waves. The first rapidly formed a cell halo around different tissue fragments after initiation of the culture and lasted about two weeks, then the constituent cells died. During the first days, several mitoses are observed.

A second migratory wave, being much more gradual in other species, may appear suddenly in the cultures of *B. fusca.* In all cases, the cells show voluminous nuclei, clear cytoplasm, and fast-outgrowing cell groups from which fibroblastic-type elements migrate. At the end of the first month tangled networks are formed in which the cellular limits are rather confused. Pulsations are noted in the whole network. Mitoses are observed especially in *B. fusca,* the cells being large and the number of chromosomes high.

The dispersion is rapid with *B. germanica* because the cells, after division, float in the medium before adhering to the bottom of the flasks. In the medium, containing 10% calf serum, the first signs of degeneration are manifest at the end of the second month in *B. fusca,* at first in the cells most distant from the original fragments. At the same time, large polyploid cells appear inside the second migration network.

An increase in the frequency of cellular division was noted when a medium with 15% (instead of 10%) fetal calf serum was used. The formation of dense plates of cells with a well-defined circumference was obtained. They may have, in certain cases, formed vesicles which were detached or remained adhering to the original fragments.

If at the end of the second month, the 10% serum medium is replaced by a 15% one, there is a net cellular reactivation and a diminution of the polyploid elements to the advantage of the survival of the fibroblasts.

The complementation of the medium by aqueous cockroach-embryo extracts (0.5–1%) gave more reproducible results, even in the 10% serum media; a continuous increase in the cell network is observed beyond the second month and the cells acquire an independence toward the fragments from which they originated. From the primary cultures of cockroach embryos, cell cultures with continuous growth were maintained by subcultures (Landureau, 1968).

The obtaining of an embryonic cell line of cockroach permitted the study of amino acid requirements of this line (Landureau and Jollès, 1969). Thus, the utilization of amino acids by the cells was measured, comportment of the cells in the absence of a given amino acid was observed, and the occurrence of transamination reactions was demonstrated. Taking in account the symptoms observed after the suppression of the amino acids from the culture medium, these components were separated into four groups: (a) amino acids essential for cell survival (proline, cysteine, glycine, phenylalanine, methionine, valine, leucine, tryptophan, histidine, and tyrosine), (b) amino acids essential for obtaining the optimum growth of the cultures (lysine, thréonine, serine, and isoleucine), (c) facultative amino acids (glutamic acid and aspartic acid), and (d) nonessential acids (glutamine, α-alanine, β-alanine, and asparagine).

The requirements of this cell line in hydrosoluble vitamins was also studied (Landureau, 1969). As for the amino acids, it was possible to classify those (a) vitamins essential for survival of the cells (calcium pantothenate, cyanocobalamin, riboflavin, inositol, and thiamine), (b) vitamins essential for obtaining the optimum growth of the culture (choline, pyridoxine, folic acid, nicotinic acid), and (c) nonessential vitamins (ascorbic acid and para-aminobenzoic acid).

The improvement from primary cultures of Dictyoptera to stabilized cultures of very long durations which can be subcultured has been demonstrated by the work of Vago et al. (1968); Vago and Quiot (1969) on cardiac cells of B. fusca, L. maderae (Fig. 6), and P. americana cultured from explanting fragments or after digestion with trypsin.

In spite of rinses during the first hours, blood cells, frequently fusiform, are found and eliminated during the first medium changes.

At the same time, during the first 24 hours numerous large cells (about 60 μ) migrate and form cell sheets more or less dense. They are characterized by extensive cellular granulation localized around the nucleus and sometimes arranged in a regular manner. The rest of the cytoplasm is nonvacuolated and clear, and the nucleus sometimes contains a few nucleoli. These cells, when they migrate individually, emit long pseudopodia or a thin, wavy membrane, but when they are joined in sheets, they are sometimes so packed that it is difficult to distinguish their contours. The cells multiply and mitotic figures are regularly observed. They maintain themselves alive for several months.

When the culture is one or two months old, new cells can suddenly appear. These are smaller, fusiform, and strongly attached to the substratum. Their cytoplasm is more dense, and less granulations are present. They constitute a tangled and packed network where numerous mitoses are seen. These cell sheets develop very rapidly and spread over the whole surface of the bottom of the flask. Cell activity is so intense that the medium must be renewed every four days. These cultures have

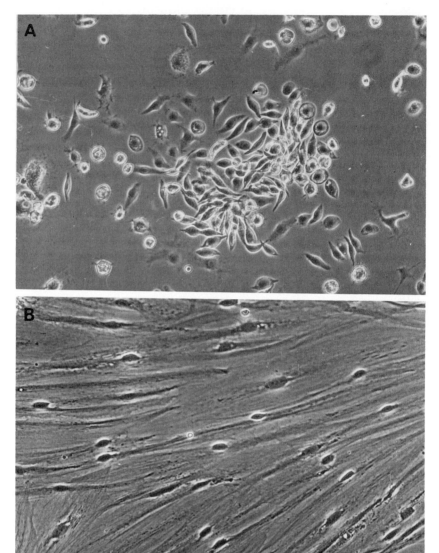

Fig. 6. Two types (a,b) of one-year cultured heart cells from *Leucophaea maderae* (Dictyoptera). Phase contrast, ×175.

been subcultured numerous times and have maintained their intense mitotic activity, which enables the establishment of strains of cardiac cells of Dictyoptera.

In the cell cultures of different cockroaches, many authors also notice the curious phenomena of vesicle formation by cells in the process of multiplication. Thus, during Larsen's experiments (1964), cultures from pieces of the heart, the Malpighian tubules, and the head of B. fusca excised from embryos were set up. The cell proliferation appeared, about five months after culture initiation, as hollow vesicles, the walls of which are formed from a single layer of cells. Though these cells appear similar to those of the epidermic sheath, it is difficult to know from what tissue the vesicles originated. They can detach themselves from the explants and settle at the bottom of the culture flasks. Their maximum size is about 0.5 mm in diameter.

Also in the cultures of the dorsal vessel, the Malpighian tubules, and the embryonic intestine of another cockroach, B. discoidalis, Larsen (1967) observed hollow vesicles formed on cut surface areas, some of which reached a diameter of 2 mm, in other words, a greater size than the original explants. Thin sections of cultured organs showed that these vesicles are of epithelial origin.

In cell cultures of L. maderae, beside the cell migrations, Marks and Reinecke (1964, 1965a,b) observed the formation of vesicles and cell buds from explants coming from regenerative tissues of legs. Two types of vesicles were noted. One grew inside the explant and migrated to the surface. This vesicle appeared as a swelling after seven days of culture and, in 60 hours, tripled in size. Its walls were formed by a layer of epithelial cells interlaced with fiber-like cells.

The other vesicle type appeared in the cell sheet which surrounded the explants at first as a mass of cells forming a "signet ring." Then as the number of cells increased, a cavity appeared inside the mass giving the form of a vesicle. The authors noted that these vesicles formed sacks of epithelial cells, underlaid by fibrous cells, and filled with the culture medium. In one case, the wound of a vesicle healed except for a small opening, across which (after 12 days) a flow of medium was established.

The effect of various chemical and cellular substances was examined many times on the cell cultures of Dictyoptera.

Thus, on the cultures of different embryonic tissues of B. discoidatis (Larsen, 1967) the effect on cell outgrowth of numerous chemical substances (added to 125 ml of TC 199) were tested, i.e., Raben-type growth hormone (0.015 gm), cholesterol (0.03 gm), bovine lyophilized serum (0.025 gm), glycerol (4 ml), royal jelly (2 ml), and phytol (1 ml), all these substances being considered as growth stimulators. The explants, kept alone in TC 199 containing none of the above-mentioned substances, showed only a slight growth after 15 days of culture. The only notable events were the migration of several fibroblasts. These were vacuolated and showed no vesicle formation. The explants maintained in the same medium but complemented with royal jelly formed numerous vesicles in 50% of the experiments. When cultures are started in a medium to which Raben-type growth hormone is added and placed three days later in a medium containing phytol, cell sheets and vesicles appear after five days.

With cholesterol, and especially with bovine serum, the growth was indicated only by the formation of vesicles or clusters of vesicles which become, in some cases, larger than the original explants.

In the medium complemented with glycerol, after the third day of culture, there was fibroblast proliferation forming cell sheets which continued to spread for about two months.

Cell cultures of Dictyoptera have attained such a degree of development that they were used in the study of certain biological actions at the cellular level.

Thus, in cell cultures of regenerating tissues of the legs of L. maderae nymphs (Marks and Reinecke, 1964, 1965a,b) cell migration was stimulated when a drop of fresh, homologous hemolymph was deposited near an explant. An interaction occurred as soon as the fourth day. The plasmatocytes emerged from the blood clot near the explant and migrated towards it. At the same time, the cell migration was greater on the side next to the blood clot. This is an interesting phenomenon because a parallel experiment where 15 drops of crude plasma of homologous hemolymph were added to 2.5 ml of medium proved that this plasma was very toxic to the cells. The blood cells could thus play an active role in this interaction.

Finally, cell cultures of Dictyoptera (L. maderae) have been used (Marks and Reinecke, 1965b) for in vitro studies on the influence of endocrine glands (such as brain, prothoracic glands, and corpus allatum) on the regenerating tissues of the legs, with particular reference to the developmental stage of the nymphs and the time intervals after the amputations.

REFERENCES

Barsa, M. C. (1954). J. Gen. Physiol. 38, 79.
Bergerard, J., and Morio, H. (1963). C. R. 1er Coll. Int. Cult. Tissues Invert., Montpellier, 1962, Ann. Epiphyt. 14, 55.
Boné, G. J. (1944). Ann. Soc. Zool. Belg. 75, 123.
Bucklin, D. H. (1953). Anat. Rec. 117, 539.
Butz, A. (1957). J. N.Y. Entomol. Soc. 65, 22.
Carlson, J. G. (1946). Biol. Bull. 90, 109.
Carlson, J. G. (1950). J. Cell. Comp. Physiol. 35, 1.
Carlson, J. G. (1961). Ann. N.Y. Acad. Sci. 95, 932.

Carlson, J. G., and Hollaender, A. (1944). *J. Cell. Comp. Physiol.* **23**, 157.

Carlson, J. G., and Hollaender, A. J. (1945). *J. Cell. Comp. Physiol.* **26**, 165.

Carlson, J. G., and Hollaender, A. J. (1948). *J. Cell. Comp. Physiol.* **31**, 149.

Carlson, J. G., Harrington, N. G., and Gaulden, M. E. (1953). *Biol. Bull.* **104**, 313.

Chambers, R. (1925). *Cellule* **35**, 105.

Charpentier, R. (1968). *Ann. Epiphyt.* **19**, 533.

Charpentier, R. (1971). In press.

Duchateau, G., Florkin, M., and Leclercq, J. (1953). *Arch. Int. Physiol.* **61**, 518.

Duveau-Hagège, J. (1963). *C. R. Acad. Sci.* **256**, 5429.

Duveau-Hagège, J. (1964). *Bull. Soc. Zool. Fr.* **89**, 66.

Eagle, H. (1955). *Science* **122**, 501.

Gaulden, M. E., and Carlson, J. C. (1947). *J. Gen. Genet.* **32**, 87.

Gaulden, M. E., and Carlson, J. C. (1951). *Exp. Cell Res.* **2**, 416.

Gaulden, M. E., and Kokomoor, K. L. (1955). *Proc. Soc. Exp. Biol. Med.* **90**, 309.

Gaulden, M. E., and Perry, R. P. (1958). *Proc. Nat. Acad. Sci. U.S.* **44**, 553.

Grace, T. D. C. (1962). *Nature (London)* **195**, 788.

Landureau, J. C. (1965). *C. R. Acad. Sci.* **260**, 5379.

Landureau, J. C. (1966). *Exp. Cell Res.* **41**, 545.

Landureau, J. C. (1968). *Proc. Int. Colloq. Invertebr. Tissue Cult., 2nd., 1967* p. 3.

Landureau, J. C. (1969). *Exp. Cell Res.* **54**, 399.

Landureau, J. C., and Jollès, P. (1969). *Exp. Cell Res.* **54**, 391.

Larsen, W. (1963). *Life Sci.* **8**, 606.

Larsen, W. (1964). *Life Sci.* **3**, 103.

Larsen, W. P. (1967). *J. Insect Physiol.* **13**, 613.

Lazarenko, T. Z. (1925). *Z. Mikrosk.-Anat. Forsch.* **3**, 409.

Lender, T., and Fischer, K. R. S. (1965). *C. R. Acad. Sci.* **261**, 244.

Lewis, M. R. (1916). *Anat. Rec.* **10**, 287.

Lewis, M. R., and Robertson, W. R. B. (1916). *Biol. Bull.* **30**, 512.

Ludwig, D., Tracey, S. K. M., and Burns, M. L. (1957). *Ann. Entomol. Soc. Amer.* **50**, 244.

Marks, E. P., and Reinecke, J. P. (1964). *Science* **143**, 961.

Marks, E. P., and Reinecke, J. P. (1965a). *J. Kans. Entomol. Soc.* **38**, 179.

Marks, E. P., and Reinecke. J. P. (1956b). *Gen. Comp. Endocrinol.* **5**, 241.

Meynadier, G., Quiot, J. M., and Vago, C. (1968). *Proc. Int. Colloq. Invertebr. Tissue Cult., 2nd, 1967* p. 218.

Morgan, J. F., Morton, H. J., and Parker, R. C. (1950). *Proc. Soc. Exp. Biol. Med.* **73**, 1.

Murray, M. R. (1926). *Biol. Bull.* **50**, 210.

Pepper, J. H., Donaldson, F. T., and Hastings, E. (1941). *Physiol. Zool.* **14**, 470.

Ramsay, J. A. (1953). *J. Exp. Biol.* **30**, 358.

Ris, H. (1949). *Biol. Bull.* **96**, 90.

Roberts, H. S. (1955). *J. Exp. Zool.* **130**, 83.

Roeder, K. D. (1948). *J. Cell. Comp. Physiol.* **31**, 327.

Rose, G., Ponevat, C., Shindler, T., and Trunnell, J. (1958). *J. Biophys. Biochem. Cytol.* **4**, 761.

Sen Gupta, K. (1961). *Folia Biol.* **7**, 400.

St. Aman, G. S., and Tipton, S. R. (1954). *Science* **119**, 93.

Shaw, E. I. (1956). *Exp. Cell Res.* **11**, 580.

Ting, K. Y., and Brooks, M. A. (1965). *Ann. Entomol. Soc. Amer.* **58**, 197.

Tobias, J. M. (1948). *J. Cell. Comp. Physiol.* **31**, 143.

Vago, C. (1963). *J. Insect Pathol.* **5,** 275.

Vago, C., and Chastang, S. (1958). *Experientia* **14,** 110.

Vago, C., and Quiot, J. M. (1969). *Ann Zool. Ecol. Anim.* **1,** 281.

Vago, C., Quiot, J. M., and Luciani, J. (1968). *Proc. Int. Colloq. Invertebr. Tissue Cult., 2nd, 1967* p. 110.

Van Asperen, K., and Van Esch, K. (1954). *Nature (London)* **174,** 927.

Van Asperen, K., and Van Esch, K. (1956). *Arch. Neer. Zool.* **11,** 342.

9

CELL CULTURE OF HYMENOPTERA

A. Giauffret

I. INTRODUCTION

For several years, the culturing of invertebrate cells has been considered possible in only a few highly specialized laboratories. This method has been progressively extended to most of the zoological groups of invertebrates over approximately the past 15 years. However, research on Hymenoptera has been neglected for a long time, except for Pfeiffer's work (1951), which showed a limited growth occurring in the explanted muscular tissues of *Vespa*.

Researches in this particular field concern mainly the honey bee, *Apis mellifera*. The biology and pathology of the bee, a useful, social insect, have been relatively well studied because of the economic aspect. However, up to the last few years, no cell cultures of the bee had been obtained. Recent work on cell cultures was undertaken mostly for application to pathology, in order to study the various pathogens occurring during intracellular multiplication. In this way, the culture of bee tissue might make possible *in vitro* tests on parasites such as *Nosema apis*, which have resisted attempts at artificial multiplication. But these techniques provide, above all, great scope in bee virology, which has been the subject of numerous *in vivo* works over the last few years (Vago, 1966, 1967). Thus, since the report on Sacbrood virus morphology (Brcak *et al.*, 1963), several workers have studied the morphology, chemistry, and immunology of this virus (Bailey *et al.*, 1964; Lee and Furgala, 1965b, 1967). This pathogen is all the more important in that it is also associated with certain cases of European Foulbrood (Giauffret *et al.*, 1966b, 1969). The virus of so-called Bee Paralysis or "Maladie Noire" was isolated and studied in different countries (Bailey *et al.*, 1963; Lee and Furgala, 1965; Giauffret *et al.*, 1966a; Alekseenko and Kolonietz, 1967). Viruses closely related to vertebrate orphan enteroviruses are usually latent in the adult bee and may interfere with virological tests. Finally, a rickettsia-like organism of the bee has been reported during recent years, but the cytopathic action of this microorganism has not been studied (Wille, 1963; Poltev and Grobov, 1967).

All these works were conducted on bees affected by natural or experimental diseases. However, this method does not permit an accurate study of the action of the viruses on the cell, and the interpretations of these results are difficult because viruses that cannot be excluded may interfere. Techniques of artifical rearing are rarely employed in bee research, and aseptic rearing cannot as yet be considered.

The important progress made in the study of bee viruses has shown the necessity as well as the possibility of studying tissue culture techniques applicable to this useful hymenopteran. Such a method is also of great value in other fields of bee pathology and biology.

II. CULTURE MEDIA

A. Composition of Hemolymph

The media used for cell cultures usually simulate, as closely as possible, the composition of the insect hemolymph. Considerable data is available on mineral and organic compounds of different tissues of the honey bee. In spite of the differences and due to either techniques or seasonal changes, these results make it possible to estimate the values of some mineral components of bee hemolymph in order to calculate cell culture media (Table I).

There are rather important differences between the larval and the imaginal blood, particularly in the sodium, potassium, and magnesium rates. Thus, it seems of value to adapt the media to the specific tissues being cultured. In larvae, the average values reported by different authors are 8.6 meq/liter for sodium, and 33.3 meq/liter for potassium. The magnesium ratio is high in larvae, while the calcium ratio is high in both larvae and adult bees.

The pH of the hemolymph of the worker bee is approximately 6.5–6.7 (Bishop et al., 1925; Hoskins and Harrison, 1934; Poutiers, 1969), while that of the larval hemolymph is 6.8 (Wigglesworth, 1959; Poutiers, 1969). The osmotic pressure in the larva is equivalent to that of 1.5% of sodium chloride (Wigglesworth, 1959). A high Δt (approx. 0.80°) was also noted by Bishop et al. (1925). However, a recent experimental study, using progressive concentrations of basal medium, has shown that the most

TABLE I

MAIN MINERAL COMPONENTS OF THE BEE HEMOLYMPH

Origin of the hemolymph	meq/liter				References
	Na	K	Ca	Mg	
Larva	10.0	45.0	—	—	Bone (1944)
	10.9	30.5	18.2	20.5	Duchateau et al. (1953)
	5.0	24.4	7.5	15.8	Bishop et al. (1925)
Adult	47.1	27.1	17.1	1	Florkin and Jeuniaux (1963)
	15.2	8.3	7.2	—	Poutiers (1969)

favorable Δt is in the region of 0.50°–0.53° (Poutiers, 1969). Mineral components have an influence on the rate of osmotic pressure, but the organic elements have an even more important role. The sodium potassium ratio essential for culture media is 0.11–0.21 in the case of larval hemolymph. It increases up to 1 for the adult bee.

With regard to the organic elements, the level of blood sugars is variable. The bee possesses no regulating mechanism for glycemia, and the composition of its hemolymph depends on the nature of the food ingested. The monosaccharide ratio can be very high, capable of reaching 3.7% and even 11% in certain cases. Fructose can represent an important proportion of the sugar in hemolymph, its ratio sometimes being higher than that of glucose. In certain instances there may be disaccharides, especially sucrose.

The protein level in the hemolymph reaches 5 gm/100 ml. Numerous amino acids can be identified (Pratt, 1950). The concentration of free amino acids is 87.7 moles/ml, which is in excess of 20% of all the amino acids. Altogether, proteins count for 45% in the osmotic pressure of the hemolymph, whereas the figure for mineral salts is only 19%. Under free conditions, proline, glycine, and lysine are present in high proportions. Proteins have a high level of lysine, aspartic acid, glutamic acid, glycine, valine, and leucine (Table II).

B. Basal Medium

The medium proposed by Giauffret et al. (1967) is established after the principle of standard fractions (Vago and Quiot, 1969). It contains two fractions. The salt solution has been calculated for the bee, after the formula given in Table III. It is buffered at pH 6.8. It has the same ratio of sodium potassium as bee hemolymph, as well as a high ratio of calcium and magnesium.

The organic fraction is the same as that in the medium 199 of Morgan et al. (1950). It includes the main amino acids present in bee hemolymph, in addition to an important concentration of vitamins, sugars, and various additives. This fraction, when prepared in a solution concentrated five times, is divided into doses of 20 ml and stored at −30°. It is completed by the addition of 200 or 300 mg of glucose or fructose.

Grace's medium (1962) for the culture of moth ovaries was used as a basic medium for the cell cultures of the bee (Stanley, 1968). This medium has a pH of 6.5, its buffering capacity being based on a phosphate system to which are added large amounts of organic acids. The sodium and potassium levels approximate those of bee hemolymph. Calcium

TABLE II

AMINO ACIDS PRESENT IN THE HEMOLYMPH OF WORKER BEES[a]

| Amino acids | Concentration (μmoles/ml) | |
	Free amino acids	Protein amino acids
Lysine	11.204	18.355
Histidine	2.394	10.192
Arginine	0.761	9.235
Aspartic acid	Traces	38.285
Threonine	5.148	13.365
Serine	1.293	18.040
Glutamic acid	0.633	43.415
Proline	45.600	18.840
Glycocolle	11.613	20.185
Alanine	1.632	16.045
Valine	4.051	24.590
Methionine	0.496	9.140
Isoleucine	1.454	13.935
Leucine	1.502	29.310
Tyrosine	Traces	18.965
Phenylalanine	Traces	13.310
Totals	87.766	305.115

[a] From Lenski, in Chauvin (1968), p. 495.

TABLE III

STANDARD FRACTIONS MEDIUM FOR APIS[a]

Substances	Amount
Mineral fraction	
NaCl	65 mg
KCl	300 mg
Na_2HPO_4	9 mg
KH_2PO_4	60 mg
$MgSO_4 \cdot 7H_2O$	495 mg
$CaCl_2$ (anhydrous)	140 mg
Organic fraction of 199 (5$\times$)	20 ml
Special fraction	
Glucose	300 mg
Lactalbumin hydrolysate	1000 mg
Fetal calf serum	10 ml
$NaHCO_3$ for pH 6.8	$\approx$ 35 mg
Bidistilled water	100 ml

[a] From Giauffret et al. (1967).

and magnesium are included to a sufficient degree. This medium contains all the amino acids shown to be present in bee blood, with the exception of hydroxyproline. Energy is supplied by glucose and fructose. A large amount of sucrose supplies the correct osmotic pressure and may be used as an energy-providing element. It also contains ten vitamins and two antibiotics.

C. Additional Biological Constituents

Several biological constituents are used to complete the basic medium. Fetal bovine serum is an essential constituent and is added in a proportion of 5–18%. The beneficial action of this supplement has been proved by numerous workers who noted the suitability of this constituent for vertebrate and invertebrate cultures. Bovine serum albumin, also, is a suitable supplement. Chicken embryo extracts were used at a dosage of 5 mg of lyophilized powder/100 ml of medium. The addition of larval extracts or of royal jelly (0.1 gm/100 ml) enables one to obtain more active cultures. Lactalbumin hydrolysate may be added to the medium at the rate of 0.5 gm/100 ml to increase the rate of proteins, while yeast extract (0.5 gm/100 ml) provides more vitamins.

Stanley (1968) modified Grace's medium by the addition of 5 ml of *Apis* hemolymph, 5 ml of fetal bovine serum, 1 ml of bovine serum albumin, 100 mg of reduced glutathione and 3.48 mg of potassium penicillin G in 100 ml of solution. The bee hemolymph used to provide specific homologous elements is collected by bleeding several hundred worker and drone larvae in a test tube at 4°. The heating, continued for 10 minutes at 60°, inhibits the polyphenoloxidase and thus prevents the melanization of the sample. Proteins precipitated during the heating are removed by centrifugation for 30 minutes at 20,000 g. The supernatant fluid is sterilized by filtration through membrane. The addition of reduced glutathione to the medium also prevents the melanization of the explants.

III. METHODS

A. Choice of Tissues

Explants have been chosen in order to use relatively undifferentiated tissues, such as the ovaries of developing queen bees and embryos. Bee ova are used at the end of evolution, 48 hours after oviposition, when the segmentation of the embryo commences (Giauffret *et al.*, 1967). Younger ova contain a large amount of yolk, and so, no culture occurs. Also, ova older than those in the early stages of segmentation do not give a good yield.

The optimum stage occurs within a rather short period after embryo evolution. Indeed, the yolk disappears completely approximately 10 hours before the commencement of segmentation. The embyro assumes the larval shape 53 hours after oviposition. It leaves the chorion on the third day.

The ovaries of developing queen bees are larger explants and may be used over a longer period of time. But to obtain these tissues, it is necessary to achieve artificial rearing in colonies. These organs may be taken from propupae or young pupae (white-eyed, tan-eyed, or red-eyed pupae). The oldest pupae, showing melanization of the tegument, have ovaries infiltrated with fat tissues and are less suitable (Stanley, 1968). The use of ovaries obtained from adult queen bees gave less satisfactory results and cannot be recommended. The ovaries of worker nymphs are very small and have not sufficient activity. The dorsal vessel of worker larvae were also used but with less interesting results.

B. Removal of Explants

The methods differ according to the organs required.

1. Embryos

In order to explant embryos, the ova are collected from the brood frame of a hive in full activity. Due to the disposition of the bee brood, in which the queen lays eggs according to a helicoidal pattern starting from the center of the frame, the youngest eggs are to be found at the periphery. Consequently, the eggs must be collected from the area nearest to the youngest larvae. The eggs, vertically laid, tend to assume a horizontal position at the termination of their evolution. They are stuck at the bottom of the cell by their narrower end and it is possible to cut them out by means of a thin stick of glass.

Approximately 100 to 200 eggs are placed on a cupule of plastic trellis in order to simplify the ensuing manipulation. The chorion is sterilized by immersion in a solution of 0.5% sodium hypochlorite for five minutes. This disinfection is followed by three rinsings in Hank's solution. The eggs placed in the medium are then examined at a low magnification in order to choose those which are at the suitable stage (Fig. 1). Embryos are extracted from the chorion by means of two forceps.

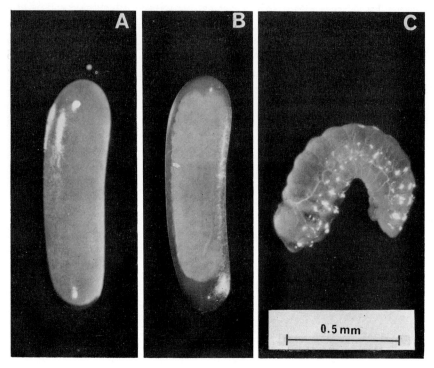

FIG. 1. Eggs and embryos of *Apis mellifera* at different stages of development. (A) The egg at the beginning of the development. (B) The egg at the beginning of the segmentation of the embryo (more suitable stage for culture). (C) The embryo at the final stage.

2. Ovaries

To excise the ovaries, developing queen bees may be obtained from hives which have been orphaned for 10 or 11 days, or from rearing in artificial cells. This latter technique gives a higher yield. Larvae and pupae are surface-sterilized in Hyamine 1622 for five minutes, rinsed three times in sterile water, and then dissected in Locke's saline solution (Stanley, 1968). It is also possible to disinfect the tegument with alcohol and to remove the ovaries after having cut out a piece of chitin in the dorsal portion of the abdomen.

C. Culture Methods

Cultures have been obtained using the hanging drop technique or in Leighton tubes and flasks. In this case, it is recommended that one use a large number of embryos fragmented by pipetting or several ovaries minced by scissors. To obtain a better dissociation of explants, it is advisable to mince them in a saline solution, containing no calcium, such as Rinaldini's solution (NaCl, 0.8 gm; KCL, 0.02 gm; $NaH_2PO_4 \cdot 2H_2O$, 0.005 gm; D-glucose, 0.1 gm; $NaHCO_3$, 0.1 gm; and sodium citrate, 0.0676 gm in 100 ml of distilled water). This solution is then replaced by the whole culture medium. In these conditions, explants and cells adhere more easily to the support.

Cultures are usually stored at 30°. They can be plated at 35° or at room temperature. The medium is changed every four to seven days.

IV. CULTURES OBTAINED

Cultures prepared under different conditions have been marked by a more or less quick cell migration. In Stanley's medium, the adaptation requires about a week. Cells, not numerous at the beginning, originally look like elongated fibroblasts, with cytoplasm sometimes granular in the cultures obtained from ovaries. These cells tend to become larger and more spreading. They then appear nonrefractile and do not show any signs of degeneration.

The growth of the culture is faster in medium of Giauffret *et al.* In that case, a diphasic evolution is also noted. Cells of a fibroblast type start to migrate 24 hours after setting up the culture. Their numbers increase rapidly, and they form important groups in which mitosis is evident. After a week of culturing, the typical fibroblasts tend to disappear and the presence of more widely spread cells of larger size is noted.

Following a few days of culturing, the appearance and number of cells show a good adaptation *in vitro*. Thus, it is possible to obtain more prolific cultures. In some instances, areas of epithelial-like cells were noted from the very commencement of the cultures, particularly from embryos and prepupal ovaries (Fig. 2). The use of numerous embryos in tubes or in flasks enables one to obtain a complete cell layer (Poutiers, 1969). In the same way, the use of the entire ovary as explant produces an important cell migration (Stanley, 1968).

After a phase of development, the cultures generally become stable. Some cultures have survived for several months. Cytokinesis and mitosis have been noted in long-term cultures. Giant cells with very large nuclei occur (Fig. 3). Polyploidal and plurinucleated cells are often present.

As yet, it has not been possible, using the cultures obtained by these methods, to produce subcultures. However, the techniques employed have provided cultures which survive sufficiently long and are prolific enough to be of value in pathology (Vol. II, Chapter 1). With these methods

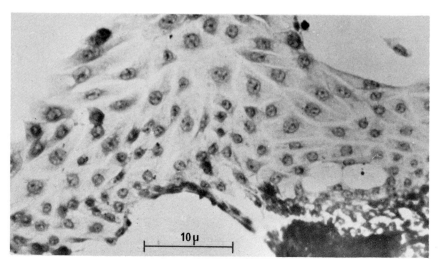

FIG. 2. Cell culture of bee embryo (fifth day of culture). Giemsa.

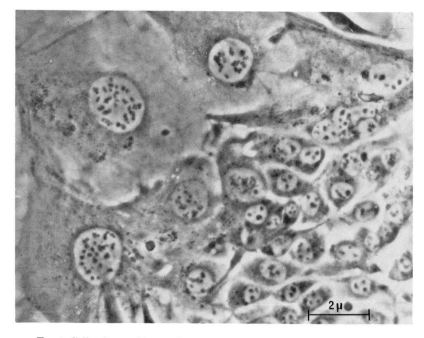

FIG. 3. Cell culture of bee embryo (15th day of culture). Phase contrast.

the cytopathogenic effect *in vitro* of different microorganisms from *Apis mellifera* or from other invertebrates has been studied. In the case of some viruses, multiplication in culture has been demonstrated by titration, and the localization of viral particles has been revealed by the examination of cell cultures studied by electron microscopy (Giauffret *et al.*, 1968; Poutiers *et al.*, 1969).

REFERENCES

Alekseenko, F. M., and Kolomietz, A. J. (1967). *21st Int. Apicult. Congr.*, p. 492.

Bailey, L., Gibbs, A. J., and Woods, R. D. (1963). *Virology* **21**, 390.

Bailey, L., Gibbs, A. J., and Woods, R. D. (1964). *Virology* **23**, 425.

Bishop, G. H., Briggs, A. P., and Ronzoni, E. (1925). *J. Biol. Chem.* **66**, 77.

Bone, G. (1944). *Ann. Soc. Roy. Zool. Belg.* **75**, 123.

Brcak, J., Svoboda, J., and Kralik, O. (1963). *J. Insect Pathol.* **5**, 385.

Chauvin, R. (1968). "Traité de Biologie de l'Abeille," Vol. 1. Masson, Paris.

Duchateau, G., Florkin, M., and Leclercq, J. (1963). *Arch. Int. Physiol.* **61**, 518.

Florkin, M., and Jeuniaux, C. (1963). *Life Sci.* **12**, 982.

Giauffret, A., Duthoit, J. L., and Caucat, M. J. (1966a). *Rec. Med. Vet. Alfort* **9**, 819.

Giauffret, A., Vago, C., Rousseau, M., and Duthoit, J. L. (1966b). *Bull. Apic. Fr.* **2**, 123.

Giauffret, A., Quiot, J. M., Vago, C., and Poutiers, F. (1967). *C. R. Acad. Sci.* **265**, 800.

Giauffret, A., Poutiers, F., Vago, C., and Rousseau, M. (1968). *Bull. Apic. Fr.* **1**, 13.

Giauffret, A., Vago, C., and Rousseau, M. (1969). *Bull. Acad. Vet. Fr.* **10**, 801.

Grace, T. D. C. (1962). *Nature (London)* **195**, 788.

Hoskins, W. M., and Harrison, H. S. (1934). *J. Econ. Entomol.* p. 924.

Lee, P. E., and Furgala, B. (1965a). *J. Invertebr. Pathol.* **7**, 170.

Lee, P. E., and Furgala, B. (1965b). *J. Invertebr. Pathol.* **7**, 502.

Lee, P. E., and Furgala, B. (1967). *J. Invertebr. Pathol.* **9**, 178.

Morgan, J. F., Morton, H. J., and Parker, R. C. (1950). *Proc. Soc. Exp. Biol. Med.* **73**, 1.

Pfeiffer, H. H. (1951). *Arch. Exp. Zellforsch. Besonders Gewebezuecht.* **24**, 273.

Poltev, V. I., and Grobov, O. F. (1967). *Pchelovodstvo* **8**, 27.

Poutiers, F. (1969). Thesis, Fac. Sci., Paris.

Poutiers, F., Giauffret, A., and Vago, C. (1969). *Ann. Soc. Entomol. Fr.* **5**, 1001.

Pratt, J. J., Jr. (1950). *Ann. Entomol. Soc. Amer.* **43**, 573.

Stanley, M. (1968). *Bull. Apic. Fr.* **1**, 45.

Vago, C. (1966). *Bull. Apic. Fr.* **1**, 5.

Vago, C. (1967). *Bull. Apic. Fr.* **2**, 109.

Vago, C., and Quiot, J. M. (1969). *Ann. Zool. Ecol. Anim.* **1**, 281.

Wigglesworth, V. B. (1959). "Physiologie des insectes." Dunod, Paris.

Wille, H. (1963). *J. Suisse Apicult.* **12**, 288.

10

CELL CULTURE OF HEMIPTERA

Hiroyuki Hirumi and Karl Maramorosch

I. INTRODUCTION

Most plant viruses are transmitted by representatives of the major insect taxa, i.e., aphids, leafhoppers, whiteflies, thrips, mealybugs, beetles, and treehoppers. Among these, two major groups of Hemiptera, the aphids and leafhoppers, carry the most important and most widely distributed plant-pathogenic viruses of temperate zones, while whiteflies play a similar role in the tropics. It has been demonstrated recently that leafhoppers and psyllids also carry mycoplasma-like agents of plant diseases, and the reader is referred to several reviews of this subject (Casper, 1969; Maramorosch et al., 1970; Shikata et al., 1969; Whitcomb and Davis, 1970).

Plant viruses, commonly termed nonpersistent or stylet borne, are transmitted by the feeding apparatus of a vector in a mechanical manner. The persistent, or circulative, viruses are transmitted biologically, often multiplying in their insect vectors as well as in plants (Black, 1959; Maramorosch, 1963). Apparently, the mycoplasma-like agents of plant diseases are also circulative and propagative in their leafhopper and psyllid vectors. Electron microscopy studies on certain arthropodborne viruses, such as rice dwarf virus (Fukushi and Shikata, 1963; Nasu, 1965), wound tumor virus (Shikata et al., 1964; Shikata and Maramorosch, 1965, 1966, 1967; Granados et al., 1967, 1968; Hirumi et al., 1967), maize mosaic virus (Herold and Munz, 1965), and maize rough dwarf virus (Vidano and Bassi, 1966) in leafhopper vectors resulted in the precise localization of virions and of their assembly sites in cells. Similarly, electron microscopy of circulative aphid-borne viruses, such as pea enation mosaic virus (Shikata et al., 1966), lettuce necrotic yellows virus (O'Loughlin and Chambers, 1967), and sawthistle yellow vein virus (Richardson and Sylvester, 1968) provided evidence for their multiplication in aphid vectors. The presence of wound tumor virus in the organs of leafhopper vectors was demonstrated by serological tests (Sinha, 1965, 1969), which provided detailed information on virus interaction with arthropod cells. Other circulative viruses have not yet been studied by these sensitive methods.

Since leafhoppers and aphids are not only common, important vectors of numerous plant pathogens but also act as alternate hosts and agents of viruses and mycoplasma-like agents, efforts have been made to culture their tissues and cells in vitro. In the past, many attempts have been made to culture cells of leafhopper vectors. The prime research objective was the study of plant-pathogenic viruses in the same manner in which bacteriophages and vertebrate viruses have been investigated. It was hoped that a system in which insect-borne viruses can be observed in invertebrate cell culture would facilitate the elucidation of insect cell penetration by these viruses, reveal the initial stages of virus proliferation, and provide practical diagnostic methods as well as accurate quantitative techniques.

Until recently, difficulties were encountered in vector tissue culture, specifically in the *in vitro* cultivation of paurometabolus insect cells such as those of Homoptera. Their cultivation was more complicated than that of holometabolus cells of Lepidoptera. These problems have been reviewed by several authors (Goodchild, 1954; Hartzell, 1958; Day and Grace, 1959; Hirumi, 1971; Jones, 1962; Maramorosch, 1962; Martignoni, 1960, 1962; Mitsuhashi, 1969a; Schneider, 1967; Vago, 1967). This chapter will be devoted to the description of the presently employed techniques for the cell and tissue cultivation of leafhoppers (Cicadellidae), aphids (Aphididae), and planthoppers (Delphacidae), the only three groups of Hemiptera in which positive results have been achieved to date. Since there is much more information available on *in vitro* leafhopper cultures, these will be discussed in greater detail. Aphid, as well as planthopper, cultures, now in their early stages of development, will be dealt with at the end of this chapter.

An early attempt to cultivate leafhopper tissues was made by Maramorosch (1956), who found that the aster yellows disease agent maintained its infectivity and probably multiplied in cultured tissue fragments of the vector *Macrosteles fascifrons* Stål. Although this first trial merely demonstrated the survival of nymphal explants, it encouraged further attempts of *in vitro* cultivation. The gut tissues of *Dalbulus maidis* Del. & W., a vector of corn stunt, and of *M. fascifrons* were maintained for a few days by Grace (1959), while he worked with one of us (K. M.) at the Rockefeller University. A few years later, various organs of *Agallia constricta* (van Duzee), a vector of wound tumor virus, and of *M. fascifrons* survived for several weeks *in vitro* (Hirumi and Maramorosch, 1963a,b). Successful growth of leafhopper cells was achieved by Vago and Flandre (1963), who used the semi-plasma-clot technique to obtain proliferation of two types of cells from various adult organs of *Cicadella viridis* L., *Macrosteles sexnotatus* Fall., and *Philaenus spumarius* L., a vector of lucerne dwarf virus.

Active cell growth from embryonic tissues of *M. fascifrons* was obtained by Hirumi and Maramorosch (1964a), who developed further the basic techniques for leafhopper tissue culture. The embryonic tissues, obtained from the blastokinetic movement stage, have been found to be the most suitable source for cell cultivation (Hirumi and Maramorosch, 1964b). A mild trypsinization technique was introduced at this time to loosen rather than to dissociate the embryonic tissues. This was found to improve the initial growth of the primary culture (Hirumi and Maramorosch, 1964a). It was also found that approximately 20% of fetal bovine serum in the culture medium gave satisfactory results, while neither insect serum nor insect extracts, earlier considered essential in arthropod tissue culture media, were necessary (Hirumi and Mara-morosch, 1964a,b,c).

Several different types of cells have been described in embryonic tissue cultures (Hirumi and Maramorosch, 1964c; Hirumi, 1965; Mitsuhashi and Maramorosch, 1964). Three of these types, one fibroblast-like and two epithelial, divided mitotically and became dominant in the cultures after two weeks of initial cultivation.

Following certain modifications of the basic techniques, mainly by introducing the use of aseptically grown insects, Mitsuhashi and Mara-morosch (1964) demonstrated the growth potential *in vitro* not only of different developmental stages of *M. fascifrons* embryos but also of nymphs and adults of this species. In addition, growth was obtained from tissues of *D. maidis* and *A. constricta*. Subsequently, the embryonic tissues of *Nephotettix cincticeps* Uhler, a vector of rice dwarf virus and rice yellow dwarf agent, have also been grown *in vitro* (Mitsuhashi, 1965a,b; Mitsuhashi and Nasu, 1967). The embryonic tissue cultures of *Nephotettix apicalis* Motschulsky, a vector of the above disease agents (Mitsuhashi, 1969a), and of *Inazuma dorsalis* Motschulsky, transmitter of rice dwarf virus (Yamada *et al.*, 1969), have also been cultured recently.

Chiu and Black (1967) succeeded in establishing cell lines from the embryonic tissues of *Agallia constricta* in the stage of blastokinetic move-ment. Nine cell lines in *A. constricta* have been obtained. One of these, AC2 (*A. constricta* cell line 2), has been successfully subcultured more than 55 times, forming monolayers with epithelial cells. Two cell lines of *Agallia quadripunctata* (Provancher), at the ninth and twentieth pas-sages, and the early stages of subculturing of *Aceratagallia sanguinolenta* (Provancher) and *Agalliopsis novella* (Say) have also been described.

II. LEAFHOPPER (CICADELLIDAE) CELL CULTURE

A. Methods of Culturing Cells

1. Developmental Stages of Insects

The first cell growth of leafhoppers was obtained from nymphal and imaginal tissues of *Cicadella viridus, Macrosteles sexnotatus,* and *Phil-aenus spumarius* (Vago and Flandre, 1963). Embryonic tissues of *Macrosteles fascifrons* were found to provide very active cell growth *in vitro* (Hirumi and Maramorosch, 1964a). Following this observation, Hirumi and Maramorosch (1964b) tested different developmental stages of the embryos to establish the most suitable material for cultivation. On the first, third, fifth, seventh, eighth, tenth, and eleventh days after oviposition, embryos were excised from leaves of rye plants (*Secale cereale* L.) and placed in the culture medium. Actively growing cells were obtained from the stage of blastokinetic movement on the seventh, eighth, and ninth days after oviposition. This stage was determined visually by the location and the size of the eye. At the beginning of blastokinesis, on the sixth or seventh day, slightly pigmented eye discs appear in the posterior positions of the eggs. These eye discs gradually move towards the anterior position during the next two or three days (Fig. 1 A–F).

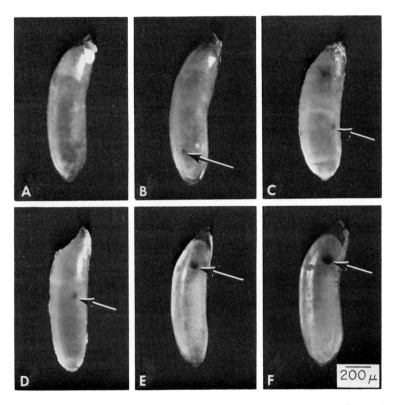

Fig. 1. Developmental stages of the embryo of *Macrosteles fascifrons* (×30). (A) One of the early developmental stages, five-day-old egg. (B–D) The eggs in the stage of blastokinetic movement during the seventh and eighth days. Slightly pigmented eye discs arise in the posterior position of the egg (B, arrow), then gradually move to the anterior position (C and D). (E–F) Eggs in late developmental stages; 10-day-old egg (E), 11-day-old egg, just before hatching (F). (From Hirumi and Maramorosch, 1964b. By courtesy of Science.)

Later it was demonstrated that the early developmental stages as well as the nymphal and imaginal tissues of *M. fascifrons,* also can be grown *in vitro* (Mitsuhashi and Maramorosch, 1964). However, the embryonic tissues of the blastokinetic movement stage provided the best source. Recently, embryonic tissues of this as well as of other species of leafhoppers in the blastokinetic movement stage were cultured and used for biological and virological studies: *Nephotettix cincticeps* (Mitsuhashi, 1965a,b, 1966; Mitsuhashi and Nasu, 1967), *Agallia constricta* (Chiu *et al.,* 1966; Chiu and Black, 1967), *Agallia quadripunctata* and *Agalliopsis novella* (Chiu and Black, 1967), *M. fascifrons* (Tokumitsu and Maramorosch, 1967; Hirumi and Maramorosch, 1968), *Inazuma dorsalis* (Yamada *et al.,* 1969), and *Nephotettix apicalis* (Mitsuhashi, 1969a).

2. Egg Collection

Primary cell cultures of leafhopper embryos required about 100 eggs for 10 small culture flasks (Hirumi and Maramorosch, 1964a). For oviposition of *M. fascifrons,* Hirumi and Maramorosch (1964a,b,c) confined approximately 200 adults to young rye plants grown in a 10-cm pot covered with a plastic transparent cage. Insects were routinely transferred once a week except when specific developmental stages of the embyro were desired. To obtain the latter, transfers were carried out daily. The caged plants with insects were maintained at a constant temperature of 25° and with 16 hours/day of light at 6600 lumens/m² provided by standard fluorescent tubes. Under these controlled environmental conditions, first instar nymphs hatched 11 days after oviposition.

To obtain embryos of *N. cincticeps,* Mitsuhashi (1965a) confined mated females to rice seedlings (*Oryza sativa* L.) in glass tubes and transferred the adults to fresh plants at two-day intervals.

For the embryonic cell culture of *A. constricta,* Chiu *et al.* (1966) excised the eggs from the petioles of crimson clover plants (*Trifolium incarnatum* L.) seven days after oviposition. We have found that eggs could be excised more easily from rye than from clover plants. Therefore, about 200 *A. constricta* adults were confined routinely to rye plants in the same manner as described for *M. fascifrons. A. constricta* embryos developed more slowly than embryos of *M. fascifrons* irrespective of the host plant.

An ingenious method of collecting leafhopper and planthopper eggs has recently been described by Mitsuhashi (1970). An oviposition cage was constructed so as to permit the insects access to a liquid medium separated from the main container by a Parafilm membrane. At 25°

under 16 hours/day of light, the insects sucked the medium through the membrane and also laid their eggs, often directly into the medium. Some eggs dropped to the bottom of the container, while others remained attached to the Parafilm singly or in clusters. For the collection of eggs, the insects were first removed from the cage and the medium container separated from the insect cage. The eggs still attached to the membrane were then pushed down and forced to sink in the medium, from which they were transferred into water by means of a pipette. Sucrose solution at a concentration of 10% was found suitable for oviposition of several planthopper and leafhopper species. As many as a thousand eggs could be collected on sucrose solutions, using *Laodelphax striatellus*. Not all species tested deposited eggs, however. *Nephotettix cincticeps* and several other leafhopper species could not be induced to oviposition into 5 or 10% solutions.

Eggs in the blastokinetic movement stage, obtained through the above-described technique or excised from the plant leaves with fine steel needles under a dissecting microscope, were then placed in a small test tube with Earle's balanced salt solution (Earle, 1943).

3. Surface Sterilization

Leafhoppers and aphids are too delicate for surface sterilization by flaming. Various sterilizing agents have been tried in the past, with varying degrees of success. Hirumi and Maramorosch (1964a) placed excised eggs for 60 seconds in 70% ethanol followed by 0.1% Hyamine 2389 solution for 10 minutes. (Hyamine is the trade name of Rohm & Haas Company's methyldodecylbenzyl trimethyl ammonium chloride' and trimethyl ammonium chloride.) The surface sterilization was obtained by the addition to the Hyamine solution of 1000 units of Penicillin G and 1000 μg of streptomycin/ml. The eggs were then washed three times with Earle's balanced salt solution. Surface sterilization with 0.1% mercuric chloride was found deleterious (Mitsuhashi and Maramorosch, 1964). Currently, leafhopper eggs are disinfected routinely by dipping them in 70% ethanol for 60 seconds (Mitsuhashi, 1965a; Hirumi and Maramorosch, 1968).

While difficulties in surface sterilization of eggs seem to have been overcome, surface sterilization of nymphal stages and of mature leafhoppers is still difficult. The usual procedure relies on the immediate disinfection of excised tissues rather than on the disinfection of the intact animals. Vago and Flandre (1963) devised a mixture containing bacitracin (5 IU/ml), penicillin (200 IU/ml), streptomycin (0.05 mg/ml), colimycin (25 μg/ml), chloramphenicol (5–10 μg/ml), and occasionally, unspecified amounts of Mycostatin. Leafhopper tissues were bathed five times in this mixture before cultivation. Hirumi and Maramorosch (1963a,b) dipped nymphs and adults of *M. fascifrons* leafhoppers in 0.1% Hyamine solution for three minutes, then dissected the insects in drops of 0.1% Hyamine solution diluted with Earle's balanced salt solution. Afterwards the tissues were washed rapidly with the same concentration of Hyamine solution, then washed several times with the culture medium.

4. Aseptic Rearing

The rearing of insects under aseptic conditions greatly facilitates cell culture work. This procedure proved especially useful in the tissue culture of leafhopper nymphs and adults that were difficult to surface sterilize. Mitsuhashi and Maramorosch (1963) employed aseptically reared leafhoppers of four species, i.e., *Macrosteles fascifrons*, *Dalbulus maidis*, *Agallia constricta*, and *Agalliopsis novella*.

After completion of blastokinesis, excised eggs were fastened with egg albumin onto strips of wax paper, sterilized by dipping the strips in 0.1% Hyamine 2389 for three minutes, then placed in glass tubes or bottles containing aseptic host plants on an agar medium. The insects were reared at 30° with 16 hours/day of light.

The plants used were rye for *M. fascifrons*, corn (*Zea mays* L.) for *D. maidis,* and crimson clover or alfalfa (*Medicago sativa* L.) for *A. constricta* and *A. novella*. To obtain aseptic plants, the seeds were sterilized by submersion for one minute in 70% ethanol, then washed in distilled water and placed in a 0.1% aqueous solution of Hyamine 2389 for five minutes. Afterwards, the seeds were washed with 70% ethanol or with sterilized distilled water and placed in the agar medium consisting of the modified Hoagland and Knop solution described by Chen *et al.* (1961). The seedlings were maintained at 25° and exposed to 16 hours/day of light. Carrot tissue cultures were also used along with rye plants as the host of *M. fascifrons*.

5. Dissection

Under a dissecting microscope on a Maximov slide with 2–3 ml of Earle's balanced salt solution, surface-sterilized eggs were dissected as follows: The posterior ends were gently pressed down with the point of a dissecting knife, while the anterior ends of the chorions were severed with a second knife. Gentle pressure was exerted to remove the embryos from their chorions and free them from yolk. Fresh salt solution was employed for three subsequent washings (Hirumi and Maramorosch,

1964a). In instances in which trypsinization was omitted, the eggs were dissected in the culture medium instead of in the salt solution. Mitsuhashi and Maramorosch (1964) used Rinaldini's salt solution (Rinaldini, 1954) for the dissection of embryos, nymphs, and adults of leafhoppers.

6. Trypsinization

Following dissection, embryonic tissues were usually subjected to mild trypsinization. Hirumi and Maramorosch (1964a) used 0.02% trypsin (commercial trypsin 1:250 solution, 2.5% in normal saline) in Earle's balanced salt solution in a water bath at 26° for 10 minutes. This treatment only loosened the tissue fragments without dissociating them. Stronger treatment caused clumping of the very viscous fragments and was, therefore, undesirable. During the initial stages of cultivation, the trypsinized tissues were found to enhance the active cell proliferation when resuspended in the culture medium.

The described mild trypsinization technique was also employed, with minor modifications, for the *in vitro* cultivation of other leafhoppers (Mitsuhashi and Maramorosch, 1964; Mitsuhashi, 1965a; Chiu and Black, 1967). Although the initial growth of cells was usually improved after trypsinization, leafhopper cell proliferation was also obtained without trypsinization (Mitsuhashi and Maramorosch, 1964; Tokumitsu and Maramorosch, 1967). Although not essential, mild trypsinization enhanced the initial growth of cells (Chiu and Black, 1967).

7. Culture Medium

During the past seven years, the initial difficulties in devising a suitable medium for leafhopper cells have been gradually overcome. Analysis of insect hemolymph provided several clues.

a. Inorganic Salts. The ionic concentration and the composition of the buffer, important in devising the balanced salt solution of the culture medium, are generally determined from hemolymph analysis. Since no complete hemolymph analysis of leafhoppers has been carried out, details of the ionic concentration are still obscure. Vago and Flandre (1963) reported that the cicadellid genera *Macrosteles* and *Philaenus* contained a high concentration of K and Mg but a low concentration of Na in the hemolymph.

Based on their findings, the concentration of sodium chloride in the leafhopper culture medium (Hirumi and Maramorosch, 1964a,b) was decreased to about two-fifths of that in a vertebrate culture medium, TC 199 (Morgan *et al.*, 1950), while the amounts of potassium chloride,

TABLE I
CULTURE MEDIUM FOR LEAFHOPPER EMBRYONIC CELLS[a,b]

Components	Concentration (mg/liter)
Inorganic salts	
$CaCl_2 \cdot 2H_2O$	510.0
$Fe(NO_3)_3 \cdot 9H_2O$	0.3
KCl	1462.0
KH_2PO_4	25.2
$MgCl_2 \cdot 6H_2O$	1333.0
$MgSO_4 \cdot 7H_2O$	1763.0
NaCl	3360.0
$NaHCO_3$	537.5
$NaH_2PO_4 \cdot H_2O$	516.0
$NaHPO_4 \cdot 7H_2O$	40.4
Carbohydrates	
Deoxyribose	0.2
Fructose	172.0
Glucose	301.0
Ribose	0.2
Sucrose	172.0
Amino acids	
L-Alanine	10.8
L-Arginine–HCl	30.1
L-Aspartic acid	12.9
L-Cysteine–HCl	0.04
L-Cystine	8.6
L-Glutamic acid	28.8
L-Glutamine	43.0
L-Glycine	21.5
L-Histidine–HCl·H_2O	9.5
L-Hydroxyproline	4.3
L-Isoleucine	8.6
L-Leucine	25.8
L-Lysine–HCl	30.1
L-Methionine	6.5
L-Phenylalanine	10.8
L-Proline	17.2
L-Serine	10.8
L-Threonine	12.9
L-Tryptophan	4.3
L-Tyrosine	17.2
L-Valine	10.8
Lactalbumin hydrolysate	4300.0
Vitamins	
p-Aminobenzoic acid	0.022
Ascorbic acid	0.022
D-Biotin	0.004

TABLE I (*Continued*)

Components	Concentration (mg/liter)
Calciferol	0.042
D-Calcium antothenate	0.004
Cholesterol	0.086
Choline chloride	0.215
Isoinositol	0.022
Menadione	0.004
Nicotinamide	0.011
Nicotinic acid	0.011
Pyridoxal–HCl	0.011
Pyridoxine–HCl	0.011
Riboflavin	0.004
Thiamine–HCl	0.004
DL-α-Tocopherolphosphate (Na$_2$)	0.004
Tween 80	2.150
Vitamin A	0.043
Other components	
Adenine–HCl·2H$_2$O	5.20
Adenosine-5'-monophosphoric acid, dihydrate (AMP)	0.09
Adenosine-5'-triphosphate disodium, tetrahydrate (ATP)	0.43
L-Glutathione	0.02
Guanine–HCl·H$_2$O	0.14
Hypoxanthine	0.13
Phenol red	19.60
Sodium acetate·3H$_2$O	35.69
Thymine	0.13
Uracil	0.13
Xanthine	0.13
Penicillin–streptomycin mixture[c]	10,000.0 (IU)
Serum	
Fetal bovine serum	127.0 (ml)
pH	6.4

[a] The culture medium is prepared by a mixing of stock solutions as follows:

Morgan's synthetic medium TC 199[c]	20 ml
Modified Vago's medium B.M. 22	20 ml
Fetal bovine serum	6 ml
Penicillin–streptomycin mixture	1 ml

[b] From Hirumi and Maramorosch (1964b).
[c] Microbiological Associates, Inc., Bethesda, Md.

magnesium sulfate, and magnesium chloride were increased. The final concentrations of inorganic salts as well as other components of Hirumi and Maramorosch's leafhopper medium are listed in Table I. This was prepared by mixing equal volumes of TC 199 and a stock solution (Table

TABLE II
MODIFIED VAGO'S MEDIUM B.M. 22[a]

Components	Concentration (mg/liter)
Inorganic salts	
$CaCl_2 \cdot 2H_2O$	1000.0
KCl	3000.0
$MgCl_2 \cdot 6H_2O$	3000.0
$MgSO_4 \cdot 7H_2O$	4000.0
$NaH_2PO_4 \cdot H_2O$	1200.0
Carbohydrates	
Fructose	400.0
Glucose	700.0
Sucrose	400.0
Amino acids	
Lactalbumin hydrolysate	10,000.0
Phenol red	25.0

[a] From Hirumi and Maramorosch (1964b).

TABLE III
BASIC MEDIUM NO. 1 FOR LEAFHOPPER CELLS[a]

Components	Concentration (mg/liter)
Inorganic salts	
$CaCl_2 \cdot 2H_2O$	200.0
KCl	200.0
$MgCl_2 \cdot 6H_2O$	100.0
NaCl	7000.0
$NaHCO_3$	120.0
$NaH_2PO_4 \cdot H_2O$	200.0
Carbohydrate	
D-Glucose	4000.0
Amino acids	
Lactalbumin hydrolysate	6500.0
Vitamins	
Yeastolate	5000.0
Serum	
Fetal bovine serum	200.0
Antibiotics	
Penicillin–streptomycin mixture[b]	10,000.0 (IU)
pH	6.5

[a] From Mitsuhashi and Maramorosch (1964).
[b] Microbiological Associates, Inc., Bethesda, Md.

II) which was modified from Medium B.M. 22 (Vago and Chastang, 1958) designed for *Bombyx mori* L. (Lepidoptera).

Although leafhopper cells were able to multiply in a wide range of inorganic salt compositions, basic medium No. 1 (Table III) provided the most adequate cell growth of the seven media tested (Mitsuhashi and Maramorosch, 1964). Mitsuhashi (1965a) increased the final concentration of sodium chloride to 436 mg/100 ml and considerably decreased the amounts of other salts. This medium was used for the cultivation of *N. cincticeps*, providing cell growth comparable to that obtained with other leafhoppers (Hirumi and Maramorosch, 1964a,b,c; Hirumi, 1965; Mitsuhashi and Maramorosch, 1964).

A concentration of sodium chloride rather high for insect cell cultures (650 mg/100 ml) was used for *M. fascifrons* cells (Tokumitsu and Maramorosch, 1966). Although this medium also supported cell growth, many cytoplasmic bubbles were observed.

Recently, Chiu and Black (1967, 1969) established a maintenance medium for leafhopper cell lines. The composition of the inorganic salts of the medium was similar to that of Schneider's Drosophila medium (Schneider, 1964). The concentrations of sodium chloride, potassium chloride, and magnesium sulfate were decreased to half the strength of those in Schneider's medium. The amounts of monobasic potassium phosphate, calcium chloride, and sodium bicarbonate were slightly decreased, and dibasic sodium phosphate was omitted (Table IV).

Although leafhopper cells have been successfully cultivated using these different balanced salt solutions, critical analyses of leafhopper hemolymph will be needed to establish an optimum salt solution. Until now, salt solutions have been developed only through trial and error by empirically modifying established mammalian culture media.

b. pH. The optimum pH of invertebrate culture media varied from 6.3 to 7.8, according to the species used. It was pointed out that the medium ought to be accurately buffered since the cultured insect cells are very sensitive to pH changes in the medium (Vago, 1967).

The pH of the hemolymph of cicadellids *M. sexnotatus* and *P. spumarius* has been established as 6.4–6.6 by means of a color indicator in a capillary (Vago and Flandre, 1963). In accordance with these findings most leafhopper culture media were adjusted to a pH 6.4–6.6 (Hirumi and Maramorosch, 1964a,b; Mitsuhashi and Maramorosch, 1964; Mitsuhashi, 1965a; Tokumitsu and Maramorosch, 1967). Chiu and Black's medium (1967) was adjusted to pH 7.0.

c. Carbohydrates. Hirumi and Maramorosch (1964a,b) used 72.3 mg of glucose, 17.0 mg of sucrose, and 17.0 mg of fructose in 100 ml of the

TABLE IV
LEAFHOPPER TISSUE CULTURE MEDIUM[a]

Components[b]	Concentration (mg/liter)
Inorganic salts	
CaCl₂·2H₂O	400.0
KCl	800.0
KH₂PO₄	300.0
MgSO₄·7H₂O	1850.0
NaCl	1050.0
NaHCO₃	350.0
Carbohydrate	
Dextrose	4000.0
Amino acids	
Lactalbumin hydrolysate	6500.0
Vitamins	
Yeastolate	5000.0
Serum	
Fetal bovine serum	200.0 (ml)
Other components	
Fungizone	2.5
Neomycin	50.0
Penicillin G	100,000.0 (IU)
Streptomycin	100.0
pH	7.0

[a] From Chiu and Black (1969).
[b] Note: A set of component solutions is prepared as follows:

    (1) 400 mg $CaCl_2 \cdot 2H_2O$ in 20 ml H_2O
    (2) 1850 mg $MgSO_4 \cdot 7H_2O$ in 20 ml H_2O
    (3) 800 mg KCl, 300 mg KH_2PO_4, and 1050 mg NaCl in 60 ml H_2O
    (4) 350 mg $NaHCO_3$ in 50 ml H_2O
    (5) 4000 mg dextrose in 100 ml H_2O
    (6) 6500 mg lactalbumin hydrolysate in 200 ml H_2O
    (7) 5000 mg yeastolate in 100 ml
    (8) 200 ml of fetal bovine serum
    (9) 100 000 units of penicillin G, 100 mg streptomycin, and 50 mg neomycin
        in 20 ml H_2O
    (10) 2.5 mg fungizone in 2.5 ml H_2O

Before starting to mix the aliquots, two aliquots of (8) should be thawed, brought quickly to 56° with stirring for 30 minutes, and then cooled (6) should be thawed, redissolved by heating to about 50°, and then cooled. (1) to (10) are added to 227.5 ml of distilled water in a 2-liter erlenmeyer flask in the order listed above.

final culture medium for *M. fascifrons* (Table I). Subsequently, it was found that glucose provided an adequate carbon and energy source for leafhopper cell growth, and substituting a part of glucose with fructose and/or sucrose did not improve the cell growth (Mitsuhashi and Maramorosch, 1964). Glucose alone at 360 mg/100 ml of the final culture medium was used later for *N. cincticeps* (Mitsuhashi, 1965a) (Table II). Tokumitsu and Maramorosch (1967) used glucose at 500 mg/100 ml of the medium for *M. fascifrons*. For leafhopper cell strains, Chiu and Black (1967) added 400 mg of glucose/100 ml of the growth medium.

d. Amino Acids. It is known that some insect hemolymphs (Lepidoptera) contain a high concentration of amino acids, as compared to vertebrates (Wyatt, 1956; Martignoni and Scallion, 1961). However, it is also known that some insect cells (Diptera) require low concentrations of amino acids to grow *in vitro* (Kitamura, 1965). Qualities and quantities of amino acids in culture media for leafhoppers and aphids have been developed empirically because of the lack of information concerning the hemolymph analysis.

Although leafhopper cells did not multiply in TC 199 culture medium (Hirumi and Maramorosch, 1963a; Mitsuhashi and Maramorosch, 1964), it was found that a substitution, a part of TC 199 with lactalbumin hydrolysates, provides adequate amino acids for the growth of leafhopper cells (Hirumi and Maramorosch, 1964a,b; Mitsuhashi and Maramorosch, 1964; Mitsuhashi, 1965a).

It was also reported that lactalbumin hydrolysate alone, at 650 mg/100 ml of the medium, could supply adequate amino acids for the growth of leafhopper cells (Mitsuhashi and Maramorosch, 1964; Chiu and Black, 1967).

Amino acids, as in Grace's medium (Grace, 1962), were also used at one-tenth concentration with 500 mg of lactalbumin hydrolysate/100 ml for leafhopper cell cultures (Tokumitsu and Maramorosch, 1967).

e. Vitamins. Vitamins, used in the vertebrate culture medium TC 199, were incorporated into the leafhopper culture media at about two-fifths concentration of TC 199, providing very active growth of embryonic cells (Hirumi and Maramorosch, 1964a,b,c; Hirumi, 1965).

Although the addition of a vitamin mixture, corresponding to that of Eagle's minimum essential medium (Eagle, 1959), did not improve leafhopper cell growth, vitamins in the form of yeast extracts (TC-yeastolate, Difco Laboratories) were found to be adequate to provide cell growth (Mitsuhashi and Maramorosch, 1964). A combination of pure vitamins, corresponding in strength to one-fifth of those in the TC 199 medium, and of yeastolate at 200 mg/100 ml, was also found satisfactory for embryonic leafhopper cell cultures (Mitsuhashi, 1965a).

For the maintenance medium of leafhopper cell lines, 500 mg of yeastolate/100 ml was used as the vitamin source instead of pure vitamins, thereby prolonging cultivation of the cell lines (Chiu and Black, 1967, 1969).

f. Sera. The addition of homologous hemolymph into culture media for invertebrate cells has been considered an important factor in successful invertebrate cell culture. It is very difficult to obtain a sufficient amount of leafhopper or aphid hemolymph. Moreover, the melanization of the hemolymph with tyrosinase presents another difficulty.

The incorporation of a leafhopper nymph extract or of a heterologous insect serum from *Leucania unipuncta* HW. (Lepidoptera) did not stimulate the outgrowth of leafhopper cells from tissue explants (Hirumi and Maramorosch, 1963a). However, the addition of fetal bovine serum, heterologous vertebrate serum, into the leafhopper culture medium provided the necessary growth factors. Leafhopper cell culture does not require homologous or heterologous arthropod sera (Hirumi and Maramorosch, 1964a). Fetal bovine serum could be substituted with newborn calf serum but not with normal calf, chicken, or horse sera. The latter was unsatisfactory, as was found by Mitsuhashi and Maramorosch (1964).

8. Culture Vessels and Techniques

The total amounts of insect materials are usually rather small, compared to those employed in vertebrate tissue cultivation. Therefore, the initial procedure employed the sitting drop technique and small culture vessels. Vago and Flandre devised a special vial (1963) which facilitated the handling of small volumes of culture medium. They obtained cell growth from leafhopper tissues by using a semi-plasma-clot technique in such vials.

To obtain better observations under high magnifications of phase contrast, Vago and Flandre's vial was modified (Hirumi, 1963; Vago, 1967) and commercially produced. In such flasks, sitting drop cultures were used for embryonic leafhopper tissues. Sitting drop cultures were prepared by placing approximately 0.2 ml of culture medium with suspended trypsinized tissue fragments, derived from about 10 embryos for each flask, on the center of the cover glass, which was sealed on the bottom of the culture flask (Hirumi and Maramorosch, 1964a,b,c; Hirumi, 1965).

The sitting drop culture technique was also employed with chambers consisting of a microslide ring and cover glasses, sealed on the top and bottom of the ring (Mitsuhashi and Maramorosch, 1964; Mitsuhashi, 1965a; Tokumitsu and Maramorosch, 1967; Hirumi and Maramorosch, 1968).

When larger populations of cells were desired, plastic T-type flasks of 30-ml capacity were used. In these, 15 drops of culture medium, with tissue fragments, were placed in the sitting drop manner. Hirumi and Maramorosch (1968) were able to obtain leafhopper cell growth of primary cultures for more than 150 days, following an initial cultivation of seven days and supplementing with 3–5 ml of the culture medium.

B. Cell Growth

1. Primary Culture

Most leafhopper cell cultures have been obtained from primary cultures except for the establishment of cell lines by Chiu and Black (1967). Only minor differences have been described in the growth of cells from different leafhopper species.

A number of dipolar single cells became attached to the surface of the culture flasks during the initial few hours of cultivation. These dipolar cells usually increased in number up to tenfold within the next two days, but their longevity was generally very limited (Hirumi and Maramorosch, 1964a,b,c; Hirumi, 1965; Chiu and Black, 1967).

One type of fibroblast-like cells began to appear from tissue explants within 24 hours of cultivation. These cells continued to grow actively, forming networks and numerous mitoses. Cell multiplication occurred along the line of dipolar cytoplasmic processes from the center of the outgrowth to the periphery. For more than 120 days this type of fibroblast-like cell continued to grow, becoming dominant in the culture (Hirumi and Maramorosch, 1964a,b,c; 1968; Hirumi, 1965; Mitsuhashi and Maramorosch, 1964; Mitsuhashi, 1965a; Chiu et al., 1966; Chiu and Black, 1967).

Besides this dominant type, two other types of fibroblast-like cells were observed. One appeared in old cultures (Mitsuhashi and Maramorosch, 1964). Both types were large, often developing irregular cytoplasmic pseudopodia at both ends. Frequent mitotic divisions were observed. Another cell type formed networks with irregular pseudopodia after six to eight days of cultivation. Nuclei in this type of cells were loosely spread, and the cells continued to divide mitotically for a long period although the outgrowths of this type were not extensive (Hirumi and Maramorosch, 1964c).

Epithelial cells became attached to the surface of the culture flask during the initial 48 hours of cultivation. The cells multiplied rapidly, with expanding cell sheets that gradually engulfed the original tissue fragments (Fig. 2). Mitotic divisions were especially numerous at the periphery of the outgrowth, and cells of this type became dominant in

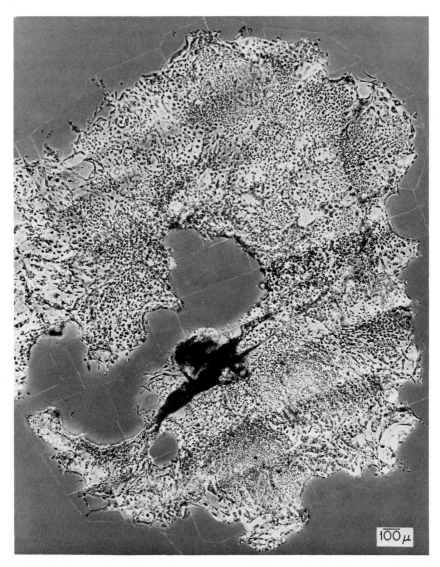

FIG. 2. Outgrowth of the embryonic tissue of *Macrosteles fascifrons* on the 33rd day of cultivation. Note a large cell sheet, consisting of two types of epithelial cells. A small dark mass at the lower center of the photograph is an original explant (×39). (From Hirumi, 1965. By courtesy of Wakayama Igaku.)

the culture (Hirumi and Maramorosch, 1964a,b,c, 1968; Hirumi, 1965; Mitsuhashi and Maramorosch, 1964; Mitsuhashi, 1965a; Chiu and Black, 1967). These epithelial cells varied in size and changed from one size to another during cultivation, especially at the periphery of the outgrowth.

Two different types were distinguished at first (Hirumi and Maramorosch, 1964c; Hirumi, 1965). Later, Mitsuhashi and Maramorosch (1964) classified them into five types based largely on their size.

The same tissue fragments yielded both fibroblast-like and epithelial cells, but in some instances only one of these two cell types grew. Larger tissue fragments provided better growing conditions than smaller fragments. Cells derived from small tissue explants generally began to deteriorate on the 15th day, while those obtained from large explants continued to grow for a long period (Hirumi and Maramorosch, 1964a,b).

The original explants yielded also two distinct types of large phagocytes, usually observed after 24 hours of cultivation, when they began to migrate by amoeboid movements. Although both types of cells increased in number by migration from the original explants, no mitotic division was seen (Hirumi and Maramorosch, 1964c; Hirumi, 1965).

Cultures of *M. fascifrons* provided two types of wandering cells that multiplied by mitosis. These cells also wandered by amoeboid movements and resembled hemocytes (Mitsuhashi and Maramorosch, 1964). Mitsuhashi (1965a) observed three different types of wandering cells in cultures of *N. cincticeps,* different from those of *M. fascifrons* and lacking mitotic divisions.

Cultures of nymphal and imaginal tissues provided various cell types that grew in the same manner as the cells from embryonic explants. Some explanted organs retained their movements for more than two months *in vitro.* Leg muscles continued to contract, while cells proliferated from their cut openings. Oviducts and alimentary tracts continued peristaltic movements for long periods. Of all cultured organs, the stomach was found to attach the most easily to the surface of the culture flasks. Not all tissues and organs provided proliferating cells, however. No cell growth was obtained from the epidermis, mycetomes, Malpighian tubules, testes, fat bodies, muscles, salivary glands, thoracic and abdominal ganglia, subesophagal ganglia, or brain (Mitsuhashi and Maramorosch, 1964).

2. Subculture

Until cell lines of leafhoppers were established (Chiu and Black, 1967), subculturing of the growing cells was not successful. Mitsuhashi and Maramorosch (1964) removed the original tissue explants and newly growing cells from the primary culture of *M. fascifrons* embryos, and after short trypsinization attempted to set up new cultures. Whenever the original explants were transferred, there was increased activity in cell proliferation. However, subcultured cells failed to continue to grow, despite their adhesion to the culture flask.

3. Cell Lines

Leafhopper cell lines have been established from embryonic tissues in the stage of blastokinetic movement by Chiu and Black (1967). In order to obtain a large number of cells per culture, 20 or more tissue fragments were placed in a small quantity of medium in the center of sealable petri dishes in the same manner as in the sitting drop culture. After obtaining primary cell growths, the cultures were exposed to 0.05% trypsin in Rinaldini's salt solution, free of calcium and magnesium ions, for 10 minutes. To stop the trypsinization, an equal volume of growth medium was added. The medium was replaced with fresh medium after most of the living cells had become attached to the surface of the culture dishes. This procedure was repeated four times at seven- to eight-day intervals with the petri dish unchanged but with the medium wetting greater areas each time. Afterwards, subculturing was carried out regularly, forming confluent monolayers of the cultured cells.

By using these techniques, nine cell lines were established from *A. constricta* embryos and two cell lines from *A. quadripunctata*. These lines consisted of epithelial cells. The cell line of *A. constricta* "line 2" (AC 2) was successfully subcultured more than 55 times, while two cell lines of *A. quadripunctata* were past the ninth and twentieth generations, respectively. There have also been attempts at establishing cell lines of other leafhopper vector species, such as *A. sanquinolenta* and *A. novella*. Cell lines of *A. constricta* have been utilized in studying the multiplication of wound tumor virus (Chiu *et al.*, 1966; Chiu and Black, 1967, 1969; Liu, 1969) and of potato yellow dwarf virus (Chiu *et al.*, 1970; Liu, 1969). At the University of California at Berkeley, Jensen (1970) obtained a cell line of *Colladonus montanus* (Van Duzee) that was carried through more than three years.

It seems that the successful subculturing of leafhopper cells requires a large number of cells at the outset of cultivation.

C. Morphological Aspects

1. Main Cell Types

The epithelial cells and the fibroblast-like cells generally become predominant in the leafhopper cell cultures. So far, four types of fibroblast-like cells, five types of epithelial cells, two types of phagocytes, and two types of wandering cells have been described. Among these a type of fibroblast-like cell and four types of epithelial cells usually dominated the primary cultures. The growth of other types of cells was not extensive

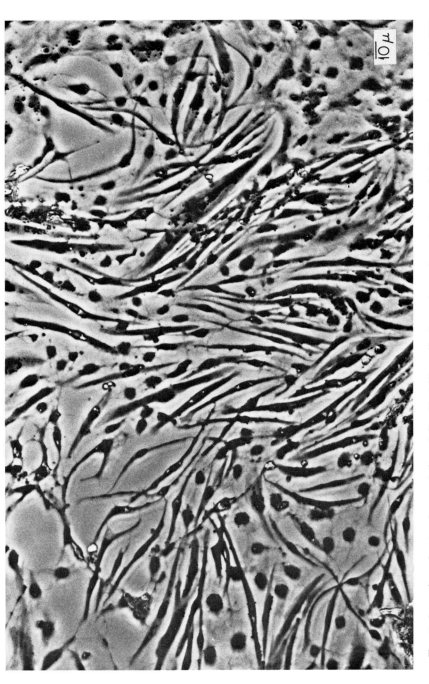

FIG. 3. A portion of networks, consisting of fibroblast-like cells from the embryonic tissue of *Agallia constricta*, on the 59th day of cultivation (×550). (Original photograph by H. Hirumi.)

and never became dominant during the cultivation (Hirumi and Mara-morosch, 1964a,b,c, 1968; Hirumi, 1965; Mitsuhashi and Maramorosch, 1964; Mitsuhashi, 1965a; Chiu and Black, 1967).

a. Fibroblast-Like Cells. Fibroblast-like cells, derived from original ex-plants, became dominant during 24 hours after initial cultivation and continued to grow actively for more than 150 days, forming networks. Nuclei of these cells were small and compact, about 7 μm in diameter (Fig. 3), and the cells had long, thin, dipolar pseudopodia approximately 40 μm in length and 8 μm in width at the widest part. During the initial period of cultivation these fibroblast-like cells were the most common type that always appeared in the cultures prior to the other types (Hirumi and Maramorosch, 1964c, 1968; Hirumi, 1965; Mitsuhashi and Maramorosch, 1964; Mitsuhashi, 1965a).

b. Epithelial Cells. The first type of epithelial cell usually became at-tached to the culture flasks and began to grow between 24 and 48 hours after initial cultivation. The cells that formed sheets and had well-spread cytoplasm with numerous cytoplasmic granules were of an average size between 75 and 120 μm, and their nuclei were approximately 30 μm in di-ameter (Fig. 4). The cytoplasmic granules were observed on the fourth day, and they increased gradually in number from the center to the periphery of the outgrowth. The cells continued to grow mitotically for a long period (Hirumi and Maramorosch, 1964c, 1968; Hirumi, 1965; Mitsuhashi and Maramorosch, 1964; Mitsuhashi, 1965a).

The second type of epithelial cells differed from the first by being devoid of large cytoplasmic granules or oil droplets and being generally smaller than the cells of the first type. These cells made their appearance somewhat later than the first type, but they multiplied more vigorously and became the dominant type in the culture after one month of culti-vation. Many cells of this type were polygonal in shape, forming fairly compact cell sheets (Fig. 5). These cells also continued to grow for more than 150 days (Hirumi and Maramorosch, 1964c; 1968; Hirumi, 1965; Mitsuhashi and Maramorosch, 1964; Mitsuhashi, 1965a).

Epithelial cells of the third type were characterized by rounded nuclei, which were surrounded by thin cytoplasms; the borders between cells were clearly delineated. The average size of the cells was about 50 μm and that of their nuclei was 12 μm in diameter. These cells were classified as type C (Mitsuhashi and Maramorosch, 1964; Mitsuhashi, 1965a); however, there were many intermediate shapes between the second type and the third type (see Fig. 5). Thus, it is possible that the third type is merely a variation of the second type.

The fourth type of epithelial cell was categorized as type D or giant

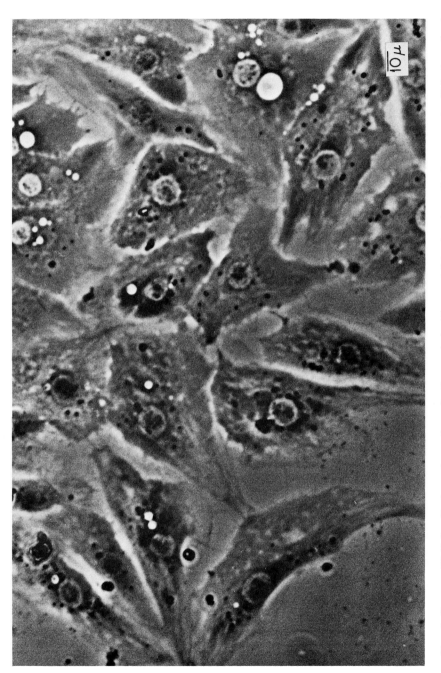

FIG. 4. Large epithelial cells from the embryonic tissue of *Agallia constricta*, forming cell sheets, on the 59th day of cultivation (×550). (Original photograph by H. Hirumi.)

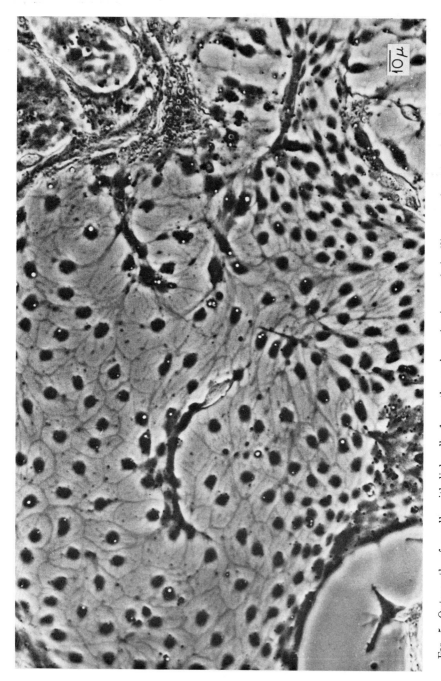

FIG. 5. Outgrowth of small epithelial cells from the embryonic tissue of *Agallia constricta*, forming a fairly compact cell sheet, on the 59th day of cultivation. Note cytoplasms of the cells free from large cytoplasmic granules (×550). (Original photograph by H. Hirumi.)

epithelial cells (Mitsuhashi and Maramorosch, 1964; Mitsuhashi, 1965a). These cells were very large and spread very thinly. Sometimes they attained 200 μm in diameter. The nuclei of the cells were generally spherical in shape, having an average of 30 μm in diameter. The cells were often polyploid, and binucleate cells were often observed. Type D cells appeared only on the outside of the growing cell sheets and were primarily found in old cultures.

c. Cell Lines. Some differences were noticed in the cell morphology and growth habit of the nine cell lines of *A. constricta*, although all consisted mainly of epithelial cell types. One line differed from the others by comprising more slender cells. Even after a steady growth rate was reached, none of the nine cell lines became uniform so far as cell morphology was concerned (Chiu and Black, 1967).

2. Cell Divisions

a. Normal Mitoses. Normal mitotic divisions were often observed in the dominant cells, either in the fibroblast-like cells or the epithelial cells, throughout the period of cultivation. Generally, mitoses appeared frequently at the periphery of the outgrowth and occasionally in other regions. Most of the cell divisions occurred parallel to the surface of the culture flask, but sometimes cell divisions, vertical to the surface, were also seen.

Late prophase was recognizable by the appearance of chromosomes under a phase-contrast microscope. Prophase lasted 30 minutes or longer at 25°. From late prophase to metaphase, the cytoplasmic processes became detached from the outgrowth, except for its bipolar ends. Thus, the cell decreased in size and became denser, forming a spindle shape. The time from late prophase to metaphase varied from 10 to 150 minutes at 25°.

At metaphase the chromosomes in the equatorial plane were recognized as a short straight line (Fig. 6A). At this stage active movements were seen in the cytoplasm. A few seconds before the beginning of anaphase the cells became more compact but did not detach from the cell sheet. The duration of metaphase varied from 10 to 60 minutes.

Anaphase lasted 2–10 minutes (Fig. 6B–G), and it took about 20 minutes for the completion of telophase (Fig. 6H–J). In the beginning of telophase, pseudopodia appeared and gradually grew out, forming well-spread cytoplasmic processes. The nuclear membrane reformed usually 30 minutes after the completion of cell division (Hirumi and Maramorosch, 1964c; Hirumi, 1965; Mitsuhashi, 1965a).

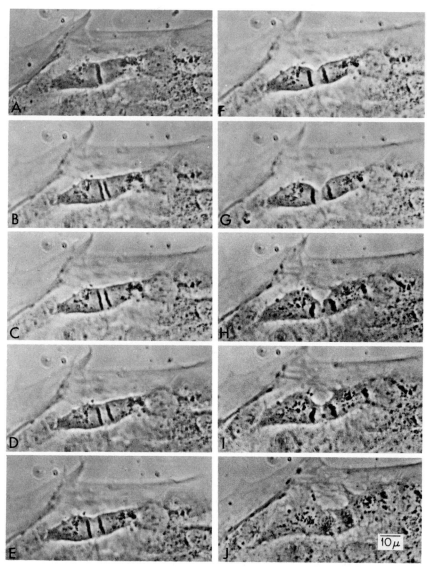

Fig. 6. Mitotic division of a large epithelial cell of *Macrosteles fascifrons* embryo, on the 18th day of cultivation. (A) Metaphase, (B–G) anaphase; (H–J) telophase (×550). (From Hirumi, 1965. By courtesy of Wakayama Igaku.)

b. Abnormal Mitoses. Abnormal cell divisions, such as multipolar mitoses and polynucleate cells, were observed in the leafhopper cell cultures. These cells appeared rather frequently in the epithelial cells. Tripolar mitoses were common in the large epithelial cells. The time for the completion of these cell divisions was almost the same as that for normal mitoses (Hirumi, 1965; Mitsuhashi, 1965a).

Sometimes cytoplasmic divisions did not follow the completion of anaphase, thus resulting in the production of binucleate cells or polynucleate cells. These occurred in the large epithelial cells (Hirumi, 1965; Mitsuhashi, 1965a).

Polyploid cells were also observed. At metaphase, it took a much longer time to complete their chromosomal arrangement than in diploid cells (Mitsuhashi, 1965a).

c. Karyotype. Karyotype analysis of *N. cincticeps* was attempted on the cultured cells 50 days following initial cultivation. Embryonic cells, which were obtained from three-day-old eggs, as well as the spermatocytes and the oocytes, which were excised from the young adults, were also examined (Mitsuhashi, 1965b). It was reported that the number of chromosomes in the diploid cells was 15 in males $(2A + X)$ and 16 in females $(2A + 2X)$. Of the 3697 cultured cells which were examined, 3484 were diploid, 57 were triploid, and 156 were tetraploid.

3. Cytoplasmic Protrusions

During a study of the effect on cell growth of different concentrations of mineral salts and glucose in the culture medium, Tokumitsu and Maramorosch (1967) observed the formation of cytoplasmic protrusions, transient protuberances, or blebs at the cell surface in epithelial cells of leafhoppers. Bubbling seemed to be a regular phenomenon in cultured cicadellid cells during mitotic divisions. There seemed to be a definite correlation between the degree of bubbling and the length of the mitotic intervals. The protuberances appeared not only during anaphase and telophase but often also at metaphase and even at very early metaphase. When they occurred at metaphase, the duration of the metaphase was prolonged. In tissue cultures of the six-spotted leafhopper *M. fascifrons*, the protuberances were most prevalent at anaphase or early telophase. The bubbling of leafhopper cells *in vitro* differed from the bubbling described for vertebrate cells, in which active cell protuberances appear mainly during late anaphase and telophase. The prolonged metaphase of bubbling leafhopper cells suggests a functional relationship between the formation of cell protuberances and the duration of the metaphase.

III. APHID (APHIDIDAE) AND PLANTHOPPER (DELPHACIDAE) CELL CULTURE

Tissue culture of Aphididae has been studied less extensively. Preliminary attempts have been carried out with cells of the pea aphid, *Acyrthosiphum pisum* (Harris), a vector of pea enation mosaic virus (Tokumitsu and Maramorosch, 1966). Tokumitsu and Maramorosch (1966) collected embryos from surface-sterilized females, immersing the adults in a Ringer-Tyrode solution (Carlson, 1946) and removing the embryos by cesarean sections. Subsequently, the embryos were divided into small tissue fragments, using steel knives. The sharp tools were made by breaking a stainless steel razor blade and soldering the small pieces (1×6 mm) onto the dissecting needles. Surface sterilization could not be applied successfully to the embryos because their chorions, when obtained by cesarean sections, were too tender. At the suggestion of Vago (1962), we employed aseptic rearing of *A. pisum* similar to that described for leafhoppers (Mitsuhashi and Maramorosch, 1964). Aseptic aphid colonies were obtained by surface-sterilizing parthenogenetic apterous females from a greenhouse insectary. The animals were immersed in 70% ethanol for approximately five seconds and, after recovery, confined to pea (*Pisum sativum* L.) plants grown from surface-sterilized seed on agar media in test tubes. Nymphs were delivered again by parthenogenetic females after a delay of a few days.

Aphid nymphs from aseptic colonies were cut into small tissue fragments to obtain cell cultures. The medium was similar to Grace's Lepidoptera medium (1962), except for the omission of calcium pantothenate. After 48 hours, fibroblast cells of two types began to migrate and to scatter on the surface of the culture flasks. The larger type of cells, derived primarily from the smaller trypsinized tissue fragments, survived and moved for up to two weeks. The second, smaller type, migrated from alimentary tract tissues. Multinucleate cells were observed in the aphid cell cultures for up to 20 days, but no cell divisions were reported (Tokumitsu and Maramorosch, 1966). Young nymphs provided the best material for *in vitro* cultivation. It soon became obvious that the medium that proved adequate for the cultivation of leafhopper cells was not suitable for cells of aphids. Attempts have continued in several laboratories to devise aphid tissue culture media that would support prolonged growth of aphid cells.

Although no prolonged cultivation has been achieved and studies of morphological aspects of the cultured cells have not been completed, some preliminary information was obtained recently. Active growth of pea aphid cells was obtained from embryonic tissues in a culture medium, consisting of 10 parts of Schneider's medium, 10 parts of modified Vago's medium B.M. 22, and 3 parts of fetal bovine serum with antibiotics. Four different types of fibroblast-like cells, an epithelial type, and large multinucleate cells grew in this medium, and some cells continued mitotic divisions for several weeks (Hirumi, 1970).

The aphid cells obtained are described below. The first of fibroblast-like cells was represented by dipolar, spindle-shaped fibroblasts, having long cytoplasmic processes. The cells were approximately 120 μm in length and 8 μm in width. They appeared during the 48 hours following initial cultivation of the original explants. Evidence of mitotic divisions in the cultured cells was not clear (Fig. 7A) (Tokumitsu and Maramorosch, 1966; Hirumi, 1970). The second type of fibroblast-like cells was smaller than Type I, 80 μm in length and 6 μm in width, with thin bipolar cyto-plasmic processes and small nuclei of 4 μm in diameter (Tokumitsu and Maramorosch, 1966). The third type of fibroblast-like cells was com-prised of more or less spindle-shaped cells which formed colonies. Mitotic divisions were observed in those cells (Fig. 7B) (Hirumi, 1970). The fourth type of cells was most likely a fibroblast type although it could have been a hemocyte. The cytoplasm of cells of that type had irregular extensions, and the cells multiplied by mitotic divisions (Fig. 7D) (Hirumi, 1970).

Large multinucleate cells were also common in the aphid cell cultures. Just after migration from the original tissue fragments, these large cells were spindle-shaped and uniform in size. Within a few hours after migra-tion, they attached to the surface of the culture flasks and began to show irregular cytoplasmic protrusions. Sometimes these cytoplasmic processes were conspicuously broad (Fig. 7C) (Tokumitsu and Mara-morosch, 1966; Hirumi, 1970). The origin of these cells is still unknown.

The survival of *in vitro* aphid cells obtained from *Hyperomyzus lactucae* L. permitted the successful inoculation of such primary cell cultures with the sawthistle yellow vein virus (Peters and Black, 1970). Cell suspensions were obtained by treating the embryonic tissues with pronase. The cells were seeded on coverslips and infected with the virus. In some of the attached tissue fragments several cells were infected and a maximum was reached after 48 hours. As many as 1700 infected cells were obtained in a single coverslip culture. Although the results were encouraging, the preparation of primary cultures on coverslips proved tedious and the cell variety in primary cultures was disadvantageous since their susceptibility to virus infection was not uniform, even though the virus was highly infectious. Attempts at subculturing were unsuccessful.

Planthopper cultivation *in vitro* has been attempted by Mitsuhashi

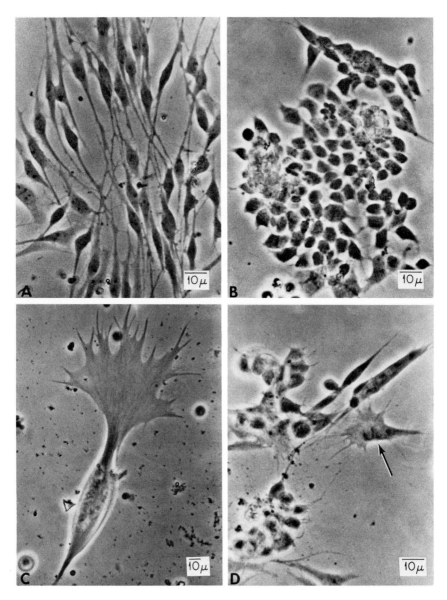

Fig. 7. Cultured cells of aphid embryos, *Acyrthosiphum pisum*, on the third day of cultivation. (A) A portion of networks, consisting of fibroblast-like cells derived from the embryonic alimentary tract. (×600). (B) Growth with mitotic divisions of fibroblast-like cells, forming cell sheets (×600). (C) A large multinucleate cell with broad cytoplasmic processes (×300). (D) Mitotic division in a small fibroblast-like cell at anaphase (arrow) (×600). (Original photograph by H. Hirumi.)

(1969b). It was found that, similarly to leafhopper cultivation, the blastokinetic stage was the most suitable for establishing primary cultures. Eggs had to be used before completion of blastokinesis because later handling was impaired by the deposition of a waxy substance (Mitsuhashi, 1969b). Surface sterilization and trypsinization followed the established procedures for leafhopper cultivation, as described earlier. The embryos had to be cut into several pieces to assure cell migration. The medium consisted of Grace's Lepidoptera medium (1962), supplemented with 20% fetal bovine serum and 1% *L. striatellus* egg extract. Cell migration started within 24 hours, and most cells that migrated were of the fibroblast type. A few epithelial cells were observed in the vicinity of the explants. Mitoses occurred in cells within the explants, but not in cells that migrated. Survival up to 40 days was obtained.

More successful was a recent attempt to culture *L. striatellus* embryonic tissues, reported by Yamada *et al.* (1970). The authors supplemented Mitsuhashi's NCM-4A basic medium with the hemolymph of *Philosamia cynthia* Pryeri and obtained active cell migration with, or without, trypsinization. One type of fibroblast-like cells, two types of wandering cells, and three types of epithelial-like cells were observed. The embryonic tissues were cultivated for over 100 days *in vitro*. Although subculturing was carried out successfully, no cell line was obtained from migrating cells.

REFERENCES

Black, L. M. (1959). *In* "Viruses" (F. M. Burnet and W. M. Stanley, eds.), Vol. 2, pp. 157–185. Academic Press, New York.
Carlson, J. G. (1946). *Biol. Bull.* **90**, 109–121.
Casper, R. (1969). *Nachrichtenbl. Deut. Pflanzenschutzdienst., Stuttgart* **21**, 177–182.
Chen, T.-A., Kilpatrick. R. A., and Rich, A. E. (1961). *Phytopathology* **51**, 799–800.
Chiu, R.-J., and Black, L. M. (1967). *Nature (London)* **215**, 1076–1078.
Chiu, R.-J., and Black, L. M., (1969). *Virology* **37**, 667–677.
Chiu, R.-J., Reddy, D. V. R., and Black, L. M. (1966). *Virology* **30**, 562–566.
Chiu, R.-J., Liu, H.-Y., Macleod, R., and Black, L. M. (1970). *Virology* **40**, 387–396.
Day, M. F., and Grace, T. D. C. (1959). *Annu. Rev. Entomol.* **4**, 17–38.
Eagle, H. (1959). *Science* **130**, 432–437.
Earle, W. R. (1943). *J. Nat. Cancer Inst.* **4**, 165–212.
Fukushi, T., and Shikata, E. (1963). *Virology* **21**, 503–505.
Goodchild, A. J. P. (1954). *Nature (London)* **173**, 504–505.
Grace, T. D. C. (1959). *Trans. N. Y. Acad. Sci.* [2] **21**, 237–241.
Grace, T. D. C. (1962). *Nature (London)* **195**, 788–789.
Granados, R. R., Hirumi, H., and Maramorosch, K. (1967). *J. Invertebr. Pathol.* **9**, 147–159.
Granados, R. R., Ward, L. S., and Maramorosch, K. (1968). *Virology* **34**, 790–796.
Hartzell, A. (1958). *Proc. Int. Congr. Entomol., 10th, 1956* Vol. 2, pp. 319–325.

Herold, F., and Munz, K. (1965). *Virology* **25**, 412–417.

Hirumi, H. (1963). *Contrib. Boyce Thompson Inst.* **22**, 113–115.

Hirumi, H. (1965). *Wakayama Igaku* **15**, 325–334.

Hirumi, H. (1970). Unpublished data.

Hirumi, H. (1971). *Curr. Top. Microbiol. Immunol.* **55**, 170–195.

Hirumi, H., and Maramorosch, K. (1963a). *Ann. Epiphyt.* **14**, 77–79.

Hirumi, H., and Maramorosch, K. (1963b). *Contrib. Boyce Thompson Inst.* **21**, 141–152.

Hirumi, H., and Maramorosch, K. (1964a). *Exp. Cell Res.* **36**, 625–631.

Hirumi, H., and Maramorosch, K. (1964b). *Science* **144**, 1465–1467.

Hirumi, H., and Maramorosch, K. (1964c). *Contrib. Boyce Thompson Inst.* **22**, 343–352.

Hirumi, H., and Maramorosch, K. (1968). *Proc. Int. Colloq. Invertebr. Tissue Cult., 2nd, 1967* pp. 203–217.

Hirumi, H., Granados, R. R., and Maramorosch, K. (1967). *J. Virol.* **1**, 430–444.

Jensen, D. D. (1970). Personal communication.

Jones, B. M. (1962). *Biol. Rev. Cambridge Phil. Soc.* **37**, 512–536.

Kitamura, S. (1965). *Kobe J. Med. Sci.* **11**, 23–30.

Liu, H.-Y. (1969). Ph.D. Thesis, University of Illinois, Urbana, Illinois.

Maramorosch, K. (1956). *Virology* **2**, 369–376.

Maramorosch, K. (1962). *Proc. Int. Congr. Entomol., 11th, 1960* Vol. 2, pp. 801–807.

Maramorosch, K. (1963). *Annu. Rev. Entomol.* **8**, 369–414.

Maramorosch, K., Granados, R. R., and Hirumi, H. (1970). *Adv. Virus Res.* **16**, 135–193.

Martignoni, M. E. (1960). *Experientia* **16**, 125–128.

Martignoni, M. E. (1962). *Proc. Annu. Biol. Colloq. [Oregon State Univ.]* **23**, 89–110.

Martignoni, M. E., and Scallion, R. J. (1961). *Biol. Bull.* **121**, 507–520.

Mitsuhashi, J. (1965a). *Jap. J. Appl. Entomol. Zool.* **9**, 107–114.

Mitsuhashi, J. (1965b). *Jap. J. Appl. Entomol. Zool.* **9**, 137–141.

Mitsuhashi, J. (1966). *Appl. Entomol. Zool.* **1**, 103–104.

Mitsuhashi, J. (1969a). *In* "Viruses, Vectors, and Vegetation" (K. Maramorosch, ed.), pp. 475–503. Wiley (Interscience), New York.

Mitsuhashi, J. (1969b). *Appl. Entomol. Zool.* **4**, 151–153.

Mitsuhashi, J. (1970). *Appl. Entomol. Zool.* **5**, 47–49.

Mitsuhashi, J., and Maramorosch, K. (1963). *Contrib. Boyce Thompson Inst.* **22**, 165–173.

Mitsuhashi, J., and Maramorosch, K. (1964). *Contrib. Boyce Thompson Inst.* **22**, 435–460.

Mitsuhashi, J., and Nasu, S. (1967). *Appl. Entomol. Zool.* **2**, 113–114.

Morgan, J. F., Morton, H. J., and Parker, R. C. (1950). *Proc. Soc. Exp. Biol., Med.* **73**, 1–8.

Nasu, S. (1965). *Jap. J. Appl. Entomol. Zool.* **9**, 225–237.

O'Loughlin, G. T., and Chambers, T. C. (1967). *Virology* **33**, 262–271.

Peters, D., and Black, L. M. (1970). *Virology* **40**, 847–853.

Richardson, J., and Sylvester, E. S. (1968). *Virology* **35**, 347–355.

Rinaldini, L. M. (1954). *Nature (London)* **173**, 1134–1135.

Schneider, I. (1964). *J. Exp. Zool.* **156**, 91–103.

Schneider, I. (1967). *In* "Methods in Developmental Biology" (F. H. Wilt and N. K. Wessells, eds.), pp. 543–554. Crowell, New York.

Shikata, E., and Maramorosch, K. (1965). *Virology* **27**, 461–475.

Shikata, E., and Maramorosch, K. (1966). *J. Nat. Cancer Inst.* **36**, 97–116.

Shikata, E., and Maramorosch, K. (1967). *Virology* **32**, 363–377.

Shikata, E., Orenski, S. W., Hirumi, H., Mitsuhashi, J., and Maramorosch, K. (1964). *Virology* **23**, 441–444.

Shikata, E., Maramorosch, K., and Granados, R. R. (1966). *Virology* **29**, 426–436.

Shikata, E., Maramorosch, K., and Ling, K. C. (1969). *FAO Plant Prot. Bull.* **17**, 121–128.

Sinha, R. C. (1965). *Virology* **26**, 673–686.

Sinha, R. C. (1969). *In* "Viruses, Vectors, and Vegetation" (K. Maramorosch, ed.), pp. 379–391. Wiley (Interscience), New York.

Tokumitsu, T., and Maramorosch, K. (1966). *Exp. Cell Res.* **44**, 652–655.

Tokumitsu, T., and Maramorosch, K. (1967). *J. Cell Biol.* **34**, 677–683.

Vago, C. (1962). Personal communication.

Vago, C. (1967). *Methods Virol.* **1**, 567–602.

Vago, C., and Chastang, S. (1958). *Experientia* **14**, 426.

Vago, C., and Flandre, O. (1963). *Ann. Epiphyt.* **14**, 127–139.

Vidano, C., and Bassi, M. (1966). *Atti Accad. Sci. Torino, Cl. Sci. Fis., Mat. Natur* **100**, 73–78.

Whitcomb, R. F., and Davis, R. E. (1970). *Annu. Rev. Entomol.* **15**, 405–464.

Wyatt, S. S. (1956). *J. Gen. Physiol.* **39**, 841–852.

Yamada, K., Tokumitsu, T., and Shikata, E. (1969). *Jap. J. Appl. Entomol. Zool.* **13**, 159–161.

Yamada, K., Tokumitsu, T., and Shikata, E. (1970). *Jap. J. Appl. Entomol. Zool.* **14**, 79–84.

11

CELL CULTURES OF CRUSTACEA, ARACHNIDA, AND MEROSTOMACEA

F. Peponnet and J. M. Quiot

I. INTRODUCTION

There has been a considerable surge of interest in the field of insect cell culture, and several successes have been reported by the few biologists using *in vitro* culture of tissues from other arthropods. Cell cultures of crabs were prepared following Vago's discovery in 1966 of the first virus of Crustacea. The crayfish cultures were undertaken for the study of various pathological and immunological problems. Among the arachnids, tick cells were cultured because these animals are vectors of numerous human and animal diseases. Toxicological and immunological investigations led to the culturing of scorpion cells, and among the Merostomacea, some work has been done on the genus *Limulus*.

II. CELL CULTURES OF CRUSTACEA

A. Introduction

Early works to maintain crustacean tissues, in natural media such as seawater enriched with proteins or coagulated plasma (Dobrowolsky, 1916; Lewis, 1916; Fischer-Piette, 1929, 1931, 1933; Cary, 1931; Cameron, 1949) often failed, due to defective nutritional media and asepsis of the explants.

More recently, the use of antibiotics, improvements in semisynthetic culture media, and the adoption of modern techniques have allowed real progress in crustacean cell culture to take place.

Crustacean organ culture was a concomitant development of great value for endocrine studies carried out on these animals (Vol. II, Chapter 5).

B. Materials and Methods

1. Asepsis of Explants

Asepsis in Crustacea raises problems other than those known in terrestrial arthropods. In fact, since bacteria exist within various tissues of these animals, surface-sterilization is not sufficient to ensure culture explant asepsis. Fischer-Piette (1929, 1931, 1933) adopted the technique of first washing out the lobster stomach region with alcohol and ether and then irradiating the explants with ultraviolet rays for 25–40 minutes.

Cary (1931) plunged the explants into sterile seawater complemented with 1% hexylresorcinol and washed them several times in sterile seawater. More recently explants have been sterilized with concentrated solutions of antibiotics such as that used by Quoit *et al.* (1968):

Chloramphenicol	20 mg
Streptomycin	100 mg
Mycostatin	5 mg
Polymyxin	2 mg
Sterile seawater	100 ml

2. Tissues Cultured

Experiments have been carried out using various tissues, not all of which may be claimed to have produced "cultures." Lewis (1916) worked on regenerating claws and on the hypodermis of the hermit crab; Fischer-Piette (1929, 1931, 1933) on the lymphoïd gland of the lobster; Cary (1931) on the cerebral ganglia and hepatopancreas of the "Martinique langouste" *Palinurus argus;* Cameron (1949) on lobster blood; and Quiot *et al.* (1968) on the embryos and the ovaries of young females of the crayfish *Astacus pallipes* and on the heart and the stomach of the crab *Pachygrapsus marmoratus.*

3. Culture Media

While natural media (seawater, coagulated plasma) were the first to be tried, recent work has been directed towards the preparation of media, of which the mineral salt composition is compatible with the osmotic pressure of the hemolymph (Table I) and the organic fraction adequate for cell requirements (Table II). There has also been an endeavor to stimulate cell activity by complementing the media with embryo extracts.

Lewis (1916) in his experiments with hermit crab tissue used the following medium: 90 ml of seawater diluted to isotonicity with the animal plasma, 10 ml of broth prepared from the muscles of the animal, and 0.25 gm of dextrose. The acidity was neutralized with 0.02 gm $NaHCO_3$. The cultures were maintained at the temperature of seawater.

Fischer-Piette (1929, 1931, 1933) explanted lobster lymphoid gland on coagulated plasma free of blood cells.

Cary (1931) used two kinds of media for his work on the cerebral ganglia and the hepatopancreas of *Palinurus argus:* either seawater (normal, diluted to one-half, or diluted and complemented with 0.5% dextrose) or classical physiological solutions (Locke, Tyrode, Goldschmidt, etc.) complemented with 5–10% of sterile and filtered muscle broth. The latter fraction, being rich in peptides, unfortunately favors the development of bacteria which interfere with the asepsis of the culture.

TABLE I

INORGANIC COMPOSITION OF BLOOD OF MARINE AND FRESHWATER CRUSTACEA

Species	meq/liter				References
	Na	K	Ca	Mg	
Marine forms					
Brachyura					
Callinectes sapidus	85.5	2.5	7.4	3.6	Florkin (1954)
Cancer borealis	85.6	1.9	4.3	8.2	Cole (1940)
Cancer pagurus	84.7	2.8	3.8	8.5	Bethe and Berger (1931)
Pachygrapsus crassipes	89.1	1.8	5.2	3.9	Schlatter (1941)
Macrura					
Homarus americanus	88.1	1.8	6.6	3.5	Cole (1940)
Homarus gammarus	89.8	2.5	5.2	2.5	Robertson (1939)
Nephrops norvegicus	90.6	1.3	4.9	3.2	Robertson (1949)
Palinurus interruptus	88.2	2.0	6.5	3.3	Schlatter (1941)
Freshwater forms					
Astacus astacus	82.7	1.5	13.0	2.7	Bogucki (1934)
Procambarus clarkii	82.4	3.0	12.6	2.1	Schlatter (1941)

Quiot *et al.* (1968) and Vago and Quiot (1969) used two fractions for cell cultures of marine and freshwater Crustacea: (a) an organic fraction composed of either the organic fraction of medium 199 of Morgan *et al.* (1950), or Eagle's (1955) maintenance medium, plus 15% fetal calf serum; (b) a mineral fraction that varied as follows: for *Astacus*, the mineral solution of a balanced medium-like type 199 (Morgan *et al.*, 1955) or Eagle's maintenance medium, with pH buffered to 7 with NaHCO$_3$; for *Pachygrapsus*, filtered and sterilized seawater with pH buffered to pH 7.5.

TABLE II

CRUSTACEA BLOOD PROTEIN CONCENTRATION

Species	Source	Percent	References
Astacus astacus	Plasma	3.7–4.7	Drilhon-Courtois (1934)
Cancer pagurus	Blood	5.69	Delaunay (1927)
Cancer pagurus	Plasma	4.1–4.4	Florkin and Blum (1934)
Carcinus maenas	Blood	1.58–8.32	Robertson (1949)
Carcinus maenas	Plasma	2.2	Damboviceanu (1932)
Homarus gammarus	Blood	4.22–5.13	Quagliariello (1920)
Homarus gammarus	Plasma	3.25	Botazzi (1908)
Nephrops norvegicus	Plasma	3.33–4.97	Florkin and Blum (1934)

4. Culture Methods

Most of the experiments were carried out by the hanging drop technique in liquid media (Cameron, 1949; Quiot et al., 1968) or on coagulated plasma (Fischer-Piette, 1929, 1931, 1933). Roller tubes (Cameron, 1949) or flat bottomed or plastic Vago–Flandre flasks were also used (Quiot et al., 1968).

C. Cultures and Observations

After Dobrowolsky's unsuccessful experiments (1916) with tissues of the crab *Gebia littoralis,* Lewis (1916) observed the migration of connective and epithelial cells from the first regenerating claw and of isolated small cells from the hypodermis. He did not mention the duration of the experiments nor the presence or absence of mitosis.

Fischer-Piette (1929, 1931, 1933) studied the histology of explanted lobster lymphoid gland. After a few hours, lymphocytes migrated from the explant, often at well-defined points corresponding to normal outlets of the gland. These cells showed amoeboid movements, and as their numbers increased, they joined together to form coherent spherical units. Under favorable conditions, the halo formed in 48 hours by the migrating lymphocytes covered an area equal to twice that of the explant.

The tissue fragments were transferred several times into fresh medium after being freed of their lymphocytes. After a few hours lymphocytes again migrated, showing mitotic divisions and some pycnosis. The explant, also called the "central fragment," maintained its compact parenchymatous appearance and continued to function, the percentage of mitoses being more or less comparable to that of a gland in the living animal.

This continuation of physiological function under *in vitro* conditions was perhaps due to the fact that in the lobster's cells the supply of nutrients and oxygen and the elimination of metabolic products could be carried out sufficiently well across the interstices between the follicles and the cells.

These organotypic cultures maintained the functions of the organ and were accompanied by cell migration.

Cary (1931) obtained from fragments of the hepatopancreas and the cerebral ganglia of *Palinurus argus,* cell migrations that increased in intensity as the percentage of the added peptide broth was raised. Thus, at 10% of broth the cultures passed through a period of cell migration before becoming quiescent; at 2.5% they did not even start any noticeable activity. No subcultures were attempted.

The first really active long-term cell cultures were obtained only recently by Quiot *et al.* (1968) using tissues of marine and freshwater Crustacea.

These authors obtained cell cultures of the crayfish *Astacus pallipes* from explants of embryos (Figs. 1–3) and ovaries or after dissociation by enzymes. In the case of embryo cells, where the yolk interfered with the observations by altering the medium, the latter was changed 12 hours after setting up the culture. After 24 hours the first cells appeared and formed a fine network. They increased rapidly in number and, after five days, produced a large layer of cells in many of which mitoses were observed.

The large fibroblast-like cells (40 to 50 μ) completely covered the substrate. Their pseudopodia were short; the cytoplasm was clear and practically unvacuolated but contained masses of granules, usually near the nucleus.

The cells generally showed great mobility, and a large number of them left the migration halo to isolate themselves farther.

By changing the medium every five days, monolayer cultures were kept in constant mitotic activity for at least four months.

For ovary and embryo cell cultures the medium was renewed after 12 hours since the fragments released a large amount of yolk or nurse cells, full of reserve materials, to the medium.

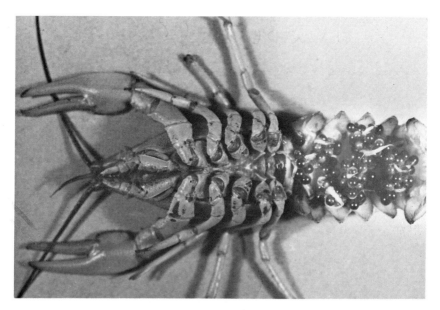

Fig. 1. Sampling incubated eggs from female of the crayfish *Astacus leptodactylus*.

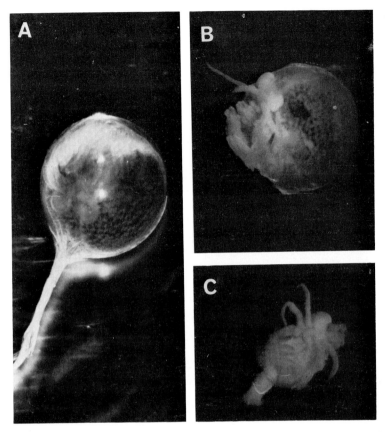

FIG. 2. Dissection of crayfish egg for removing embryos. (A) Embryo within the chorion; (B) dechorioned egg (on the left, the embryo; on the right, the vitellus); (C) entirely freed embryo.

A sheath of cells composed of fibroblasts was established around the explants and from the dissociated tissues. These cells differed in appearance from those cultured from embryos, being tapered and producing long, branched pseudopodia.

After about 10 days, these cells degenerated and were replaced by new cells of the same type. They rapidly formed a new, thick sheath of cells with constant mitoses for at least four months.

Quiot et al. (1968) cultured cardiac (Fig. 4) and stomach cells of the marine crab Pachygrapsus marmoratus.

The cardiac tissue, after four to six days of culture, produced a fine transparent network of cells that developed into a large sheath. These cells were different from the ovarian fibroblasts and were joined together by short pseudopodia. They were often compressed and superimposed.

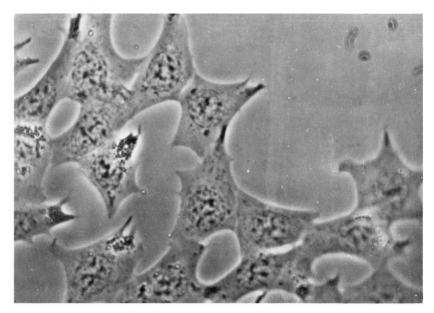

Fig. 3. Cell culture (two months) of *Astacus* embryonic cells. Phase contrast ×350.

Fig. 4. Simplified aseptic dissection of the crab *Pachygrapsus marmoratus* for removing heart (h).

348

Because of their transparency, it was always difficult to observe the cytoplasm, even under the phase-contrast microscope.

The mitotic activity in the cell layer was regular and showed periodic increase and decrease in intensity for at least four months.

From the stomach, a naturally septic organ, a thick sheath of fibroblast cells was obtained. These cells were very large and so compressed that they formed a mass in which it was hard to find the cell boundaries.

This type of culture spread progressively by mitoses and lasted for many months.

The results showed that, as with insects, it is possible to obtain from Crustacea long-lasting cell cultures with mitoses and producing large surface spreads. They also demonstrated the efficiency of culture media composed of balanced minerals and standard organic fractions. These active and long-lasting cultures enable a more thorough *in vitro* investigation of endocrinological and pathological aspects. In the latter field cell culture studies became particularly important after discovery of the first viral (Vago, 1966) and rickettsial (Vago *et al.*, 1971) diseases in Crustacea.

III. CELL CULTURES OF ARACHNIDA

A. Introduction

Arachnid cell culture is a young field, the first experiments going back not more than twenty years (Weyer, 1952). For the study of the acarine transmission of viruses and rickettsias pathogenic to animals and man, a particular effort was made to culture tissues of *Dermacentor marginatus, D. pictus, Hyalomma dromedarii, H. asiaticum* (Rehacek, 1958, 1962, 1965; Rehacek and Brezina, 1964), *Dermacentor andersoni* (Yunker and Cory, 1965, 1967), and *Rhipicephalus appendiculatus* (Martin and Vidler, 1962). More recently, attempts have been made to culture other arachnids such as opilions for the study of their neurosecretory tissues (Fowler and Goodnight, 1966) and scorpions for toxicological and immunological research (Peponnet and Quiot, 1968).

B. Materials and Methods

1. Disinfection of Surface

The principle of disinfection is the same as that employed for insects. Nymphs of the tick *Dermacentor andersoni* were disinfected by immersion in 70% ethyl alcohol for 5–10 minutes and dried with sterile gauze (Yunker and Cory, 1967). Scorpion tissues were removed after the integument of the animal had been disinfected in 95% alcohol (Peponnet and Quiot, 1968). The explants were washed several times in sterile culture medium or in medium containing antibiotics (Rehacek, 1963; Yunker and Cory, 1967; Peponnet and Quiot, 1968).

2. Tissues Cultured

The tick tissues were taken from nymphs and adults at different periods after the nymphal and imaginal moults. In scorpions and spiders only adult tissues were used. Various adult tick tissues were cultured, such as central nervous ganglia, epidermis, and appendices of *Hyalomma dromedarii* and salivary glands, nervous system, gut, Malpighian tubules muscles, trachea, and gonads of *Rhipicephalus appendiculatus* (Martin and Vidler, 1962). The whole body of nymphs from various tick species was cultured after the alimentary canal, the Malpighian tubules, and the rectum had been removed.

Cell cultures from the scorpions *Buthus occitanus* and *Androctonus australis* were obtained from heart, gonads (Fig. 5), male and female

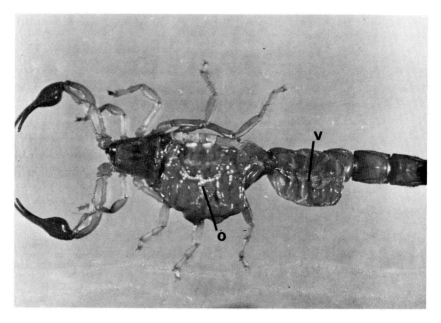

Fɪɢ. 5. Aseptic dissection of the scorpion *Androctonus australis* for removing ovaries (o).(v, dorsal vessel.)

genital organs, lymphatic glands, gut, and Malpighian tubules (Pepon-net and Quoit, 1968). The organs of the opilion *Leiobunum longipes* chosen for tissue culture were brain, separated from the pigmented mass of the ocular tubercles, and gut of male and female adults isolated from the anal and genital connections (Fowler and Goodnight, 1966).

3. Media Utilized

The first attempts to culture cells of *Dermacentor marginatus* employed the medium of Trager (1938) (Chapter 2) for cells of the Lepidoptera *Bombyx mori* (Rehacek, 1958). Other work with *D. marginatus* employed three other media, all based on the physiological solution of Hanks complemented with 0.5% of lactalbumin hydrolysate and 0.1% of yeast hydrolysate. Other media were devised by adding either 10% horse serum or 1% egg albumin (Rehacek, 1958).

For the cultures of *D. marginatus* and *D. pictus* (Rehacek and Hana, 1961; Varma and Wallers, 1965), Eagle's (1955) and Vago and Chastang's (1958) media were mixed together in equal parts; for the culture of *Hyalomma dromedarii*, in the ratio of 2:1 (Rehacek, 1965). These media were modified by adding 5% dextran or tick egg extract; 5% dextran plus 0.1% dried calf serum prepared by Michl (1961); or simply by 0.1% calf serum.

The TC 199 medium of Morgan *et al.* (1950) was complemented by sera and extracts of tick or spider eggs and larval and adult sera from various beetles, crayfishes, or cockroaches (Rehacek and Hana, 1961). Cultures of *D. andersoni* developed on media made up from Hanks saline solution complemented by lactalbumin hydrolysate, 10% heat-inactivated normal rabbit serum, 10% whole chicken egg ultrafiltrate, 10 mg of bovine plasma albumin (Fraction V), 100 IU/ml of penicillin G, and 100 μg/ml of streptomycin sulfate (Yunker and Cory, 1967).

These media were buffered to pH 6.5 (Rehacek, 1965), 6.9 (Varma and Wallers, 1965), or 7.2 (Rehacek, 1958).

For attempts to culture cells of the tick *Rhipicephalus appendiculatus*, Martin and Vidler (1962) used the following three media:

1. Medium A: Wyatt (1956) saline solution, vitamins, amino acids of Eagle's medium and lamb serum (5–20%).

2. Medium B: Hanks saline solution, vitamins, amino acids of Eagle's medium, and 20% calf serum.

3. Medium C: medium B plus 0.5% lactalbumin hydrolysate and folic acid (0.00882 gm/liter).

Each of these media contained 100 IU of penicillin and 100 IU of streptomycin/ml. Their pH ranged from 6.8 to 7.0.

The *Buthus occitanus* and *Androctonus australis* scorpion culture media were prepared according to the principle of standard and variable fractions (Vago and Quiot, 1969). This medium "72" was prepared for the cell culture of invertebrates of which the hemolymph Na/K ratio is greater than 1 (see Chapter 8, Table II). For cell cultures of scorpions the pH was fixed at 6.9 and the osmotic pressure kept at $\Delta t = -0.57°$ (Tables III and IV).

Tissue cultures of the opilion *Leiobunum longipes* were grown in the medium of Martin and Vidler (1962), which consisted of Hank's saline solution, the amino acids and vitamins of Eagle's medium, glutamine, a pH buffer ($NaHCO_3$), a pH indicator (phenol red), and bovine serum. Antibiotics (penicillin and streptomycin) were also added to the medium (Fowler and Goodnight, 1966).

TABLE III

CONSTITUENTS OF PLASMA OF HEMOLYMPH OF *Androctonus australis* ACTIVE ON OSMOTIC PRESSURE[a]

Constituents	Concentration (mg/100 ml)
Alanine	2.48
Arginine	4.92
Aspartic acid (total)	3.32
Glutamic acid (total)	15.80
Glycine	5.37
Histidine	1.60
Isoleucine	1.26
Leucine	0.97
Lysine	2.96
Phenylalanine	1.61
Proline	9.40
Serine	4.28
Thréonine	3.44
Tyrosine	1.64
Valine	3.49
Dialysable N (total)	20.5
Taurine	40.3
Sodium	752.25
Potassium	16.48
Calcium	41.85
Magnesium	10.09
Trehalose	28.75
Osmotic pressure	530 mOsm/liter

[a] From Bricteux-Grégoire *et al.* (1963).

TABLE IV

SOME INORGANIC CONSTITUENTS AND THE OSMOTIC PRESSURE OF THE
BLOOD OF THE SCORPIONS *Heterometrus fulvipes*[a,b]

	Concentrations (mmoles/liter)		
Blood constituent	Males	Females	Average for males and females
Sodium	221.7 ± 52.5	197.8 ± 34.7	209.7 ± 44.6
Potassium	1.4 ± 0.83	1.35 ± 0.84	1.37 ± 0.83
Calcium	6.68 ± 1.36	5.52 ± 2.24	6.08 ± 1.07
Magnesium	10.08 ± 3.35	10.83 ± 3.16	10.43 ± 3.27
Chloride	251.4 ± 44.3	277.10 ± 63.1	266.5 ± 56.1
Sulfate	1.21 ± 0.66	1.04 ± 0.71	1.02 ± 0.69
Amino acids	5.13 ± 0.81	5.28 ± 0.83	5.22 ± 0.82
Sugar	40.67 ± 20.7	38.05 ± 19.7	38.80 ± 20.2
Nonprotein nitrogen	42.50 ± 6.55	40.38 ± 4.84	41.40 ± 5.56
Protein nitrogen	12.07 ± 1.21	11.47 ± 1.55	11.76 ± 1.4
Protein	75.45 ± 6.95	71.76 ± 9.88	73.48 ± 8.60
Osmotic pressure	1.35 ± 0.13[c]	1.35 ± 0.10[c]	1.35 ± 0.011[c]

[a] From Padmanabhanaidu (1966).
[b] Standard deviations are calculated from the data.
[c] % NaCl.

4. Culture Methods

a. Explants. This method was employed in hanging drop cultures using tissue from the ticks *Dermacentor marginatus* and *D. pictus* (Rehacek, 1958; Rehacek and Hana, 1961); in tube cultures of *Rhipicephalus appendiculatus* adult and nymphal tissues (Martin and Vidler, 1962); and in tissue cultures of *D. andersoni* nymph tissues (Yunker and Cory, 1965, 1967). The same technique was used also for culturing various tissues and organs of the scorpions *Buthus occitanus* and *Androctonus australis*, in reversible (Vago and Flandre, 1963) or plastic bottles (Pepconnet and Quiot, 1968). In the case of the cell cultures of the opilion *Leiobunum longipes* (Fowler and Goodnight, 1966), the organs were not cut into explants. The brain and intestine (prepared as described above) were placed side by side in a 30-ml culture flask. The tissues were gently dried so that they adhered to the bottom of the flask and were then covered with 2 ml of culture medium. The flasks were kept at room temperature under conditions of alternating light and darkness and placed in a receptacle with a carbon dioxide enriched atmosphere (Fowler and Goodnight, 1966).

b. Enzymatic Dissociation. Recent cell cultures of *D. marginatus, D.*

pictus (Rehacek, 1962), and *H. dromedarii* (Rehacek, 1965; Varma and Wallers, 1965) have been made after digestion of the tissues or the organs in a 0.25% trypsin solution agitated either by pipetting (Rehacek, 1962, 1965) or with a magnetic stirrer (Varma and Wallers, 1965). The cells dissociated in this way were introduced directly into culture tubes. For viral and rickettsial studies, the cells were placed on a thin cover glass and, after 48 hours, put into the tubes in order to ensure a good fixation (Rehacek, 1965). The cultures were found to develop better if the dissociated cells were placed in tubes inclined at 7° and recovered by a cover glass that completely covered the free surface of the culture medium. Under such conditions cell metabolism, as judged by the more rapid changes in pH, appeared to be greater (Varma and Wallers, 1965).

C. Cultures Obtained and Observations

After the first attempts at tick cell cultures made by Weyer (1952) for the study of rickettsial development, the survival of adult *D. marginatus* explants on various media for up to 10 days was observed. But these cells did not divide (Rehacek, 1958). The explants from nymphs dissected three to five days after feeding gave cultures in 10% of cases where the migration of fibroblast-like cells was noticed during six days. By the eighth day, however, all the cells had degenerated.

For *Dermacentor marginatus* and *D. pictus*, survival was prolonged up to 10 days (Rehacek and Hana, 1961). The most prolific growth took place between the fourth and the eight day in the medium containing 5% dextran. It appeared that some cells, such as those of the salivary glands, dedifferentiated to produce fibroblast-like cells. It was expected that these results would be useful for the study of various viruses.

In a medium prepared from Eagle's and Vago and Chastang's media in equal parts and complemented by 5% dextran and 0.1% dried calf serum extract, the cells were observed to proliferate from the first to the fourth day, after they had grown only in size. The medium was renewed every five days, and the cultures survived up to the 20th day; but no mitosis was seen after the fifth day, and attempts to obtain subcultures were unsuccessful (Rehacek, 1962).

With *Hyalomma dromedarii*, cell cultures (Rehacek, 1965) prepared by trypsinization of various tissues, particularly epidermis and central ganglion, adhered to the cover glass after 24 hours and migrated from the fragments of the tissues. Most of the cells were of the fibroblast-like cells. Mitoses were observed around the 10th day and the cells survived for 14–20 days. In subcultures the number of cells gradually diminished, and a month later, large macrophage cells, about 50 μ in length, appeared and were examined during a period of six months.

Cellular debris present at the beginning of the culture are phagocytized by cultured cells. It is possible that phagocytosis and pinocytosis play a role in the infection of cultured cells.

Several cell cultures have been carried out with adult and nymphal *Rhipicephalus appendiculatus* tissues (Martin and Vidler, 1962). Explants of salivary glands of fasting adults survived for 77 days but showed no growth, mitosis, or migration. Similar results were obtained with explants of the nervous system, the alimentary canal, and the Malpighian tubules removed from adults either 1 or 21 days after the moult.

Explants of the alimentary canal, Malpighian tubules, muscles, trachea, and gonads taken from adults six days after the moult sometimes showed a migration of fibroblast-like cells followed by epithelial-like cells. The latter continued to accumulate for over three months, while the former diminished in number after the second month. In one culture that survived for over 170 days, each change of medium was followed by a temporary inhibition of growth and a degeneration of the cells. Adult tissues with low metabolic activity did not appear to be good material for culture.

With nymphs, the best results were obtained with animals dissected on the fourth to seventh day after a meal. Shortly after the outset, most of the cultures showed contractile movements and migration of large fibroblast cells, sometimes very elongated, containing large vacuoles, followed by small epithelial cells which survived for about 50 days. Finally, large epithelial cells arose from the mid-intestinal epithelium and survived up to the 175th day of the culture.

Attempts were made to transfer explants to fresh containers without establishing subcultures. From the first day following the transfer, a migration of two types of fibroblasts was observed around the explant and this process increased in intensity up to the fourth day. A histological examination of the explant, fixed 10 days later, showed several healthy tissues alongside large fibroblasts and epithelial-like cells of the midgut, some of which were in division phases. Explants from *Dermacentor andersoni* nymphs (Yunker and Cory, 1967), after a few hours of culture, liberated fibroblast-like cells which remained alive for two months and presented a few mitoses, especially around the fourth day of culture.

In scorpion cell cultures (Peponnet and Quiot, 1968) the tissue of the dorsal vessel of *Buthus occitanus* and *Androctonus australis* produced a net of migratory elongated fibroblast-like cells.

In cultures of lymphatic glands of *B. occitanus* and *A. australis* (Fig. 6), two types of cells were noted: (a) numerous fibroblasts, 40–50 μ in length, with a clear, vacuole-free cytoplasm and medium-sized globular nuclei and (b) round cells moving freely in the medium almost without being attached to the surfaces of the container. These cells resembled those observed *in vivo* in the gland but not the blood cells circulating in the hemolymph. They seemed to have phagocytic properties. After a few weeks they became more numerous than the fibroblasts in the culture. Within the first 24 hours, the ovarian tubes of *Androctonus* produced numerous cells with vacuolated cytoplasm. They were progressively replaced by small fibroblasts with a clear nonvacuolated cytoplasm.

The vas deferens tissues of *Buthus* produced, in addition to numerous bundles of spermatozoids, migratory fibroblasts which persisted for only a few weeks.

Gut and brain fragments of the opilion *Leiobunum longipes* (Fowler and Goodnight, 1966) were maintained in culture for periods ranging from several weeks to one year. These cultures were organ cultures, but since migration of cells occurred, they are mentioned here. About 5% of the cultures could not be maintained, and this percentage increased

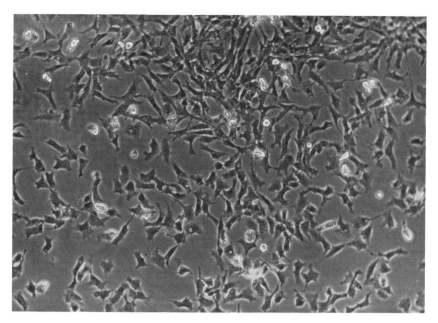

Fɪɢ. 6. Cell culture (one month) of lymphoïd gland from the scorpion *Androctonus australis*. Phase contrast ×350.

when the explants used were taken from old animals or from those which had passed through periods of excessive drought.

The migrating cells belong essentially to two categories: (a) small, round cells, the cytoplasm of which seem to contain a yellow pigment, and (b) numerous large, irregular, transparent cells spreading over the surface of the culture flask.

Such organ cultures had been kept for about a year and used for neurosecretion studies, in which surviving organs are essential.

IV. CELL CULTURES OF MEROSTOMACEA

A. Introduction

This class of primitive arthropods is represented by only a few species of the genus *Limulus* inhabiting the coasts of the American North Atlantic and the seas of the Far East. It is probably their primitive characteristics which early attracted the attention of workers searching for material for cell (Lewis, 1916; Sanborn *et al.*, 1959) and organ cultures (Wolff, 1962, 1963).

B. Materials and Methods

Explants were taken from various organs of *Limulus polyphemus*, i.e., heart, pericardium, muscles, hypodermis, ovary, hepatopancreas, and nervous tissue.

Two types of media were used: one based on seawater (Lewis, 1916) (Table V), the other (Sanborn *et al.*, 1959) prepared from mineral salts, sugar, organic acids, and 5–10% sterilized *Limulus* serum (Table VI).

TABLE V

CULTURE MEDIUM FOR *Limulus polyphemus*[a]

Substances	Amounts
Seawater (diluted to become isotonic to plasma of the animal)	90 ml
Bubble of muscles of *Pagurus*	10 ml
Dextrose	250 mg
NaCl	1000 mg
$NaHCO_3$	20 mg

[a] From Lewis (1916).

TABLE VI

AMINO ACIDS OF BLOOD OF *Limulus polyphemus*[a]

Amino acids[b]	Concentration (mg/100 ml)
Alanine	1.4
Arginine	0.8
Aspartic acid	1.1
Glutamic acid	0.3
Glycine	±0.0
Histidine	0.3
Isoleucine	0.4
Leucine	0.2
Lysine	0.2
Methionine	0.2
Phenylalanine	0.2
Proline	0.9
Thréonine	0.2
Tyrosine	0.3
Valine	0.3

[a] From Bricteux-Grégoire *et al.* (1966).

[b] Estimated by microbiographical method (Duchateau and Florkin, 1954).

Cultures were made using the hanging drop technique and incubated at 15°–18°.

C. Cultures Obtained and Observations

Lewis reported the migration of small cells from a hypodermis explant. From heart and muscle tissue only a few cells migrated, while the pericardium gave rise to many unidentified migratory cells.

Sanborn *et al.* (1959) observed two types of cells around the explants of ovary, hepatopancreas, nervous tissue, and heart: (a) small round cells, free in the medium, and (b) spindle-shaped cells fixed to the glass wall or to the liquid–air interface of the drop. Both cell types persisted for at least a month, but after 10 days, increasing numbers of granules and vacuoles were observed.

The free cells were kept for at least six weeks by replacing the original explants by fragments of fresh tissue each week.

Explants taken from the peripherial nerves and muscles produced mostly fusiform cells, while the other tissues gave rise to a greater proportion of round cells. After several days, fibers appeared at the edges of the explants of the hepatopancreas and the ovary, surrounding the migratory cells.

REFERENCES

Bethe, A., and Berger, E. (1931). *Pfluegers Arch. Gesamte Physiol. Menschen Tiere* **227**, 571.

Bogucki, M. (1934). *Arch. Int. Physiol.* **38**, 172.

Bottazzi, P. (1908). *Atti Accad. Naz. Lincei, Cl. Sci. Fis., Mat. Natur., Rend.* **17**, 16.

Bricteux-Grégoire, S., Duchateau-Bosson, G. H., Jeuniaux, C., Schoffeniels, E., and Florkin, M. (1963). *Arch. Int. Physiol. Biochim.* **71**, 393.

Bricteux-Grégoire, S., Duchateau-Bosson, G. H., Jeuniaux, C., and Florkin, M. (1966). *Comp. Biochem. Physiol.* **19**, 729.

Cameron, G. (1949). *Anat. Rec.* **103**, 431.

Cary, L. R. (1931). *Pap. Tortugas Lab. Carnegie Inst.* **30**, 279.

Cole, W. H. (1940). *J. Gen. Physiol.* **23**, 575.

Damboviceanu, A. (1932). *Arch. Roum. Pathol. Exp. Microbiol.* **5**, 239.

Delaunay, H. (1927). "Recherches biochimiques sur l'excretion azotée des Invertébrés." Sinaudeau, Bordeaux.

Dobrowolsky, N. A. (1916). *C. R. Soc. Biol.* **79**, 789–792.

Drilhon-Courtois, A. (1934). *Bull. Inst. Oceanogr.* **644**, 1.

Duchateau, G., and Florkin, M. (1954). *Arch. Int. Physiol.* **62**, 487.

Eagle, H. (1955). *Science* **122**, 501.

Fischer-Piette, E. (1929). *C. R. Soc. Biol.* **3**, 764.

Fischer-Piette, E. (1931). *Arch. Zool. Exp. Gen.* **74**, 33.

Fischer-Piette, E. (1933). *Arch. Exp. Zellforsch. Besonders Gewebezuecht.* **14**, 345.

Florkin, M. (1954). *In* "Traité de Zoologie" (P. P. Grassé, ed.), Vol. XII, pp. 1064–1088. Masson, Paris.

Florkin, M., and Blum, H. F. (1934). *Arch. Int. Physiol.* **38**, 353.

Fowler, D. J., and Goodnight, C. J. (1966). *Trans. Amer. Microsc. Soc.* **85**, No. 3, 378.

Lewis, L. R. (1916). *Anat. Rec.* **10**, 287.

Martin, H. M., and Vidler, B. O. (1962). *Exp. Parasitol.* **12**, 192.

Michl, J. (1961). *Exp. Cell Res.* **23**, 234.

Morgan, J. F., Morton, H. J., and Parker, R. C. (1950). *Proc. Soc. Exp. Biol. Med.* **73**, 1.

Padmanabhanaidu, B. (1966). *Comp. Biochem. Physiol.* **17**, 157.

Peponnet, F., and Quiot, J. M. (1968). *C. R. Acad. Sci.* **266**, 1589.

Quagliariello, G. (1920). *Atti Accad. Naz. Lincei, Cl. Sci. Fis., Mat. Natur., Rend.* **29**, 213.

Quoit, J. M., Vago, C., and Luciani, J. (1968). *Proc. Int. Colloq. Invertebr. Tissue Cult., 2nd, 1967* p. 102.

Rehacek, J. (1958). *Acta Virol. (Prague), Engl. Ed.* **2**, 253.

Rehacek, J. (1962). *Acta Virol. (Prague), Engl. Ed.* **6**, 188.

Rehacek, J. (1963). *Ann. Epiphyti.* **14**, 199.

Rehacek, J. (1965). *Acta Virol. (Prague), Engl. Ed.* **9**, 332.

Rehacek, J., and Brezina, R. (1964). *Acta Virol. (Prague), Engl. Ed.* **8**, 308.

Rehacek, J., and Hana, L. (1961). *Acta Virol. (Prague), Engl. Ed.* **5**, 57.

Robertson, J. D. (1939). *J. Exp. Biol.* **16**, 387.

Robertson, J. D. (1949). *J. Exp. Biol.* **26**, 182.

Sanborn, R. C., Haskell, J. A., and Fisher, F. M. (1959). *Biol. Bull.* **117**, 399.

Schlatter, M. J. (1941). *J. Cell. Comp. Physiol.* **17**, 259.

Trager, W. (1938). *Amer. J. Trop. Med.* **18,** 387.

Vago, C. (1966). *Nature (London)* **109,** 1290.

Vago, C., and Chastang, S. (1958). *Experientia* **14,** 110.

Vago, C., and Flandre, O. (1963). *C. R. 1er Coll. Int. Cult. Tissues Invert. Montpellier, 1962, Ann. Epiphyt.* **14,** 127.

Vago, C., and Quiot, J. M. (1969). *Ann. Zool. Ecol. Anim.* **1,** 281.

Vago, C., Meynadier, G., Juchault, P., Legrand, J. J., Amargier, A., and Duthoit, J. L. (1971). *C. R. Acad. Sci.* **271,** 2061.

Varma, M. G. R., and Wallers, W. (1965). *Nature (London)* **208,** 262.

Weyer, F. (1952). *Zentralbl. Bakteriol Parasitenk., Infektionskr. Hyg., Abt. I, Orig.* **159,** 13.

Wolff, Emm. (1962). *Bull. Soc. Zool.* **87,** 120.

Wolff, Emm. (1963). *C. R. 1er Coll. Int. Cult. Tissues Invert., Montpellier, 1962, Ann. Epiphyt.* **14,** 113.

Wyatt, S. S. (1956). *J. Gen. Physiol.* **39,** 841.

Yunker, C. E., and Cory, J. (1965). *J. Parasitol.* **51,** 686.

Yunker, C. E., and Cory, J. (1967). *Exp. Parasitol.* **20,** 267.

12

CELL CULTURE OF MOLLUSKS

O. Flandre

I. INTRODUCTION

The improvements achieved in the field of invertebrate tissue culture are closely related to the development of virology and, in particular, to the increasing interest which is being given to the study of virus diseases of insects. The attempts made with mollusk cell culture are far fewer and are concerned with but a small number of species. We can distinguish three trends in the development of mollusk tissue cultures: the production of organ cultures, the culture of cells of those mollusks that are inter-mediate hosts for parasites or viruses, and the study of certain problems of cellular physiology proper to those species.

More than 30 years ago, Gatenby (1931), Gatenby and Duthie (1932), Bohuslav (1932, 1933), and Gatenby and Hill (1933) observed the *in vitro* proliferation of cells from fragments of the heart, mantle, pulmo-nary cavity wall, and receptaculum seminis from *Helix* sp.

These studies were further developed by Hanghton (1934), Hill (1934), Hill and Gatenby (1934), and Gatenby *et al.* (1934) on explants of tis-sues cultured in hanging drops. These authors obtained prolonged cultures of several tissues but never observed any mitosis in the cultured cells.

Gatenby (1932) believed that cell multiplication took place in the cultures of small fragments of the wall of the pulmonary cavity; how-ever, he did not detect cells displaying mitosis, and one may presume that "cell multiplication" simply describes an increase in size of the cellu-lar outgrowths.

Tissues from mantle (Bevelander and Martin, 1949) were kept for several weeks in balanced salt solution, with cells migrating from the explants to form outgrowths.

Benex (1961) observed that tentacles from *Australorbis glabratus* iso-lated in a complex medium showed ciliary and muscular activity for about 3 weeks.

Vago and Chastang (1958, 1960) cultured and kept *in vitro* cellular clones of various tissues of snails and oysters and observed mitosis in those conditions. These authors obtained such results in nutritive media adapted to the biological requirements of the species studied.

After an analysis of the composition of the hemolymph and with a complex nutritive medium, Chernin and Schork (1959) and Chernin (1963) obtained long-lasting cultures of *Australorbis glabratus* heart. From explants of heart Chernin obtained a migration of amoebocytes and epithelial cells, but never observed any mitosis.

The culture of insect tissues in plasma coagulum was obtained by Flandre *et al.* (1962) and Vago and Flandre (1963). This method permits long-lasting cultures with cellular mitosis. These cultures are obtained by successive explants as in vertebrate tissue cultures. Flandre and Vago (1963) were able to apply this technique to cultures of mollusk tissues by adapting the nutritive medium to suit these species. This method was successful in the culture of heart, mantle, and foot muscle of various species.

II. TECHNIQUES FOR CELL CULTURE OF MOLLUSKS

A. Culture Medium

1. Balanced Salt Solution (BSS)

The culture medium consisted of a salt solution balanced and adjusted to a suitable pH. The composition of the BSS was determined from the results of a qualitative and quantitative analysis of the hemolymph of the particular species cultured. The BSS contained the main mineral salts in variable proportions.

These solutions can be very simple. The simplest is seawater, as used by Vago and Chastang (1960) to culture tissues of sea mollusks. Formulae of several BSS follow below:

1. Bohuslav's BSS (1932) has been used for the cell cultures of a variety of species of mollusks, for example, *Helix pomatia, H. austriaca, H. obvia,* and *Arion empiricorum* (Table I).

2. Ripplinger and Joly's solution (1961) was used for short subcultures,

TABLE I
BOHUSLAV'S BALANCED SALT SOLUTION

Substances	Concentration (gm/1000 ml of distilled water)
NaCl	7.40
KCl	0.45
CaCl$_2$	0.50
MgCl$_2$	0.02
NaCHO$_3$	0.15
Na$_2$HPO$_4$	0.05
pH	8.8

TABLE II
RIPPLINGER AND JOLY'S SOLUTION (1961)

Substances	Concentration (gm/1000 ml of distilled water)
NaCl	3.58
KCl	0.313
CaCl$_2$	0.710

This solution is based upon the analysis of normally hydrated *Helix pomatia's* hemolymph. It is completed by

NaH$_2$PO$_4$	0.500 gm/1000 ml

and it may be included in the composition of nutritive media destined to organ cultures (Durchon, 1964) (Table II).

3. Vago and Chastang's (1958) BSS is particularly adapted to the tissue culture of *H. aspersa* and *H. pomatia* (Table III).

4. Chernin's BSS is used for culture of *Australorbis glabratus;* it is based partly on the chemical determination of snail hemolymph composition and partly on empirical modification (Table IV).

5. Vago's BSS Ha 78 is used for culture in semisolid medium by Flandre and Vago (1963) (Table V).

These solutions generally contain an indicator, i.e., 0.4% phenol red, 5 ml/1000 ml of salt solution, to monitor variations in pH during storage and in use.

Once prepared, the saline solution is sterilized by filtration through a millipore membrane filter (type "H.A."), 0.45-μ pore size, and stored in rubber-stoppered vessels at 5° until required for preparing nutrient medium.

TABLE III
VAGO AND CHASTANG'S (1958) BALANCED SALT SOLUTION

Substances	Concentration (gm/1000 ml of bidistilled water)
NaCl	6.50
KCl	0.14
CaCl$_2$	0.12
NaH$_2$PO$_4$	0.01
CO$_3$NaH	0.20
pH	7.6–7.9

TABLE IV
CHERNIN'S (1963) BALANCED SALT SOLUTION

Substances	Concentration (gm/1000 ml of bidistilled water)
NaCl	2.80
KCl	0.15
Na₂HPO₄ (anh)	0.07
MgSO₄·7H₂O	0.45
CaCl₂·2H₂O	0.53
NaHCO₃	0.05

All components except calcium are dissolved in 800 ml of bidistilled water. Calcium is dissolved separately in 200 ml of water, and the solution was mixed by stirring. The pH of this solution is between 7.3 and 7.5.

2. Antibiotics

Antibiotics are not systematically used in the culture medium. If septic tissues are cultured, the explants can be washed in a solution of antibiotics before being cultured. Penicillin can be incorporated at a concentration of 200 units/ml. Streptomycin can be used at a concentration of 0.05 mg/ml, but with caution. Indeed, Chernin (1957) and Chernin and Shork (1959, 1960) showed that this antibiotic had a cytopathic effect upon snail cells.

After excision, septic samples can be washed for some minutes in the antibiotic solution (Vago and Flandre, 1963) (Table VI). Washing in the antibiotic solution is advisable, when dealing with tissues like branchiae, intestine, and foot muscles.

TABLE V
VAGO'S (1959) BALANCED SALT SOLUTION HA 78

Substances	Concentration (gm/1000 ml of bidistilled water)
NaCl	7.20
KCl	0.40
CaCl₂	0.30
CaH₂PO₄	0.20
MgSO₄	0.20
CO₃NaH	5.50
pH	7.6

TABLE VI
Antibiotic Solution[a]

Substances	Concentration
Bacitracin	5 IU/ml
Penicillin	200 IU/ml
Chloramphenicol	5–10 μg/ml
Colimycin	25 μg/ml
Streptomycin	0.05 mg/ml

[a] From Vago and Flandre (1963).

3. Natural Media

a. Mollusk Hemolymph. Mollusk hemolymph was used as an additive to nutritive media by Bohuslav (1933), Hanghton (1934), Friedl (1958), Vago and Chastang (1958, 1960), Flandre and Vago (1963), and Chernin (1963).

Collection of snail hemolymph is achieved by heart puncture, the heart being located by direct illumination through the shell.

The external surface of the shell should be sterilized with 70% alcohol, then air dried. An incision is made with iris scissors in the region of the heart, and this is punctured and hemolymph withdrawn with a thin needle fixed to a sterile syringe or with a thin sterile Pasteur pipette. The hemolymph is collected in sterile, ice-cooled conical tubes and centrifuged at 2000 rpm for 5–10 minutes to remove hemocytes and fragments of shell or tissues which could contaminate the sample. The supernatant is taken off and stored in sterile tubes. A bacteriological assay is made on every sample. Heart punctures of 15 to 20 snails yield 5–6 ml of hemolymph.

Vago and Chastang (1960) removed hemolymph from oysters (*Ostrea edulis* and *Gryphoea angulata* by a puncture of the pericardial sac and of the lacunes situated there. After lifting the shell, the muscular fasciculus of the valves is sectioned with a thin scalpel close to the shell. It is possible to insert a sharp Pasteur pipette into the pericardial sac through the released membrane, and the blood can thus be collected without suction.

b. Heterologous Media. These are necessary to introduce growth factors and proteins in the culture medium.

Heterologous Embryonal Extracts. Chernin (1963) used beef embryo extract conditioned according to Ender's method (1953); it was prepared in Hanks' solution, stored at $-20°$ in screw-cap tubes, thawed, centrifuged (2000 rpm for 30 minutes), and the supernatant utilized.

Chicken embryonal extracts were used by Flandre and Vago (1963) for the culture of *H. aspersa* and *H. pomatia* on semisolid medium. Chicken embryonal extracts are obtained from eggs which have been incubated for 9 days. The embryos are crushed under sterile conditions. The resulting pulp is diluted with equal proportions of the BSS Ha 78. The mixed solution is then centrifuged at 3000 rpm for 10 minutes; the light-colored supernatant is retained and stored at 4°. The sterility of the extract is checked before use by bacteriological assay.

Such extracts are prepared each week to ensure that the medium used is always fresh. Embryonal extracts are mixed with plasma to form one of the bases for the plasma coagulum.

COCKEREL PLASMA. Cockerel plasma was used in the culture of insect tissues by Gavrilov and Cowey (1941), by Carlson (1946), by Flandre *et al.* (1962), and by Vago and Flandre (1963) to obtain cultures capable of transplantation in coagulated plasma; Flandre and Vago (1963) then used it in the culture of mollusk tissues.

Blood is collected by a puncture in the carotid of cockerel (Carrel and Ebeling, 1921), without anticoagulants, in siliconized tubes previously sterilized and cooled and immediately centrifuged. The plasma is stored in siliconized tubes in a cold room. These operations must be carried out under very strict conditions of asepsis. Test for sterility were done by transferring plasma sample to tubes of nutrient broth, thioglycollate, and heart infusion broth.

The resultant plasma is introduced into the culture medium in sufficient quantity to produce a semisolid coagulum in which mollusk cells can multiply easily. Cockerel plasma is not cytotoxic for mollusk cells.

HETEROLOGOUS SERA. Calf and horse sera classically used in cultures of vertebrate tissues can be employed in liquid media adapted to cultures of invertebrate tissues. Heterologous sera are mostly used for cultures in liquid medium.

Calf serum was used by Vago and Chastang (1962) and Burch and Cuadros (1965); horse serum was employed by Chernin (1963) for heart cultures of *Australorbis glabratus*.

Serum is taken after blood coagulation. Complement is destroyed by heating to 56° for 30 minutes and filtered through millipore membrane (Type "H.A.," 0.45-μ pore size). Sterile serum is stored in a refrigerator at 4°.

Chernin (1963) used bovine amniotic fluid for the culture of *A. glabratus*. This fluid was obtained by trochar drainage from bovine uteri and stored in rubber stoppered flasks at 5° (Enders, 1953; Neva *et al.*, 1961).

4. Examples of Media

See Tables VII–XII.

TABLE VII
MEDIUM FOR SNAIL[a]

Substances	Concentration (gm/1000 ml)
BSS	
NaCl	7.40
KCl	0.45
CaCl₂	0.50
MgCl₂	0.02
NaHCO₃	0.15
NaHPO₄	0.05
Sugar	
Glucose	0.60

Extract of explant tissue: 3.00 gm in 100 ml of distilled water

pH	8.8
Cultured tissues	

Heart, foot, tunic from *Helix pomatia, H. obvia, H. austriaca, Arion empiricorum*

[a] From Bohuslav (1932).

Vago and Quiot (1969) have studied the possibility of standardization of media used for the cell cultures from many invertebrate species. These authors established formulations, on the basis of Na/K ratio, Δt^0 values, and hemolymph pH, which allowed the culture of cells of numerous species with similar basic needs.

The media comprised two fractions: a constant element composed of organic salts, antibiotics, and sera; the amino acid and vitamin formulae are those established for vertebrate tissue culture, i.e., medium TC 199, Eagle's minimum essential medium supplemented with fetal calf serum, a variable element including mineral fractions, pH, and Δt^0 regulation, and eventually, specific supplements.

These media made it possible to obtain extended cell cultures from many invertebrate species belonging to various orders.

5. Temperature

Mollusk cells are often cultured at 20°–25° in an incubator, but Burch and Cuadros (1965) have observed that cultures seemed to do better at 15°.

TABLE VIII

MEDIUM FOR SNAIL[a]

Substances	Concentration (gm/1000 ml)
BSS	
NaCl	6.50
KCl	0.14
CaCl₂	0.12
NaH₂PO₄	0.01
CO₃NaH	0.20
Sugar	
Glucose	1.0
Amino acids	
Casein hydrolysate	0.5
Glutamine	0.1
Choline	0.002
Yeast extracts	2 ml
Homologous serum	10%
Antibiotics	
Penicillin	200,000 IU
Streptomycin	50 mg
pH	7.6–7.9
Cultured tissues	
Foot tunic, mantle, heart from *Helix aspersa, H. pomatia*	

[a] From Vago and Chastang (1958).

TABLE IX

MEDIUM FOR OYSTER[a]

Substances	Concentration
Seawater	100 ml
Lactalbumin hydrolysate	500 mg
Glucose	100 mg
Antibiotics	
Penicillin G	20,000 IU
Streptomycin	2 mg
Oyster serum	10–20%

The pH is brought to 6.6 with sodium bicarbonate

Cultured tissues
  Mantle, heart, branchiae from *Ostrea edulis* and
    Gryphoea angulata

[a] From Vago and Chastang (1960).

TABLE X
MEDIUM FOR SNAIL[a]

Substances	Concentration (gm/1000 ml)
Part A: BSS	
NaCl	2.80
KCl	0.15
Na₂HPO₄ (anh)	0.07
MgSO₄·7H₂O	0.45
CaCl₂·2H₂O	0.53
NaHCO₃	0.05
Sugar	
Glucose	1.00
Trehalose	1.00
Antibiotics	
Penicillin G	100 IU/ml
Streptomycin sulphate	100 μg/ml
Phenol red (0.4%)	5 ml/1000 ml
Part B: Nutritive medium	
Balanced salt solution	850.00 ml
Bovine amniotic fluid	110.00 ml
Horse serum	12.5 ml
Beef embryo extracts	12.5 ml
Lactalbumin hydrolysate	10.0 ml
Yeast extract (10%)	5.0 ml
pH	7.3–7.5
Cultured Tissues	
Heart from *Australorbis glabratus*	

[a] From Chernin (1963).

B. Preparation of Tissues

1. Choice of the Tissues to be Cultured

Although most of mollusk organs can be maintained *in vitro*, only hematocytes and heart, mantle, and foot muscles are commonly cultured.

The tissue culture of the terrestrial gasteropods has attracted much attention; Bohuslav (1933), Gatenby *et al.* (1934), Hill (1934), Wagge (1955), Vago and Chastang (1958), and Flandre and Vago (1963) devoted themselves to tissue culture of various *Helix*, i.e., *H. aspersa, H. pomatia, H. obvia, H. austriaca*. The snail tissues cultured were those of *H. pomatia, A. glabratus*, and *Pomatiopsis lapidaria* and were taken from the foot muscle, mantle, esophagus, oviduct, and gonad. Foot muscle and gonad were the two tissues most commonly used.

TABLE XI

MEDIUM FOR SNAIL (Culture in Plasma Clot)[a]

Substances	Concentration (gm/1000 ml)
BSS Ha 78	
NaCl	7.20
KCl	0.40
CaCl₂	0.30
NaH₂PO₄	0.20
MgSO₄	0.20
CO₃NaH	5.50
Sugar	
Glucose	0.50
Amino acids	
Lactalbumin hydrolysate	1
Snail serum	10%
pH	7.6
Embryonal extracts	
Medium Ha 78	3 parts
Chicken embryonal extract	2 parts
Plasma clot	
Cockerel plasma	1 part
Embryo extract	20 parts
Medium Ha 78	
Cultured tissues	
Heart, foot muscle, mantle from *Helix*	

[a] From Flandre and Vago (1963).

Tissues of aquatic gasteropods have also been used: Benex (1961) and Chernin (1963) maintained fragments of heart of *A. glabratus;* Friedl (1958) used the heart and blood vessels of *Lymnea stagnalis* in a culture medium essentially composed of homologous hemolymph. The mantle, branchiae, and heart tissue of various oysters were cultured by Vago and Chastang (1960). Various tissues of mussel were cultured by Karnik and Kamat (1961), Havinga (1964), and Nikolic and Stojnic (1964). These authors usually observed a migration of cells from the explant and a growth of the culture although mitosis was seldom observed.

There are two types of cultured cells: Amoebocytes resemble blood cells and rapidly appear around the explant; fibroblasts form a continuous crown around the fragment, are less mobile, and resemble the fibroblasts of the connective tissue in vertebrates.

The heart is favored for several reasons. It is easy to reach in dissection and is seldom contaminated. The fragments of the heart muscle can be uniform; thus, various cultures can easily be compared.

It is necessary to wash the explants in a bath of salt solution to obtain

TABLE XII
MEDIUM FOR SNAIL CELLS[a]

Substances	Concentration
Part 1: Snail Medium[b]	
1. Bidistilled water	480 ml
2. Medium 199 T.C. + 0.5% Peptone (Difco)	500 ml
3. BHI Bacteriological Broth	20 ml
4. S.L. Broth	20 ml
5. M 9 Stock A	4 ml
6. M 9 Stock B	8 ml
7. Calf fetal serum	40 ml
8. Snail extract[c]	40 ml
9. Antibiotic mixture	8 ml
Part 2: S.L. Broth[d]	
Trypticase (B.B.L.)	10 gm
Yeast extract (Difco)	5 gm
K_2HPO_4	6 gm
Ammonium citrate	2 gm
Glucose	20 gm
Sodium acetate	25 gm
Glacial acetic acid	1.32 ml
Salt solution	5 ml
Tween 80	1 gm
Bidistilled water	500 ml
Part 3: Salt Solution	
$MgSO_4 \cdot 7H_2O$	11.5 gm
$MnSO_4 \cdot H_2O$	2.86 gm
Bidistilled water	100 ml
Part 4: M-9 Stock Solutions[e]	
Solution A	
Na_2HPO_4 (anh)	150 gm
K_2HPO_4 (anh)	75 gm
Bidistilled water	1,000 ml
Solution B	
$MgSO_4$	20 gm
NaCl	50 gm
NH_4Cl	1 gm
Bidistilled water	1,000 ml
Antibiotic Mixture	
Fungizone	50 mg
Penicillin	1,000,000 IU
Streptomycin	1 gm
Bidistilled water	100 ml

[a] From Burch and Cuadros (1965).
[b] *Preparation of Snail Medium:* All components were pooled and mixed in a 2-liter

a culture of heart cells, and this washing eliminates the blood contained in the tissues.

In snails, the heart is removed through a cut made in the disinfected shell. It is reached by slightly putting aside the hepatopancreas and organ of Bojanus (Fig. 1).

In oysters, the heart tissue is removed after denuding the pericardial membrane by cutting the adducent muscle. The heart beat is easily observed and helps in the operation (Fig. 2).

The foot muscle of snails is taken from under the foot tunic. This tissue is often contaminated, so it should be washed in the antibiotic solution described by Vago and Flandre (1963). The foot muscle is cut in small regular fragments. A migration of fibroblasts is observed within 48 hours following the initiation of the culture.

The foot muscle of oyster can also be cultured. The mantle is removed after a window has been cut in the disinfected shell. This tissue is often contaminated, so it must be washed in the antibiotic solution before culture.

---

flask in the order given in Part 1. The pH was adjusted by adding steam-sterilized 0.3 N sodium hydroxide. The indicator (Phenol red) contained in the 500 ml of medium 199 was enough to indicate the pH even though diluted by the other components. The medium was filtered through a millipore filter, dispensed in 100-ml Pyrex bottles, and stored at $-5°$.

[c] *Snail Extract:* The snails were kept in a vivarium and fed on lettuce. Prior to removing organs their shells were washed, dried, disinfected with 70% ethanol, and cracked with sterile pliers. The tissues were cut with sharp, sterile scissors and pooled in separate, previously weighed beakers which had been kept cool in ice throughout the process. The foot, the mantle, the floor of the pulmonary cavity, the hermaphrodite genital tract, and the albumen gland were used. Tissues of the alimentary canal, liver, head, and anal region were discarded. Final weights of the snail tissues were as follows:

Mantle	31.0 gm
Foot	120.4 gm
Albumen gland ⎰ Lower oviduct ⎱	91.9 gm
Rest of the reproductive system	39.1 gm

The total weight of the tissues used was 285.8 gm, to which was added 285.8 ml of bidistilled water. The tissues pooled in a cold Waring blender were minced in water for 30 minutes at 0°, and the homogenate was centrifuged for 10 minutes at 2000 rpm at 10°. The supernatant was collected. Using this medium Burch and Cuadros cultured foot muscle, mantle, esophagus, oviduct, and gonad of *H. pomatia, A. glabratus, Pomatiopsis lapidaria.*

[d] *Preparation of SL Broth:* The components were dissolved with 500 ml of sterile bidistilled water. When the mixture was fully dissolved the volume was adjusted to 1 liter by adding bidistilled water.

[e] *Preparation of M-9 Stock Solutions:* Stock solutions A and B were prepared separately, and each was made up to 1 liter with bidistilled water.

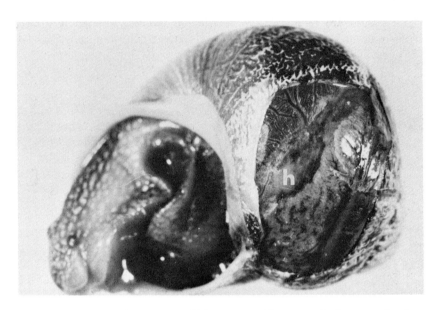

Fig. 1. Simplified dissection of *Helix aspersa* (Gasteropod) for removing heart tissues (h).

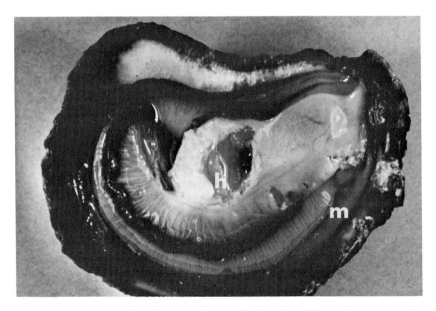

Fig. 2. Simplified dissection of *Ostrea edulis* (Lamellibranch) for removing heart (h) and mantle (m) tissues.

The tissues are removed with sterile microknives, minced into small pieces, washed several times in a sterile saline solution, and placed in sterile petri dishes.

2. Preparation of Tissues

Like vertebrate tissue culture, the culture of mollusk tissues can be achieved in two different ways. The first consists of culturing organ fragments in a suitable medium, and cellular migration starts from the explant.

In the second method, culturing is preceded by a dissociation of the tissue so that the cells are separated from each other.

1. The culture of tissue explants is the oldest technique. It bears a resemblance to the one developed by Carrel (1914, 1923) for vertebrates. It has the advantage of keeping a beneficial environment around the cells, and thus, the cellular differentiation is less rapid. This method is used when one wants to make hanging drop cultures of small tissue fragments. It does not yield a large quantity of cells.

2. The culture of dissociated cells is achieved by various processes: Mechanical dissociation consists in cutting the tissue into tiny fragments. This has been replaced by enzymatic dissociation, which is a more adaptable process and easier to use. Enzymatic digestion can be done with several enzymes. Hyaluronidase was used to dissociate insect tissues (Aizawa and Vago, 1959) and mollusk tissues (Vago and Chastang, 1960). Nowadays it would be preferable to use trypsin, as employed in cultures of vertebrate cells (Dulbecco, 1952). Trypsin was used to dissociate various mollusk tissues by Chardonnet and Peres (1963). Chernin (1963) applied it to the dissociation of the heart tissues of *A. glabratus* (Fig. 3). The fragments are placed in a 25% trypsin solution prepared in appropriated salt solution (pH 7.6–7.8) for 50–60 minutes. It is stirred gently during the whole period of dissociation. The enzyme action can be stopped either by cooling the cellular suspension in melted ice or, preferably, by the use of a natural inhibitor. If a pancreatic inhibitor is introduced, it blocks the action of trypsin irreversibly. Trypsin is inhibited by one-third of its weight of pancreatic inhibitor. This method, used by Santucci *et al.* (1962) for cell culture of vertebrates, can also be applied to mollusk cells without any modification.

Cecil (1969) applied enzymatic fragmentation to dissociate the cardiac tissue of the surf clam, *Spisula solidissima*. Cell cultures have been grown as cell monolayers for extended periods. Disaggregated cells from pooled cardiac tissue were obtained by treatment with 0.25% trypsin-EDTA in

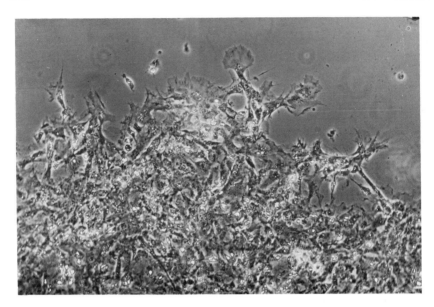

Fig. 3. Heart cell culture from *Australorbis glabratus* (Gasteropod). Phase contrast; ×175.

a 2.6% NaCl medium. This consisted of known components supplemented with fetal calf serum and whole egg ultrafiltrate.

C. Culture Techniques

Cultures of mollusk tissues and cells can be achieved by several methods, using instruments comparable to the ones employed in vertebrate tissue culture. The choice of the culture support is a function of the size of the explant to be cultured, of the cell multiplication rate, and of the desired end result.

The hanging drop technique (Harrison, 1906) has considerable advantages in exploratory tissue culture work on invertebrates, particularly if the explants tend to be small. When invertebrate tissues can be dissociated by enzymes into separate cells, the primary cultures may then be sown with large numbers of cells derived from pooled tissues from several animals. The dissociated cells can be cultured in roller tubes, Carrel flasks, and V.H. flasks.

1. Equipment

Glass or sterilizable plastic depression slides allow hanging drop and sitting drop cultures. Carrel D_5 and D_3 flasks, direct observation flasks

(Vago, 1959), can be used when the culture develops slowly. Roller tubes with flattened surfaces or Leighton tubes with flat surfaces can also be used for stationary cultures in fluid phase.

The coverslip technique is the simplest. A fragment of tissue is placed in a drop of medium on a coverslip, covered with a depression slide, and sealed and incubated at 25°. The cells migrate and multiply and may be studied under the microscope. This method is mainly used for short cultures. When a semisolid plasma clot is used, the method may be extended by repeated transfers of the cultures.

The flask and roller tube techniques are better adapted to the growth of larger amounts of tissue and to long-term culture with maintenance of activity. The tissue, fixed on the slide and nourished by a supernatant fluid, may be left undisturbed for long periods since only the fluid medium is changed. In flasks, the supernatant fluid is stationary, whereas in roller tubes the tube is rotated so that the tissues are alternatively exposed to nutrient and to air.

2. Cultures in Fluid Medium

This technique is used by most authors who obtained cultures of mollusk cells. These cultures can be made on coverslips, flasks, and roller tubes.

The technique is quite simple: 1-mm-diameter fragments of tissue are placed into the medium, in touch with the support. After some time, cells migrate from the explant and some of them remain in suspension in the fluid, while others are fixed onto the surface of the slide. After a time varying with the nature of the cultured tissue the cells which have multiplied are removed with a pipette and are transferred into a fresher medium.

This method enabled Vago and Chastang (1958) to establish a real cell strain from tissues of *H. aspersa* and of oysters. The cells thus cultured are mostly fibroblasts, but it has been also possible to culture blood cells, heart tissue, and epithelial cells (Chernin, 1963).

3. Cultures in Plasma Clot

Cultures of mollusk tissues in coagulated medium can be made in depression slides, V.H. flasks, Carrel flasks, and Leighton tubes. The merit of this method is in the ease of interpretation and the possibility of keeping cells with preserved cytological characters indefinitely.

Flandre and Vago (1963) defined the conditions under which these cultures are successful. The culture medium has two phases: a solid phase (plasma clot) and a fluid phase.

The solid phase, or coagulum, is formed by cockerel plasma and the complete Ha 78 medium (Vago, 1959) with addition of chicken embryo extracts. This coagulum must be semisolid since it has to fix the explant and to keep the cells well grouped in a zone of growth, but it must be fluid enough to allow some cell migration from the explant. A coagulum fulfilling these standards is obtained by dilution of 1/20. The fluid phase is made with a complete Ha 78 medium.

When the cultures are in hanging drops, explantations are made about every fifth day; the culture is cut when it reaches the limit of the outgrowth, then washed in the salt solution and placed in a new coagulum.

Culture can also be done in roller tubes and in V.H. flasks, and here the explant is fixed in a very thin coagulum spread on the cover slide of the tube or of the flask. After coagulation, the complete medium Ha 78 is added. Growth is observed in the coagulum. The fluid phase can be changed every fifth day without the culture being touched. The explants are planted out every fortnight. This method gives large cultures which can be planted out indefinitely.

4. Cultures of Dissociated Cells

This technique, which is directly adapted from those applied in vertebrate virology, makes it possible to obtain cultures of cells in monocellular layers.

After dissociation by trypsin, the cells are placed into the culture medium in roller tubes or V.H. flasks. The cells fix themselves on the slide and multiply.

The cells are separated from the support for transplantation with trypsin and washed in a salt solution before placing in a new medium. This method is used mostly for the culture of fibroblasts.

III. CELL CULTURES OBTAINED

The techniques above described make it possible to culture various mollusk cells and to study cytology and physiology.

A. Foot Tissue Culture

The fragments of this complex tissue composed of muscles, connective tissue cells, and deep epithelium are taken under the foot tunic (Flandre and Vago, 1963).

The cellular emission from the explant appears as a multiplication of cells which form an outgrowth around the explant and can be observed early as the second day of culture. These cultures have been maintained by successive transplantation for several months, keeping the outgrowth which was a starting point for new cells.

After 1-month development *in vitro*, cultures of two types of cells can be observed.

1. Fibroblasts are characterized by their polymorphism and their large size. They are surrounded by an undulating, thin, transparent membrane which can change shape and forms a hyaline veil in perpetual movement. This membrane does not contain granules. It vanishes or withdraws during mitosis or fixation. In the cytoplasm there is an important chondriome formed by granulous, filamentous, and highly mobile mitochondria. The nucleus has various shapes and sizes and is often polylobed; it comprises nucleolae which are small, dense, and very polymorphic. Their number varies, and there are at least two of them in every nucleus. These fibroblasts are highly mobile.

2. Ciliated cells are the second type of cell, and they are very different. They are only slightly mobile, their growth is regular, and they keep a contact between one another, thus forming a tissue with a loose epithelial structure type. These cells are triangular and have a denser base formed by granulations and vibratile cilia. The nucleus is situated at the apical pole of the cell; it is dense and regular and possesses one or two nucleolae. These cells divide actively; they preserve their initial morphology during a considerable period, yet tend to evolve towards a fibroblastic form.

In mixed cultures connective tissue cells dominate over epithelial cells after a few weeks and form a thin layer near to the explant. Burch and Cuadros (1965) have cultured foot tissue with surrounding outgrowth for 60 days, and ciliated cells were still active at the end of the experiment.

B. Heart Culture

The formation of the outgrowth is fast, it is visible after 3 days of culture, and it has a characteristic aspect (Flandre and Vago, 1963).

From the explant, cells migrate and form compact groups here and there whence new cells migrate in their turn. Once these small groups are linked to one another, they eventually form a crown around the explant. In this zone, the coagulum is rapidly lyzed by the cells, which thus multiply in a more fluid medium. The progression of the peripheric zone causes the coagulum to be partly lyzed so that the latter must be often replaced. After several explantations two types of cells can be identified.

Fixed cells are the most numerous; they form islets around the explant. These elements are spread out, regular, and seldom possess cytoplasmic prolongations. Inside the cytoplasm there are granulous, dense areas not stained by fat dyes and, also, MacManus negative. They are sometimes replaced by vacuoles of variable sizes which extend to a large part of the cytoplasm. In such cells, the nucleus is driven off to the periphery; it is irregular in shape and contains one or several dense oblong nucleolus. A thick chromatin network is often visible.

Mobile cells have a small cytoplasm with thin branching prolongations. The nucleus is small, very dense, and bears several thick nucleolae. These cells can move very quickly.

Others are typical fibroblasts of fairly large size; the chondriome is plentiful and the nucleus is regular. These fibroblasts make a continuous layer between the big accumulations of cells, mainly in the lyzed area of the coagulum.

Chernin (1963), in trypsin-treated hearts explanted in plastic flasks, observed two types of cells, i.e., amoebocytes, and "epithelial" cells (*Australorbis glabratus*).

Amoebocytes were usually observed within an hour or two, and always within 24 hours, near the margins of the explants. Migration was first evidenced by the appearance at the tissue margin of numerous clear filipodia simulating a brush border. Emergence of individual cells and their subsequent movements were readily observed as the cell processes rapidly made contact with the surface and flattened. As a rule, amoebocytes moved out independently of each other while actively forming lamelliform pseudopodia and interconnecting filipodia, but sometimes the cells emerged initially in dense masses. The nucleus of the unstained amoebocyte was not visible, but in stained preparation the nucleus appeared vesicular and contained scattered chromatin. Stained preparations also occasionally detected their presence within intracellular vacuoles. The number of amoebocytes usually increased during the first 2–4 days or so.

The "epithelial" cells were large, polygonal, hyaline, and lacked large inclusions or vacuoles; the nucleus was visible and cell boundaries were sharply delineated and contiguous. These cells appeared to be derived from the border of the explant and typically moved outward as a sheet resembling pavement epithelium.

Chernin (1963) and Flandre and Vago (1963) observed that the heart pulsed *in vitro*. Pulsation was often ventricular; on occasion it was confined to the auricle, and more rarely, the auricle pulsed alternately. Approximately 50% of the explanted hearts pulsed at one time or another.

C. Mantle Culture

The cultures are made of pure connective tissue, whose growth is fast. (See Fig. 4.) Fibroblasts form a cellular layer around the explant. They exhibit different sizes; some are small and highly mobile. Large fibroblasts are very numerous; they are edged with a wide undulating membrane formed by cytoplasmic prolongations. Inside the cytoplasm the chondriome is represented by granulous and filamentous mitochondria. Granulous mitochondria are numerous around the nucleus, whereas the filamentous ones are more mobile and move about in the whole cell. The nucleus is large, light-colored, often irregularly shaped, and limited by a well-individualized membrane. Some cells possess a very regular nucleus comparable to the nucleus of vertebrate fibroblasts. The nucleolae are punctiform and scattered all over the nuclear surface.

The fibroblasts form a cellular layer by their cytoplasmic prolongations; they remain mobile, however, but their motions are slow. Cells in mitosis are visible in the peripherical area of the culture, even after several explantations.

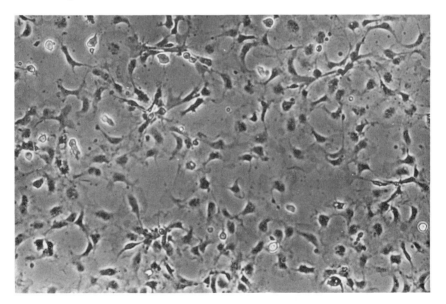

Fig. 4. Culture (8 month) of dissociated mantle tissue from *Ostrea edulis* (Lamellibranch). Phase contrast; ×230.

D. Gonad Culture

Gonad tissues of *H. pomatia*, *A. glabratum*, and *Pomatiopsis lapidaria* were cultured by Burch and Cuadros (1965). Several observations are particularly pertinent. Actively motile mature sperm were visible continually over 60 days. Various prophase I, stages of meiosis, diakinesis, were seen in great abundance. Numerous metaphase I cells were also seen. After 14 days of culture many mitotic metaphase cells were seen in primary explants of *H. pomatia*, indicating actual cell division and quantitative growth of the cultures. Farris (1968) observed that after dissociation of the ovotestes of *H. pomatia* by trypsin the cells reaggregated into histotypically organized tissue. Reaggregation is facilitated by centrifugation, but pseudopodial activity of the cells is another important factor.

REFERENCES

Aizawa, K., and Vago, C. (1959). *Ann. Inst. Pasteur. Paris* **96**, 455.
Benex, J. (1961). *C. R. Acad. Sci.* **253**, 734.
Bevelander, G., and Martin, J. (1949). *Anat. Rec.* **105**, 614.
Bohuslav, P. (1932). *Arch. Exp. Zellforsch.* **13**, 673.
Bohuslav, P. (1933). *Arch. Exp. Zellforsch.* **14**, 139.
Burch, J. B., and Cuadros, C. (1965). *Nature, London* **206**, 637.
Carlson, J. G. (1946). *Biol. Bull.* **90**, 109.
Carrel, A. (1914). *J. Exp. Med.* **20**, 1.
Carrel, A. (1923). *J. Exp. Med.* **38**, 407.
Carrel, A., and Ebeling, A. H. (1921). *J. Exp. Med.* **34**, 599.
Cecil, J. T. (1969). *J. Inverteb. Pathol.* **14**, 407.
Chardonnet, Y., and Peres, G. (1963). *C. R. Soc. Biol.* **157**, 1593.
Chernin, E. (1957). *Amer. J. Hyg.* **66**, 321.
Chernin, E. (1963). *J. Parasitol.* **49**, 353.
Chernin, E., and Schork, A. R. (1959). *Amer. J. Hyg.* **69**, 146.
Chernin, E., and Schork, A. R. (1960). *Exp. Parasitol.* **9**, 9.
Colin Nicol, J. A. (1967). "The Biology of Marine Animals." Interscience (Wiley), New York.
Dulbecco, R. (1952). *Proc. Nat. Acad. Sci. U. S.* **38**, 747.
Durchon, M. (1964). *Bull. Soc. Zool. Fr.* **89**, 45.
Dutko, V. P. (1967). *Tsitol. Genet.* **1**, 61.
Enders, J. F. (1953). *Proc. Soc. Exp. Biol. Med.* **82**, 100.
Farris, V. K. (1968). *Science* **160**, 1245.
Flandre, O., Vago, C., and Chastang, S. (1962). *C. R. Acad. Sci.* **255**, 1654.
Flandre, O., and Vago, C. (1963). C. R. Colloq. Int. Cult. Tissue Invertebr. 1st, Montpellier, 1962. *Ann. Epiphyt.* **14**, 161.
Friedl, F. E. (1958). "Doctoral dissertation." Univ. Minnesota.
Gatenby, J. B. (1931). *Nature* **128**, 1002.

Gatenby, J. B. (1932). *Nature* **130**, 628.
Gatenby, J. B., and Duthie, E. S. (1932). *J. Roy. Microsc. Soc.* **52**, 395.
Gatenby, J. B., and Hill, J. C. (1933). *Quart. J. Microscop. Sci.* **76**, 331.
Gatenby, J. B., Hill, J. C., and Macdougald, T. J. (1934). *Quart. J. Microsc. Sci.* **77**, 129.
Gavrilov, W., and Cowey, S. (1941). *Ann. Parasitol. Hum. Comp.* **18**, 180.
Guardabassi, A., and Piacenza, M. L. (1958). *Arch. Anat. Microsc. Morphol. Exp.* **47**, 25.
Hanghton, I. (1934). *Quart. J. Microsc. Sci.* **77**, 157.
Harrison, R. G. (1906). *Anat. Rec.* **7**, 116.
Havinga, B. H. (1964). *Sea Frontiers* **10**, 155.
Hill, J. C. (1934). *J. Roy. Microsc. Sci.* **54**, 163.
Hill, J. C., and Gatenby, J. B. (1934). *Arch. Exp. Zellforsch.* **18**, 195.
Hirumi, H. (1963). *Contrib. Boyce Thompson Inst.* **22**, 113.
Jones, B. M. (1966). *In* "Cells and Tissues in Culture. Methods, Biology, and Physiology" (E. N. Willmer, ed.), Vol. 3, pp. 397–457. Academic, New York.
Karnik, A. G., and Kamat, D. N. (1961). *J. Univ. Bombay* **29B**, 172.
Konicek, H. (1933). *Arch. Exp. Zellforsch.* **13**, 709.
Lewis, M. R. (1916). *Anat. Rec.* **10**, 287.
Michelson, E. H. (1959). *Trans. Amer. Microsc. Soc.* **78**, 256.
Neva, F. A., Malone, M. F., and Myers, B. R. (1961). *Amer. J. Trop. Med. Hyg.* **10**, 140.
Nikolic, M., and Stojnic, I. (1964). *Proc. Gen. Fish. Counc. Mediter.* **7**, 251.
Pan, C. (1958). *Bull. Mus. Comp. Zool. Harvard Univ.* **119**, 237.
Parker, R. C. (1961). "Methods of Tissue Culture." Hoeber, New York.
Paul, J. (1959). "Cell and Tissue Culture." Livingstone, Edinburgh.
Rannou, M. (1967). *Vie et Milieu* **18**, 525.
Ripplinger, J., and Joly, M. (1961). *C. R. Soc. Biol.* **155**, 825.
Santucci, J., Haag, J., Choay, J., and Thely, M. (1962). *C. R. Acad. Sci.* **254**, 955.
Trager, W. Y. (1938). *Amer. J. Trop. Med.* **18**, 387.
Vago, C. (1959). *Entomophaga* **4**, 23.
Vago, C., and Chastang, S. (1958). *Experientia* **14**, 110.
Vago, C., and Chastang, S. (1960). *C. R. Acad. Sci.* **251**, 902.
Vago, C., and Flandre, O. (1963). C. R. Colloq. Int. Cult. Tissus Invertebr. 1st Montpellier, 1962, *Ann. Epiphyt.* **14**, 127.
Vago, C., and Quiot, J. M. (1969). *Ann. Zool. Ecol. Anim.* **1**, 281.
Wagge, L. E. (1955). *Int. Rev. Cytol.* **4**, 31.
Waymouth, C. (1957). *J. Nat. Cancer Inst.* **19**, 495.

13

CELL CULTURE OF INVERTEBRATES OTHER THAN MOLLUSKS AND ARTHROPODS

Michel Rannou

I. INTRODUCTION

In this chapter I shall review only those studies which have increased our knowledge of morphology and physiology by means of *in vitro* cell culture technique. It is not my intention, however, to mention every single study of cells *in vitro*. Some of these investigations are outside the scope of this treatise. For example, I shall not take into account the observations of sexual cells (which are emitted naturally by organisms) nor the descriptions of coelomic or blood cells maintained in their natural media, outside the organism, and for brief periods of time. Also, the considerable research on embryonic cells *in vitro* will not be discussed here.

II. DEVELOPMENT OF CULTURE MEDIA

Attempts to maintain invertebrate cells were made quite early in the history of tissue culture. It should be remembered that it was as long ago as 1910 that Burrows obtained mitoses *in vitro*. M. R. Lewis and Lewis (1911a,b) and W. H. Lewis and Lewis (1912) used an artificial salt solution and seawater as media for vertebrate cells. Wilson (1907, 1908, 1910) and Huxley (1911) kept sponge cells alive for considerable periods. Wilson (1911a,b), de Morgan and Drew (1914), and Hargitt (1914) published results on work on Cnidaria. Finally, Goldschmidt (1915) succeeded in obtaining the division of insect spermatocysts in a nutritive medium composed of a salt solution and hemolymph. The demonstration by Frederic and Macallum of the similarity between seawater and the internal medium of some invertebrates and her own experience in the field of cell culture enabled M. R. Lewis to maintain cells of various invertebrates in easily constituted media. Lewis used media made up of 90% seawater, 10% animal broth, and 0.1, 0.25, or 0.5% dextrose. She was thus able to keep alive with some success chicken, fish, grasshopper, horseshoe crab, hermit crab, and sea anemone cells.

Some years later, Cary (1931, 1933) attempted to culture the cells of 11 marine animals (three cnidaria, one platyhelminthe, one annelid, two mollusks, one crustacean, two echinoderms, and one stomochordate) in different physiological solutions. She experimented with Locke and Goldschmidt solutions, seawater, diluted seawater (50%), Tyrode and Drew solutions, and Locke–Lewis and Goldschmidt solutions supplemented with 0.5% dextrose. The best results were obtained with artificial solutions in which the salt concentration had been doubled; in these conditions, the substitute with osmotic pressure of the solutions was the same as that of diluted seawater.

Information on the nutrition of cells in culture continued to increase. M. R. Lewis and Lewis (1911a,b) added amino acids and peptides to their media. Dobrowolski (1916) studied invertebrate tissues in a "milieu nutritif artificiel composé non pas de matières albuminoïdes simples, mais des produits de dédoublement de ces matières, pour constater dans quelle mesure la cellule animale en croissance peut produire ses propres matières albuminoïdes par voie de synthèse."* Burrows and Neymann (1917, 1918) noted the toxicity of amino acids in their cultures; Carrel (1924) pointed out that, in certain conditions, amino acids could encourage cell migration, though they could not be used as growth substances. Krontowsky and Rumiazev (1922) maintained pieces of head and tail of earthworms in a medium composed of agar and tissue extract and obtained outgrowth and mitoses for 3 to 5 days. Murray had already supplemented culture media with amino acids present in the animal diet, and long before completely synthetic media were used for vertebrate cell culture, she had stated that "these experiments make it appear possible however that, in contrast to the conditions found by Carrel to obtain multiplication in the cells of chicken, the cells of *Planaria* may be able to use for growth purposes substances other than embryo extracts."

Murray (1926, 1927a,b) also examined the problem of the disinfection of tissues with ultraviolet rays, to remove bacteria from *Planaria*.

Over the last 20 years, synthetic media used in the culture of vertebrate cells (TC 199, Eagle medium) have enabled the development of invertebrate cell culture media. These media are described in various chapters of this book. In this chapter, media are mentioned only when a knowledge of their composition is essential for the understanding of a particular study. Nutrient solutions have often been supplemented with animal tissue extracts homologous serum, vertebrate serum, or semisynthetic nutrients (Table I).

Occasionally, experiments have been made with entirely synthetic media. If the nutritive elements of all these media do not fulfill the particular needs of all invertebrate cell categories, they do, however, seem to constitute "an environment sufficiently close to the normal passive environment of the cells that they can modify it to fulfill completely their peculiar nutritional requirements" (Waymouth, 1954). If, indeed, "when the medium is adequate for prolonged survival of cells, the additional

---

* Dobrowolski (1916) studied invertebrate tissues in a "nutritious artificial medium composed not of simple albuminoid materials, but of the diluted products of these materials, in order to establish to what degree the animal cell, in growing, can produce its own albuminoid materials by means of synthesis."

TABLE I^a
CULTURE MEDIUM FOR HYDRA CELLS

Substances	Concentration for 1000 ml
Eagle medium	100 ml
Modified Earle's solution*	100 ml
Horse serum	100 ml
Distilled water	700 ml
Penicillin	200 IU
Fumaril B	500 IU
Tampon phosphate	0.15 M for pH 6.8
* The modified Earle's medium in milligrams/100 ml	
NaCl	5.8
$MgSO_4 \cdot 7H_2O$	100
$NaHCO_3$	168
KCl	7.5
$CaCl_2$	111
Dextrose	1000
Phenol red	10
Streptomycin	12.5

[a] From Y. Y. F. Li et al. (1963).

conditions which will permit growth can be recognized" (Waymouth, 1954), the prolonged survival of isolated cells from different animal sources in media containing the same nutritive elements should help in the comparative study of cell nutrition and in the perfecting of media.

III. CELL CULTURE OF PORIFERA

At the beginning of this century, Wilson (1907, 1908, 1910) described the disaggregation of tissues. Small pieces of tissue, knotted in cheesecloth, were immersed in freshwater or seawater; the knot was then squeezed between forceps; this pressure was enough to overcome the cell adhesion. The disaggregated cells were forced through the mesh and dispersed in the water. This technique, as described by Wilson (1937), is still widely used. However, the disaggregation is not always complete, and many cells remain joined together. In order to increase the efficiency of this method, Humphreys et al. (1960a,b) broke by chemical means the intercellular bonds which had survived the treatment. After being passed through the cheesecloth, the cells of a sea sponge were collected in seawater free of calcium and magnesium and centrifuged; the deposit was then suspended at 0° in a trypsin solution in seawater free of calcium and magnesium. After vigorously stirring and pipetting, all the cells were perfectly separated.

A purely chemical method was used by Curtis (1962): Pieces of sponge were subjected to EDTA (0.004 M) in a buffered sodium chloride solution.

The hardiness of the separated cells has meant that research into their nutritional requirements has been neglected so that one cannot speak of a real culture medium as far as sponge cells are concerned. Despite the disillusioned remark that "their history in ordinary seawater is a history of gradual starvation, followed by involution, since the fluid does not contain sufficient nutriment . . . ," Huxley (1921b) has been, to our knowledge, alone in attempting to feed isolated sponge cells. He tried unsuccessfully to feed sea sponge cells on diatoms, suspensions of dead marine bacteria, spores of the alga *Ulva*, solutions of peptone in seawater, sponge broth, and ammonium lactate. All other workers used cells surviving in simple water.

Even before the development of techniques for vertebrate cell culture, the ability of sponge cells to survive in water has drawn attention to certain biological problems which have since been the subject of numerous experiments:

1. Is there any dedifferentiation in isolated cells? Are some cells totipotential?
2. What is the process of cellular reaggregation?
3. Can bispecific aggregates be obtained?
4. How do the components of the cell surface function in aggregation?

These questions will be discussed in detail in the following pages.

A. Cellular Categories, Dedifferentiation, and Totipotency

Wilson (1907, 1908, 1910), the pioneer of sponge cell culture, distinguished several categories of dissociated *Microciona prolifera* cells; the most numerous were spherical granular red amoebocytes which produced pseudopods. Next were modified choanocytes, also fairly numerous. These cells were elongated and collarless but still had their flagellum, which, however, soon stopped moving. Other categories of cells were less common. Soon after the cells had sedimented, reaggregation began and it became impossible to distinguish the different categories. Wilson concluded that cell dedifferentiation took place within the aggregates which then contained only archeocytes, and that this was followed by a redifferentiation of the cells.

Müller (1911a) attempted to define the role of different cell types in the formation of the restitution body. He found in filtrates of *Spongilla lacustris* and *Ephydatia mülleri* all of Wilson's cell types, i.e., nucleolated cells (archeocytes, amoebocytes, thesocytes, chromatocytes, phagocytes), dermal cells with no nucleole (pinacocytes, collencytes, spherular cells, silicoblasts, spongioblasts, cytencytes), and choanocytes without flagellum or collar. However, 3 hours after cell regrouping, the aggregates contained only archeocytes and dermal cells and were surrounded by hyaline zone. The ciliated chambers formed from polynucleated elements deriving from the archeocytes.

The regressive differentiation of sponges in confined media also resulted in the formation of masses containing only archeocytes and dermal cells. This confirmed Müller's hypothesis (1911b), which agreed with Wilson's, that totipotential archeocytes were the result of dedifferentiation.

In the same year, Huxley (1911) showed that the regeneration from dissociated cells which Wilson had observed in monaxonid sponges and in Cnidaria (Wilson, 1911a,b) also took place in the heterocoelic calcareous sponges. About 24–30 hours after separation, *Sycon coronatus* cells formed regeneration spherules and a new olynthus appeared between 17 to 30 days later. Like earlier workers, Huxley described the dedifferentiation of choanocytes, which, he said, was incomplete. He also considered that cells could redifferentiate only into cells of their own type. This meant that during reorganization, the evolution of the cells was not determined by their position but that their position depended on their type. Huxley (1921a) attempted to repeat his experiments with the homocoelic calcareous sponges *Leucosolenia* and *Clathrina* but met with little success. He developed a method for isolating *Sycon* choanocytes and studied the reorganization of tissues thus formed. He obtained aggregates composed almost entirely of choanocytes, thus corroborating his earlier hypothesis that dissociated cells differentiated but did not, however, become totipotential. During these experiments, the author noticed the penetration of sponge spermatozoa into somatic cells.

De Beer (1922), repeating one of Huxley's experiments (1921a) with *Sycon raphanus,* obtained masses composed entirely of choanocytes. He had collected large numbers of these cells by lacerating the sponge with a needle, rubbing it against a silk sieve, or squeezing it between the fingers.

Galtsoff (1923, 1924) demonstrated that aggregates formed solely from *Microciona prolifera* archeocytes did not survive and that combination with pinacocytes was necessary. When the aggregate spread over the surface to which it was adhering, organenesis began; the pinacocytes migrated to form the outer epithelium, subdermal cavities, and canals. Most of the elements of the central mesenchyme were newly formed and derived from the archeocytes. Aggregates without choanocytes were able to regenerate. The author considered that the choanocytes were derived from the pinacocytes. The tissues of the new sponge could therefore differentiate, through a process of neo-formation, from the archeocytes and pinacocytes. For Galtsoff, however, and contrary to Wilson's conclusions, this did not mean that dissociated cells dedifferentiated and reverted to an embryonic state.

Using the same material, Wilson and Penney (1928, 1930) continued Galtsoff's research on cellular dedifferentiation. Detailed histological study led the authors to consider the outer epithelium of *Microciona prolifera* as a syncytium. They also suggested a simplification of the terminology used for cell categories. After dissociation, they were able to distinguish two types of amoebocyts which played very different roles in regeneration; first anucleolated cells and grey cells, and second, choanocytes. Hyaline cells were extremely numerous in the suspension, but pinacocytes and mesenchymal cells seldom passed through the cheesecloth mesh. The grey cells formed the syncytial epithelium of the aggregates and demarcated the canals. As Huxley had concluded, the choanocytes derived from the original sponge tissue, as did the collencytes. The glandular and rhabdiferous cells, on the other hand, derived from the archeocytes. By study of these results and detailed examination of what earlier workers had observed, Wilson and Penney were able to conclude that the cells did not revert to an undifferentiated stage.

With *Reniera*, Galtsoff (1929) obtained aggregates which separated from the substrate after 24 hours. They contained in particular, archeocytes, small round cells with or without intracellular bodies. Choanocytes were numerous and active. However, cell activity ceased after a few hours, the aggregates became round, and separated from the substrate.

According to Fauré-Frémiet (1932a) four cell types were present in the aggregates of *Ficulina ficus*, i.e., choanocytes, archeocytes (which could fuse to form giant multinucleated cells), collencytes, and fuchsinophilic cells. Fauré-Frémiet questioned whether the syncytium described by Wilson and Penney was, in fact, present around the aggregates. In his opinion the pinacocytes, scleroblasts, and numerous fuchsinophilic cells of the aggregates derived from the archeocytes. However, despite an apparent dedifferentiation caused by the mechanical dissociation of the tissue, several cell types retained their specific properties, notably, the choanocytes. Contrary to Galtsoff, however, Fauré-Frémiet observed that aggregates without choanocytes never had ciliated chambers. These normally appeared in the form of polynucleated masses composed of de-differentiated choanocytes. The author concluded, therefore, that the reorganization of sponges consisted largely in cellular regroupings. Fauré-Frémiet (1932b) also studied cell involution especially under the effect of ultraviolet radiation.

Brønsted (1936) showed that after dissociation the sponge was rebuilt from the different cell types, and he admitted that the archeocytes, apparently the least differentiated cells, could differentiate into cells of another type. The experiments undertaken to study the limit of the differentiation potential of the archeocytes during the development of gemulae (Brønsted, 1953) will be described in the chapter on invertebrate organ culture. It need only be pointed out here that the author observed a decrease in the differentiation power of archeocytes as the sponge was constructed.

Having identified the cells remaining after dissociation of *Ephidatia fluviatilis,* Brien (1937) considered their role in histogenesis and morphogenesis. All the cells of the parental sponge survived without structural change and were to be found in the reorganized spherule in the same proportion as in the normal sponge. Like Huxley, Brien thought that reorganization was the repositioning of the different cells of the parental sponge and that these cells retained their distinctive character without dedifferentiation. He considered that histogenesis was limited to the formation of scleroblasts, vacuolar and spherulous granular cells. Only in the case of organogenesis from the larva or the gemula was there any real ontogenesis and evidence of archeocytic totipotency.

Tuzet (1945), Shivaramakrishnan (1951), Agrell (1951), and Connes (1966) studied more particularly the evolution of the choanocytes.

Ganguly (1960a,b) studied the formation of the restitution bodies of *Ephydatia* from the beginning of dissociation to the 15th day. The cells first became rounded, and after 4 to 6 hours the choanocytes, archeocytes, and scleroblasts redifferentiated into their original type.

Levi (1960) studied the reconstitution of the skeleton of *Ophlitaspongia seriata* by means of cell suspension from adult sponge. During the second month, the main spicules and the microscleres appeared in all parts of the sponge and the spongine built up an incomplete basal layer which gradually covered the spicules. Further developments were the lengthening of the fibers upon a framework of slender spicules and the lateral growth of connecting fibers which generally contained no spicules. The reconstituted skeleton rapidly recovered its normal reticulated structure.

The filtrates of *Sycon raphanus* cells made by Tuzet and Connes (1962) contained moving elements (choanocytes, amoebocytes) and inert cells (mesenchymal cells, pinacocytes, collencytes, eosinophilic amoebocytes, megacytes, hyalin amoebocytes). In aggregate, dedifferentiation was complete in 3 days; all the cells were more or less spherical, only their sizes were different. Redifferentiation began on the 5th day. There was intensive cell multiplication. The outer cells redifferentiated into pinacocytes, the first ciliated chambers formed. The first spicules appeared in binucleated cells. The number of pinacocytes and chambers increased until the 15th day.

By means of Agrell's method (1951, 1952) and differential centrifugation, Borojevic (1963a,b) obtained almost pure suspensions of choanocytes of *Ficulina ficus* and *Hymeniacidon sanguinea*. These cells, which had neither collar nor flagellum, became amoeboid but were soon destroyed by cytolysis before any choanosome was formed.

After an electron microscope study of the reorganization of dissociated *Ophlitaspongia seriata* cells, Borojevic and Levi (1964) questioned whether dedifferentiated and totipotential archeocytes were present. According to these authors, the cells did not revert to a polyvalent embryonic state; no syncytium was observed.

Sara (1965) studied the mitotic activity of cells during aggregation.

Borojevic and Levi (1965) observed the reaggregation of cells of swimming larvae of *Mycale conteranii*, after chemical dissociation, and were able to state that it was an adult sponge that formed, not an organism of the larvae type. Dissociation of the larvae cells produced the same effect as fixation. However, it was suggested that the dissociation of younger embryos might give a different result. The authors noted the formation by the collencytes of the basal and marginal membranes of the spherules and the disappearance of the vacuolar larval cells. Some ciliated larval cells became choanocytes.

Borojevic (1966) maintained the different cell groups of *Mycale conteranii* larvae in separate cultures. The central parts of the larvae gave, mainly, collencytes and archeocytes. In culture, the larval epithelium rapidly formed a normal sponge unless the archeocytes and collencytes were in insufficient numbers, in which case the culture degenerated. Ciliated cells could not form other cell types. A detailed electron microscope study of the fixation apparatus of the aggregates has also been made (Borojevic and Levi, 1967).

B. Mechanisms and Factors of Aggregation

From his very first observations, Wilson (1907, 1908, 1910) noted the tendency of sedimented dissociated cells to regroup. The coalescing of granular cells began immediately; they formed small masses surrounded by pseudopods and to which choanocytes and hyaline cells soon joined. Cellular membranes were soon no longer discernable; the masses joined together and large syncytia were formed which differentiated to become small sponges.

Müller (1911a) noted that aggregates formed by amoebocytic activity developed only if their diameter was about 1.5 mm and if they adhered to the support. De Beer (1922) subjected aggregates to hypotonic and hypertonic solutions and observed increases and decreases of volume. Galtsoff (1924) demonstrated that in *Microciona prolifera* the formation of cell groups was mostly due to the activity of archeocytes which could adhere one to another, the cells joining together randomly. After 4 hours, coalescence became evident in reticulated form and after 5 to 6 hours this divided into spherules. However, the mobility of the archeocytes was not indefinite and generally lasted between 40 to 170 minutes. Galtsoff (1925a,b, 1926) also examined the action of physical and chemical factors on the aggregation, the contraction of the aggregates, and their cell stability. He considered that archeocytic activity was the only cause of cell coalescence.

Fauré-Frémiet (1925e) studied the factors and mechanism of the aggregation of dissociated sea sponge cells (*Halichondria panicea, Hymeniacidon sanguinea*) and freshwater spongilles. As the cells sedimented from suspension, Fauré-Frémiet observed the formation of small, regularly distributed primary aggregates. Amoeboid cell movements determined further contacts and the formation of secondary masses. The retraction of cell masses, necessary for the formation of structures able to develop, was associated with the reciprocal cellular activity. The physicochemical properties of the medium modified the form and number of the cellular structures; thus, temperature changes not only influenced archeocytic activity but also determined the stability of the cellular structure. At low temperatures structures were not formed, and in high temperatures they were destroyed as they formed. The ionic composition and the pH of the medium influenced the form of pseudopods and, thus, the retraction of the mass. Further studies on the influence of the medium were carried out by Galtsoff and Pertzoff (1926) and, later, by de Laubenfels (1932).

Brien (1937) described cell agglutination and coalescence which resulted in the formation of the network and, later, of nodules. Cell coalescence came about through the retraction of a network of long pseudopods. Several conditions were necessary for the reorganization of the spherules: (a) It had to be of sufficient size (1–1.5 mm); (b) the water had to be pure, flowing, and aerated; (c) the spherules had to attach to the support by the pinacocytes surrounding them. The formation of a protoplasmic network between isolated cells, observed by Galtsoff (1925b) and Brien

(1937), was again noted by Tuzet (1945) in silicious and calcareous sponges, and by Shivaramakrishnan (1951) in *Callyspongia*. Tuzet and Connes (1962) noted that in *Sycon raphanus* the first aggregates were formed mainly from choanocytes to which mesenchymal cells and pinacocytes were joined. Spicule fragments formed centers of reaggregation to which the cells adhered.

Humphreys (1963) employed the method developed by Humphreys *et al.* (1960) to facilitate by rotation the aggregation already dissociated by chemical means. The role of bivalent cations in adhesion was once more noted. At 5° the cells remained dispersed; the optimum temperature was between 18° and 25°. It should be noted that at low temperature cells of *Microciona prolifera* and *Haliclona oculata*, which had been mechanically dissociated, were capable of reaggregation (Humphreys, 1963; Moscona, 1963).

C. Bispecific Aggregation

Wilson's first attempts (1907, 1908, 1910) to obtain bispecific aggregation were unsuccessful. When dissociated cells of *Microciona prolifera* and *Lissodendoryx* and of *L. carolinensis* and *Stylotella heliophila* were placed in the same container, restitution bodies were built up from the cells of one species of sponge only. The mixed aggregates which sometimes occurred soon disintegrated or died. De Laubenfels (1926, 1928, 1932) had more success. By mixing dissociated cells of different sponges (*Halichondria, Haliclona viridis, H. rubens, H. longleyi, Lotrochota birotulata*) he obtained mixed aggregates, capable of surviving 2 weeks, from the last two species mentioned. In 1956, as a confirmation of de Laubenfels's experiment, Sara obtained mixed aggregates with two related *Leucosolenia*. In further experiments he obtained the same result with other sponges (Sara, 1966; Sara *et al.*, 1966a) and even succeeded in inducing the coalescence of sponge cells and cells of the sea anemone *Anemonia sulcata* (Sara, 1966; Sara *et al.*, 1966b).

D. Role of the Cell Surface

In 1929, Galtsoff published a report of experiments done in Bermuda on the specific segregation of dissociated cells. The silicious marine sponges *Reniera cinerea, Pachycalina* sp., *Spinosella sororia, Tedania ignis, Donatia* sp., *Suberites carnosus*, and the horny sponges *Aplysina hirsuta, A. crassa, Euspongia irregularis* were used. Heteroaggregation was observed in numerous cases, but it was not always reciprocal. Thus,

Reniera, which aggregates the cells of all other sponges, was itself aggregated by *Tedania* and *Aplysina crassa* but not by *Pachychalina.* The volume of cellular suspension that had to be added to obtain aggregation varied according to the combinations. Galtsoff also demonstrated that in experiments with *Reniera,* the substance which caused cell aggregation was soluble in seawater. The inhibition of archeocytic movement in the presence of cells of an other species, as observed in *Microciona* and *Cliona,* was again noted with *Reniera.*

In his experiments on the marine sponge *Iotrochota birotulata,* de Laubenfels (1932) noticed that an aqueous extract from *Haliclona rubens* prevented cell aggregation; this inhibition could be removed by heating to 90°. A colloidal substance liberated on cell dissociation was of some importance in the reaggregation phenomenon.

Agrell (1951) demonstrated that cells of *Halichondria panicea* could reaggregate in the presence of citrate and oxalate, and Spiegel (1954) showed that calcium, also indispensable for cell movement, was not always necessary for adhesion. Spiegel also pointed out specific antigenic substances present in the adhesion of *Microciona prolifera* and *Cliona celata.* A detailed analysis of these experiments can be found in Weiss's recent work (1967).

Curtis (1962) attempted to study the relative position of the cells that make up regeneration tissue. He was not entirely satisfied by the hypothesis [which Margoliash *et al.* (1965) and Gasic and Galenti (1966) were later to support, however] that specific proteins were responsible for the adhesion of isolated cells. Chemical dissociation would inhibit these proteins, whereas they would be activated in a suitable culture medium. Curtis postulated a mechanism determining the relative position of the cells and, thereby, their specificity. Cells of *Microciona sanguinea, Halichondria panicea, Suberites ficus,* and *Hymeniacidon perleve* were dissociated chemically. Immediately after dissociation or after some time (2–10 hours) bispecific mixtures were made; different types of tissue were obtained, corresponding to different stages in cell association (Fig. 1):

1. Complete separation of the cells of each species
2. Contiguity of aggregates, each containing cells of a single species
3. Groups of cells of one species surrounded by cells of the other species
4. Homogeneous mixture

To explain these results, Curtis concluded that, for a very short period of time each of the different cell types of each species of sponge could accept heterologous cells. If two cell types could be synchronized during the

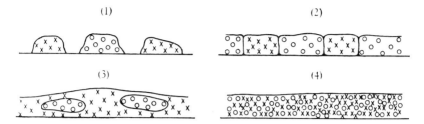

FIG. 1. The four types of reaggregate seen in idealized section. (1) Complete separation of two cell types. (2) Chain aggregates: types separate in groups, but each group adheres to another. (3) Concentric coating; one cell type invests the other. (4) Intermingling. ○, cells of one type; ×, cells of second type. [Courtesy of Professor A. S. G. Curtis (1962) and *Nature (London)*.]

crucial phase of the process, they would accept each other. Viscosimetric measurements were performed (Curtis, 1970).

Study of the components of the cell surface and their role in adhesion was begun by Spiegel (1954, 1955) and continued by Moscona (1963) and by Humphreys (1965, 1967) with experiments on *Microciona prolifera* and *Haliclona oculata*, and by Yazykov (1965a,b, 1967) with experiments on *Reniera cinerea*, *Halichondria panicea* and *Ephydatia fluviatilis*. Loewenstein (1967) studied, with intracellular electrodes, the genesis of communication between the cells of *Haliclona oculata* and *Microciona prolifera* during reaggregation. The author confirmed that an organic factor (as well as calcium and magnesium) was of fundamental importance in establishing intercellular communication. The importance of calcium and magnesium in cell adhesion had already been emphasized by Humphreys (1963, 1965), Moscona (1963), and Margoliash *et al.* (1965).

IV. CELL CULTURE OF CNIDARIA

Using cheesecloth, Peebles (1897) was the first to obtain cell dissociation of Cnidaria. After applying this method to sponges, Wilson (1911a,b) dissociated Cnidaria cells in the same way and kept them alive in water. It was noted that dissociated cells of *Eudendrium carneum* and *Pennaria tiarella* joined together in irregular masses surrounded by a perisarc. On the 4th day, the ectoderm and the endoderm could be distinguished, and on the following day hydranths were formed. As in the case of sponge reconstitution, Wilson thought that dedifferentiated totipotential cells made up the restitution masses.

These experiments were continued by de Morgan and Drew (1914), Hargitt (1914), and Okada (1927).

De Morgan and Drew (1914) were less successful than Wilson. The restitution masses of *Antennularia*, *Plumaria*, *Tubularia*, and *Clava*, which were histologically different from those that Wilson had observed, did not produce hydranths. Ectodermal and endodermal cells, as well as syncytia, which might temporarily surround the ectodermal cells, could, however, still be distinguished. According to these authors, therefore, there was no real dedifferentiation.

In answer to the doubts expressed by de Morgan and Drew as to the accuracy of Wilson's results, Hargitt (1914) published a report of experiments done some years earlier which supported the theory of a return to an embryonic state. An hour after the dissociated cells of *Podocoryne carnea* began to reaggregate, morphological differences between the cell types disappeared. A perisarc was rapidly secreted and a polyp formed. The cells of hydranths of *Eudendrium rameum* and *E. racemosum* gave less constant results. Aggregates of *Tubularia mesenbryenthemum*, *T. larynx*, *Halecium*, and various campanularians and serratularians and of medusea did not develop. Okada (1927), too, concluded from his observations that cells returned to an embryonic state.

The work mentioned thus far was concerned with cells which had already been dissociated. Other workers, however, have used the tissue fragment method. A piece of tissue placed in a suitable medium is soon surrounded by isolated cells which have broken off to colonize the nutritive medium. In this way, it is easy to verify that the cells moving on the glass surface of the container are in good physiological condition. On the other hand, it is much more difficult to ascertain whether an increase in the number of isolated cells is the result of active migration or cell multiplication. Since early experiments contain no cytological confirmation, care is needed to interpret the results.

M. R. Lewis (1916) successfully maintained cells from pieces of sea anemone. The culture medium was composed of 95% seawater, 0.25% dextrose, 0.1% broth, sodium bicarbonate, and about 5% distilled water. Abundant outgrowth was noted.

Fifteen years later, Cary (1931) did systematic research into the most favorable solution for the survival of numerous invertebrate cells; further references to her work will be made in this chapter, but mention should be made here of her experiments in cultivation of fragments of the tentacles, the bell margin, and the wall of the polyp of *Stoichactis heliantus*, *Aurelia aurita*, and *Briareum asbestinum* to obtain "actively growing cultures."

Other experiments were carried out by Macallum (1926), Child (1928) and Weimer (1934). Papenfuss (1934) cultured cells of the freshwater hydra, *Chlorohydra viridissima*, in petri dishes containing a layer of agar covered with well water. The dissociated cells were placed in small cavities, but no cellular aggregation could be obtained and the author had to use small tissue fragments for his experiments on regeneration. Beadle and Booth (1938) demonstrated that endodermic and ectodermic cells were necessary for the reconstitution of *Cordylophora*.

Using fragments of the marine hydrozoan *Clava leptostyla*, Rudzinska (1951) studied the influence of sterilization (by heat or filtration) of the media on culture behavior. She did not succeed in obtaining migration with seawater sterilized by porcelain filter but obtained good results in all other cases.

Sanyal and Mookerjee (1960) dissociated cells of *Hydra vulgaris* by squeezing between slide and coverslip, isolated them with a micropipette and kept them in hanging drops for 2 or 3 hours. Epitheliomuscular, interstitial, muscular-nutritive, and secretory cells were noted. Philips (1961) succeeded in keeping alive cell cultures of *Entopleura elegantissima* for more than a year. The tissues were sliced and dissociated by squeezing through a cheesecloth. The cells were centrifuged and washed in sterile artificial seawater. The culture medium was composed of seawater, antibiotics, and a variable percentage of edamine, a product of the enzymatic digestion of lactalbumin. The cells kept in petri dishes or culture tubes "showed certain peculiarities, some of which it is hoped, may be corrected through the use of a better nutrient medium."

Y. Y. F. Li *et al.* (1963) succeeded in obtaining division of interstitial *Hydra* cells in culture. The tissues were first sterilized and then dissociated in trypsin or EDTA. The nematoblasts were eliminated by slight centrifugation. The cells in suspension soon assumed their typical shape. The culture medium was composed as indicated in Table I.

Despite the many difficulties encountered by earlier workers (Sanyal and Mookerjee, 1960; Philips, 1961) in the study of the morphogenetic potential of Cnidaria cells, R. Martin and Tardent (1963) and Tardent (1965) traced the evolution, in culture, of the isolated cnidoblasts of the colonial hydrozoan *Tubularia larynx*.

The living tissues from which the epibionts and hydrocauls had been removed were treated with antibiotics for 24 hours. Tissue fragments were placed in a semisynthetic medium composed of buffered seawater (pH 7.5), serine, taurine and glycine, yeast extract, and glucose. A semisolid medium was formed by addition of crayfish plasma, chosen for its bacteriostatic properties. In hanging drops of rolling tubes, the cells soon migrated out of the tissue fragments and dispersed. Musculoepithelial type cells, in particular, formed a network on the glass, while retaining close contact with each other. In these primary cultures, most of the cell degenerated after 4 to 8 days. Only a few cnidoblasts escaped this regression. After an adaptation period, their number suddenly increased. After 1 month of culture in the medium which was renewed every week, the first stages of the differentiation of the cnidoblasts were observed; they could divide again when the nematocyst capsule was formed.

In a chemically defined medium, Burnett et al. (1968) obtained the growth of Tubularia cells and their differentiation into nervous cells and cnidoblasts.

Another type of morphogenetic differentiation (the formation of calcareous skeletal pieces) was obtained in vitro by Rannou (1968). The swimming larva of gorgonians (planula) is a small ciliated ovoid organism without skeleton. When it settles, it soon changes into a polyp, in the tissues of which the primary calcareous spicules appear. Fragments of the planula were cultured in a medium composed of seawater, the organic fraction of the vertebrate cell culture medium TC 199, 10% bovine embryo serum, and antibiotics. The tissues first retracted into small spheres. After 4 days, the cells of these spheres dissociated and dispersed through the culture fluid. After several weeks, different stages of the differentiation of the scleroblasts could be seen, from the appearance of fine rods to the elaboration of spicules similar to those of young polyps. Mention should be made here of comparable results, observed by Levi (1960), in cell cultures of sponge larvae.

The mixed aggregation of sponge and sea anemone cells obtained by Sara et al. (1966a,b) has already been mentioned in the previous section.

V. CELL CULTURE OF PLATYHELMINTHES

Cell culture of Platyhelminthes was attempted in 1911 by Morse, who, following Harrison's method, placed fragments of tissue of the worms Callobothrium and Crossobothrium, which are shark parasites, into shark serum. After 12 hours of culture at 17°–23° migrating cells dispersed in the medium, where they survived for several weeks. Good results were also obtained by placing the tissue fragments in pure seawater and in various saline solutions. The serum of Limulus was noted to have a harmful effect and the cultures were often invaded by bacteria.

Bacterial invasions were the principal obstacle to prolonged observation of the cells in vitro, at the time when Murray described (1926, 1927a,b) a method she had developed for the cultures of planaria cells.

Rinsing the worms was impossible because of the sticky mucus that covered the animals. Washing off the germs introduced by the tissue fragments was of no use. The disinfection by bactericidal products such as mercurochrome, mercuric chloride, and gentian violet did not give good results as "the tolerance of the planarians to the bactericidal agents was found to be lower than that of the majority of the bacteria." On the other hand, the use of ultraviolet rays seemed to be very effective. The worms were placed in a thin film of water and exposed to uv radiation. If the power of the lamp, its distance from the animal, and the length of exposure were carefully selected and if the usual aseptic procedures were observed, sterile cultures could be obtained.

One of the physiological solutions used by Murray had been formulated by M. R. Lewis and Lewis (1911a,b):

NaCl	0.8%
KCl	0.02%
CaCl$_2$	0.02%
NaHCO$_3$	0.02%

This solution was prepared with filtered, boiled, and aerated well water. Cells from different parts of the worms (whole or regenerating) had a varying tolerance to the concentration of the medium; the optimum concentration for the muscular and epithelial cells was from 1/9 to 1/10. For parenchymatous cells, it was from 1/11 to 1/12. The survival of the tissue fragments was very short, but the cells deriving from them could survive 3–7 days in the buffered solutions and 4–6 days in a solution of sodium chloride at 0.9%. When 0.1–1% dextrose was added to a buffered solution, the cells survived for as long as 10–15 days. With glycogen, they would live only for 9–10 days. With dextrose plus 0.1% peptone in Locke's solution, the cells divided more frequently and they survived.for 10 days. The cultures were placed in hanging drops in a liquid or solid medium (a drop of agar at 1 or 1.5% to 10 drops of nutritive solution). The cells that migrated were mainly muscular, ciliated, and digestive cells. The author concluded from the observation that cellular division was amitotic.

Since whole planarians could be fed on coagulated egg white, Murray tried to supplement the culture media by adding the three principal amino acids of egg white. Arginine (0.2%) in Locke's solution made the medium toxic, and the cells survived only 3 days. They survived 6 days with 0.2% tyrosine, 9 days with 0.2% leucine, and 6 days with the mixture of the three amino acids.

Media supplemented with serum or extracts of platyhelminths, mollusks, or isopods could no longer be sterilized, but during the 2 or 3 days they survived, "the cells in these foreign extracts appeared to be markedly stimulated to migration and probably to division." Sheep serum in Locke–dextrose solution failed to improve the survival.

Murray (1928a) noticed that worms kept in saline solutions made up with distilled water soon became paralyzed; this did not happen when well water containing Ca and K ions was used. The behavior of whole *Planaria dorotocephala* and of cultured cells was observed in solutions of KCl, NaCl, and $CaCl_2$ at pH 7.6 and at Δt 0.2°. In solutions of KCl and NaCl the cultures rapidly died. In solutions of $CaCl_2$ muscular cells and the cells with pseudopods remained alive for at least 2 weeks. The study of the role of the Ca/K ratio with different quantities of sodium showed that when the Ca/K ratio was high, the cultures remained in good condition. The Ca/K ratio had no effect on the behavior of the cultures. In solutions unfavorable for the survival of whole worms, the epithelial and muscular cells, which are not very adaptable, soon died. Parenchymatous and endodermic cells survived the longest. Their adaptability seemed to be related to their great activity during regeneration.

Later, Murray (1931) attempted to prepare a medium which might take the place of embryonic extracts as a growth stimulator, by making peptic digests of blood fibrin, liver, and other substances and using the proteoses thus obtained. As a culture medium for parenchymatous cells, she used a salt solution with high Ca/K and Na/K ratios:

NaCl	0.5 gm
KCl	0.01 gm
$CaCl_2 \cdot 2H2O$	0.07 gm
$NaHCO_3$	0.01 gm
Distilled water	150 gm
(Δt: 0.2°)	

The cells survived for 4 weeks in the medium supplemented with proteoses and only two weeks in the unsupplemented salt solution. When peptones from planarians were added to the salt solution, the cells survived for 6 weeks at 12°–15°. The parenchymal cells soon migrated and after 24–36 hours became mono- or bipolar. When muscular cells were present in the culture, the pseudopods of the parenchymal cells often came in close contact with them and seemed to become adherent to them, in the same way as nerve cells do.

Mention must also be made of Cary's experiments (1931) in survival of cell of the marine platode *Bdelloura candida*. By culturing pieces of pharynx of *Planaria gonocephala*, Seilern-Aspang (1958) succeeded in achieving cell proliferation between two glass slides. When the cells had more room, a three-dimensional development was possible and parenchymatous masses surrounded by ciliated epithelial cells were formed.

Freisling and Reisinger (1958) obtained restitution bodies from mechanically dissociated cells of *Planaria polychroa*. In Holtfreter's liquid there was rapid reorganization of the aggregates whenever there were ectodermic cells in the crushed tissues.

Ansevin and Buchsbaum (1961) experimented with the freshwater planarian *Dugesia tigrina*. After the worm had been washed in antibiotics for 30 minutes (2500 units/ml of penicillin and streptomycin) and rinsed in sterile distilled water, tissue fragments were obtained either by slicing or by use of EDTA (0.2%) for an hour. The cultures developed in hanging drops. The authors experimented with three media: a solid medium (2% agar in water plus extracts of planarian tissue) and two liquid media containing extracts of planarian tissue diluted in a physiological solution (Hanks' solution at half strength or Holtfreter's solution at 1/10 strength) or in chicken plasma (4/1). The medium contained 100 μg of neomycine/ml and its pH was adjusted to 8. Cell migration began a few hours after the cells were placed in culture, and it was much more active in the solid medium than in the liquid ones, which seemed to inhibit it. The cells survived 7–10 days.

Occasionally, during organ culture experiments with freshwater Planaria, Chandebois (1963) observed cell migrations. The culture medium, which was solid, contained amino acids, antibiotics, agar, and a salt solution based on Murray's (1931).

VI. CELL CULTURE OF ANNELIDS

Attention was drawn in Section III to the results obtained by Krontowsky and Rumiazev (1922) in the culturing of earthworm tissues. Fragments of regenerated head and tail of *Lumbricus terrestris*, the earthworm, placed in a solid medium (agar and earthworm hydrolysate) gave rise to an outgrowth of cells which survived only 1 week. On the other hand, chloragogenic cells, from fragments of blood vessels, remained in good condition for 20 days.

Fauré-Frémiet (1925a–f) succeeded in keeping blood cells of *Arenicola* alive in lymph diluted in a solution of sodium chloride. The agglutination of the amoebocytes was noted and the action of the cations on these cells studied. Similar observations were made in subsequent years (Fauré-Frémiet, 1928; Garrault, 1931) (Fig. 2).

Cary (1931) reported that "actively growing cultures" had been obtained from regenerated tail ends of sabellid worms placed in various chemically defined media. Fragments of the intestinal lining of *Lum-*

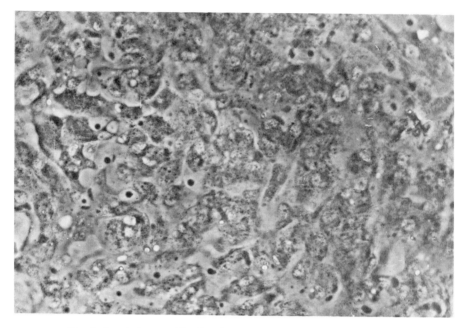

FIG. 2. *Lumbricus* sp. blood cells in culture. Phase contrast; ×660.

bricus, kept in culture by Janda and Bohuslav (1934), formed cysts. Some of the cysts survived for 13 months in a culture medium containing glucose, the product of the peptic digestion of blood fibrin, and earthworm tissue, but most of the cysts disaggregated into numerous large cells, generally spherical. At temperatures between 15° and 26° the cells survived for several months without any visible modification. The authors noted also that the phototactic activity of the amoebocytes seemed to be negative and that during 8 months they were able to move by means of pseudopods.

VII. CELL CULTURE OF SIPUNCULIDS

For a long time, various free bodies in the coelomic liquid of the sipunculids were mistaken for protozoans. Thus, the urns of the *Sipunculus*, with their discoidal ciliated cells, were first considered to be ciliates. Hence, Thomas's observation (1932): "La facilité relative avec laquelle on peut cultiver les vesicules enigmatiques et les urnes de siponcles, déjà si différenciées, semble être un argument en faveur de leur origine parasitaire, sinon il faudrait interpréter ces résultats comme représentant une culture de tissus d'invertébrés en milieu purement liquide."* Thomas mixed 20 drops of plasma, previously centrifuged and sterilized by porcelain filtration, with two to five drops of *Sipunculus nudus* plasma collected in sterile conditions. Multiplication of the vesicles and urns soon began. After 3 months during which time several more subcultures were made (five drops of the culture in 20 drops of new plasma), the urns disappeared but the enigmatic vesicles continued to multiply. After 4 months, they began to degenerate, but some still survived after 6 months.

VIII. CELL CULTURE OF ECHINODERMS

The egg of the sea urchin has been used for experimentation for many years. In 1877, Fol described fertilization *in vitro*. Driesch (1891a,b, 1895) dissociated a fertilized egg at stage 2 and observed the formation of two whole larvae, thus discovering the phenomenon of regulation. Herbst (1900) dissociated blastula cells by placing them in seawater without calcium. They reassociated in normal seawater. No attempt will be made to describe the many experiments since carried out on echinoderm eggs. We shall describe only the original method used by Okazaki (1965) to observe the formation of the skeleton *in vitro*. Making use of Herbst's discovery, Okazaki placed fertilized *Mespilia globulus* eggs in seawater with a low calcium content (1/20 of that of normal water). The blastula soon stuck to the glass, and the ectoderm cells moved about centrifugally by means of their pseudopods; the larva then opened and flattened into two low hemispheres. The medium was replaced by normal seawater to avoid excessive flattening. The blastula was then cultured in gently running seawater.

Since Wilson's (1911a) experiments on *Asterias*, where he reported some success, there have been few attempts to culture cells of adult echinoderms.

Some results were obtained by Cary (1931) with the intestine, nerve, and gonad cells of *Centrechinus setosum* and *Tripneustes esculenta*, and by Koizumi (1939) with holothurian tissues.

Several observation of cells maintained *in vitro* are found in Konichev's and Mourachova's work (1965) on the primary immunological reactions of echinoderms. Tissues of adult starfish and sea urchins were crushed and

---

* "The relative ease with which one can cultivate the enigmatic vesicles and the urns of the sipunculids, already very differentiated, seems to be an argument in favor of their parasitic origin; otherwise, it is necessary to interpret these results as representing a culture of invertebrate tissues in a purely liquid medium."

mixed *in vitro* with the internal liquid of these animals. After 18–24 hours of incubation at 8°–10°, the cells of the internal fluid aggregated. The authors observed an "antibody-like" substance in the internal liquid incubated this way.

Coagulation of the coelomic liquid has been studied by Abraham (1964) and by Johnson and Beeson (1966). It was a reversible phenomenon, as the cells forming the clot dispersed after 48–96 hours. They could be observed in hanging drops for 5–74 days. Johnson studied the morphology and dynamics of the coelomic elements in hanging drops (1969a) and their *in vitro* reaction to bacteria (1969b).

Quiot and Rannou (1971) succeeded in culturing cells of different tissues of the sea urchin (podial ampullae, gonads, gonoducts, brown glands, digestive tract) and *Holothuria* tissues (digestive tract, blood vessels, gonads, respiratory trees, Polian vesicles) (Fig. 3). The culture medium consisted of seawater, nutrient substances from the TC 199 medium for vertebrates, antibiotics, and 10–20% embryonic bovine serum. The cells which migrated from the tissue fragments behaved as fibroblasts and formed a network connected by pseudopods or a mono-cellular epithelioid layer.

Similar results were obtained by Rannou (1971) with an entirely synthetic medium without serum.

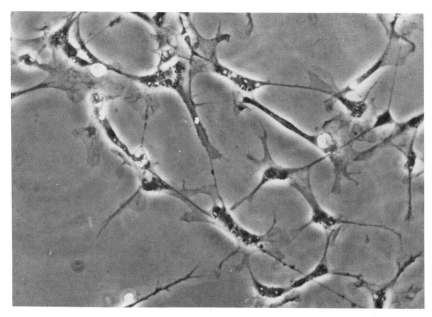

Fig. 3. Culture of cells from the respiratory system of *Holothuria* sp. Phase contrast; ×330.

IX. CELL CULTURE OF STOMOCHORDATES

Cary (1931, 1933) appears to be the only worker to have experimented on cell culture of stomochordates.

Basing her work on M. R. Lewis (1916) and Murray (1928a,b), she maintained cells of *Ptychodera bahamensis* in seawater or in physiological solution. The best results were obtained in media with a Δt of about 0.9°. The cells remained alive for a long time in the salt solutions. The addition of 0.5–1% dextrose, 10% snail broth, and *Ptychodera* peptones caused a more active but shorter outgrowth. Sterilization was obtained by washing the whole animal and the tissue fragments in a solution of hexylresorcinol; 10% of this product could be added to the culture media without causing any harm to the cells. Ultraviolet rays were also satisfactory.

Connective, nervous, and ectodermic cells were maintained in hanging drops. The endodermic cells were subcultured 10 times. Dedifferentiation and redifferentiation of the muscular cells were reported.

X. CELL CULTURE OF PROTOCHORDATES

Phase microscope studies of living blood cells led Andrew (1961) to describe a new type of cell appendage. With the same methods used in their work on echinoderms, Konychev and Murachova (1965) observed the aggregation of blood cells of Ascidia at the point of contact of the tissue extracts from another animal of the same species. The presence of antibody-like substances was also noted.

REFERENCES

Abraham, M. (1964). *Pubbl. Sta. Zool. Napoli* 34, 43.
Agrell, I. (1951). *Ark. Zool.* [2] 2, 519.
Agrell, I. (1952). *Ark. Zool.* [2] 3, 23.
Andrew, W. (1961). *Quart. J. Microsc. Sci.* 102, 89.
Ansevin, K. D., and Buchsbaum, R. (1961). *J. Exp. Zool.* 146, 153.
Beadle, L. C., and Booth, F. A. (1938). *J. Exp. Biol.* 15, 303.
Borojevic, R. (1963a). D. E. S., Fac. Sci., Université de Strasbourg.
Borojevic, R. (1963b). *C. R. Acad. Sci.* 257, 961.
Borojevic, R. (1966). *Develop. Biol.* 14, 130.
Borojevic, R., and Levi, S. (1964). *Z. Zellforsch. Mikrosk. Anat.* 64, 708.
Borojevic, R., and Levi, C. (1965). *Z. Zellforsch. Mikrosk. Anat.* 68, 57.
Borojevic, R., and Levi, C. (1965). *Z. Zellforsch. Mikrosk. Anat.* 68, 57.

Borojevic, R., and Levi, C. (1967). *J. Microsc. (Paris)* **6**, 857.
Brien, P. (1937). *Arch. Biol.* **48**, 185.
Brønsted, H. V. (1936). *Acta Zool.* **17**, 75.
Brønsted, H. V. (1953). *Quart. J. Microsc. Sci.* **94**, 177.
Burnett, A. L., Ruffing, F. E., Zongker, J., and Necco, A. (1968). *J. Embryol. Exp. Morphol.* **20**, 73.
Burrows, M. T. (1910). *J. Amer. Med. Ass.* **55**, 2057.
Burrows, M. T., and Neymann, C. A. (1917). *J. Exp. Med.* **25**, 93.
Burrows, M. T., and Neymann, C. A. (1918). *Proc. Soc. Exp. Biol. Med.* **15**, 138.
Carrel, A. (1924). *Physiol. Rev.* **4**, 1.
Cary, L. R. (1931). *Carnegie Inst. Wash., Yearb.* **30**, 379.
Cary, L. R. (1933). *Carnegie Inst. Wash., Publ.* **28**, 125.
Chandebois, R. (1963). *Ann. Epiphyt.* [2] **14**, 141.
Child, C. M. (1928). *Physiol. Zool.* **2**.
Connes, R. (1966). *Bull. Soc. Zool. Fr.* **91**, 43.
Curtis, A. S. G. (1962). *Nature (London)* **196**, 245.
Curtis, A. S. G. (1970). *Nature (London)* **226**, 260.
de Beer, G. R. (1922). *Arch. Zool. Exp. Gen.* **61**, 47.
de Laubenfels, M. W. (1926). *Carnegie Inst. Wash., Yearb.* **26**.
de Laubenfels, M. W. (1927). *Carnegie Inst. Wash., Yearb.* **27**, 219.
de Laubenfels, M. W. (1928). *J. Elisha Mitchell Sci. Soc.* **44**, 82.
de Laubenfels, M. W. (1932). *Tortugas Lab. Pap., Carnegie Inst. Wash.* **28**, 39.
de Morgan, W., and Drew, G. H. (1914). *J. Mar. Biol. Ass. U. K.* **10**, 440.
Dobrowolsky, N. K. (1916). *C. R. Soc. Biol.* **79**, 789.
Driesch, H. (1891a). *Z. Wiss. Zool.* **53**, 160.
Driesch, H. (1891b). *Z. Wiss. Zool.* **55**, 10.
Driesch, H. (1895). *Mitt. Zool. Sta. Neapel* **11**.
Fauré-Frémiet, E. (1925a). *C. R. Soc. Biol.* **92**, 1187.
Fauré-Frémiet, E. (1925b). *C. R. Soc. Biol.* **92**, 1287.
Fauré-Frémiet, E. (1925c). *C. R. Soc. Biol.* **92**, 1367.
Fauré-Frémiet, E. (1925d). *C. R. Soc. Biol.* **92**, 1436.
Fauré-Frémiet, E. (1925e). *C. R. Soc. Biol.* **93**, 618.
Fauré-Frémiet, E. (1925f). *C. R. Acad. Sci.* **181**, 573.
Fauré-Frémiet, E. (1928). *Arch. Exp. Zellforsch. Besonders Gewebezuecht.* **6**, 264.
Fauré-Frémiet, E. (1932a). *Arch. Anat. Microsc.* **28**, 1.
Fauré-Frémiet, E. (1932b). *Arch. Anat. Microsc.* **28**, 121.
Fol, H. (1877). *Arch. Zool. Exp. Gen.* **6**, 145.
Freisling, M., and Reisinger, E. (1958). *Arch. Entwicklungsmech. Organismen* **150**, 581.
Galtsoff, P. S. (1923). *Biol. Bull.* **45**, 153.
Galtsoff, P. S. (1924). *Anat. Record* **29**.
Galtsoff, P. S. (1925a). *J. Exp. Zool.* **42**, 183.
Galtsoff, P. S. (1925b). *J. Exp. Zool.* **42**, 223.
Galtsoff, P. S. (1926). *J. Gen. Physiol.* **20**, 239.
Galtsoff, P. S. (1929). *Biol. Bull.* **57**, 250.
Galtsoff, P. S., and Pertzoff, V. (1926). *J. Gen. Physiol.* **10**, 239.
Ganguly, E. (1960a). *Proc. Indian Sci. Congr.*, **47**, 434.
Ganguly, E. (1960b). *Arch. Entwicklungsmech. Organismen* **152**, 22.
Garrault, A. (1931). *Arch. Exp. Zellforsch. Besonders Gewebezuecht.* **11**.
Gasic, G. J., and Galanti, N. L. (1966). *Science* **151**, 203.

Goldschmidt, R. (1915). *Proc. Nat. Acad. Sci. U. S.* **1**, 220.

Hargitt, C. W. (1914). *Biol. Bull.* **27**, 370.

Herbst, C. (1900). *Arch. Entwicklungsmech. Organismen* **9**, 424.

Humphreys, T. (1963). *Develop. Biol.* **8**, 27.

Humphreys, T. (1965). *Exp. Cell Res.* **40**, 539.

Humphreys, T. (1967). *Ann. Meeting Soc. Gen. Physiol., Englewood Cliffs,* p. 195.

Humphreys, T., Humphreys, S., and Moscona, A. A. (1960a). *Biol. Bull.* **119**, 249.

Humphreys, T., Humphreys, S., and Moscona, A. A. (1960b). *Biol. Bull.* **119**, 295.

Huxley, J. S. (1911). *Phil. Trans. Roy. Soc. London, Ser. B,* **202**, 165.

Huxley, J. S. (1921a). *Quart. J. Microsc. Sci.* **65**, 293.

Huxley, J. S. (1921b). *Biol. Bull.* **40**, 127.

Janda, V., and Bohuslav, P. (1934). *Publ. Fac. Sci. Univ. Charles, Prague* **133**, 1.

Johnson, P. T. (1969a). *J. Invertebr. Pathol.* **13**, 25.

Johnson, P. T. (1969b). *J. Invertebr. Pathol.* **13**, 42.

Johnson, P. T., and Beeson, R. J. (1966). *Life Sci.* **5**, 1641.

Koizumi, A. (1939). *Sci. Rep. Tohoku Univ.* **7**, 269.

Konychev, V. A., and Murachova, A. I. (1965). *J. Gen. Biol.* **26**, 451.

Krontowsky, A., and Rumiazev, A. (1922). *Pfluegers Arch. Gesamte Physiol. Menschen Tiere* **195**, 291.

Levi, C. (1960). *Cah. Biol. Mar.* **1**, 353.

Lewis, M. R. (1916). *Anat. Rec.* **10**, 287.

Lewis, M. R., and Lewis, W. H. (1911a). *Anat. Rec.* **5**, 277.

Lewis, M. R., and Lewis, W. H. (1911b). *Bull. Johns Hopkins Hosp.* **22**, 126.

Lewis, W. H., and Lewis, M. R. (1912). *Anat. Rec.* **6**, 207.

Li, Y. Y. F., Baker, F. D., and Andrew, W. (1963). *Proc. Soc. Exp. Biol. Med.* **113**, 259.

Loewenstein, T. (1967). *J. Cell Biol.* **33**, 235.

Macallum, A. B. (1926). *Physiol. Rev.* **6**, 316.

Margoliash, E., Schenck, T. R., Margie, M. P., Borokas, S., Richter, W. R., Barlow, M., and Moscona, A. A. (1965). *Biochem. Biophys. Res. Commun.* **20**, 383.

Martin, R., and Tardent, P. (1963). *Rev. Suisse Zool.* **70**, 312.

Morse, M. W. (1911). *Science* **34**, 770.

Moscona, A. A. (1963). *Proc. Nat. Acad. Sci. U. S.* **49**, 742.

Müller, K. (1911a). *Zool. Anz.* **37**, 83.

Müller, K. (1911b). *Zool. Anz.* **37**, 114.

Murray, M. R. (1926). *Proc. Soc. Exp. Biol. Med.* **23**, 754.

Murray, M. R. (1927a). *J. Exp. Zool.* **47**, 467.

Murray, M. R. (1927b). *Zentralbl. Bakteriol., Parasitenk. Infektionskr. Hyg.* **86**, 228.

Murray, M. R. (1928a). *Physiol. Zool.* **1**, 137.

Murray, M. R. (1928b). *Proc. Soc. Exp. Biol. Med.* **6**, 1.

Murray, M. R. (1931). *Arch. Exp. Zellforsch. Besonders Gewebezuecht.* **11**, 656.

Okada, Y. K. (1927). *Arch. Zool. Exp. Gen.* **66**, 7.

Okazaki, K. (1965). *Exp. Cell Res.* **40**, 585.

Papenfuss, E. J. (1934). *Biol. Bull.* **67**, 223.

Peebles, F. (1897). *Arch. Entwicklungsmech. Organisem* **5**, 794.

Philips, J. M. (1961). "Biology of the Hydra." Univ. of Miami Press, Coral Gables, Florida.

Quiot, J. M., and Rannou, M. (1971). In press.

Rannou, M. (1968). *Vie Milieu* **19**, 53.
Rannou, M. (1971). In press.
Rudzinska, M. A. (1951). *Proc. Soc. Exp. Biol. Med.* **78**, 67.
Sanyal, S., and Mookerjee, S. (1960). *Arch. Entwicklungsmech. Organismen* **152**, 131.
Sara, M. (1956). *Boll. Zool. Agr. Bachicolt.* **23**.
Sara, M. (1965). *Naturwissenschaften* **52**, 503.
Sara, M. (1966). *Boll. Zool.* **32**, 1067.
Sara, M., Liaci, L., and Melone, N. (1966a). *Nature (London)* **210**, 1167.
Sara, M., Liaci, L., and Melone, N. (1966b). *Nature (London)* **210**, 1168.
Seilern Aspang, F. (1958). *Zool. Anz.* **160**, 1.
Shivaramakrishnan, V. R. (1951). *Proc. Indian Acad. Sci. Sect. B* **34**, No. 6, 273.
Spiegel, M. (1954). *Biol. Bull.* **107**, 130.
Spiegel, M. (1955). *Ann. N. Y. Acad. Sci.* **60**, 1056.
Tardent, P. (1965). *In* "Regeneration in Animals and Related Problems (Kiortsis-Trampush, ed.). North-Holland Publ., Amsterdam.
Thomas, J. A. (1932). *C. R. Soc. Biol.* **110**, 451.
Tuzet, O. (1945). *Arch. Zool. Exp. Gen.* **84**, 224.
Tuzet, O., and Connes, R. (1962). *Vie Milieu* **13**, 703.
Waymouth, C. (1954). *Int. Rev. Cytol.* **3**, 1.
Weimer, B. R. (1934). *Physiol. Zool.* **7**, 212.
Weiss, L. (1967). "The Cell Periphery Metastasis and Other Contact Phenomena," p. 135. North-Holland Publ. Amsterdam.
Wilson, H. V. (1907). *Science* **25**, 912.
Wilson, H. V. (1908). *J. Exp. Zool.* **5**, 245.
Wilson, H. V. (1910). *Bull. U. S. Fish. Bur.* **30**, Doc. No. 750.
Wilson, H. V. (1911a). *J. Exp. Zool.* **11**, 281.
Wilson, H. V. (1911b). *Proc. Amer. Zool. Soc.* **33**.
Wilson, H. V. (1925). *Carnegie Inst. Wash., Yearb.* **24**.
Wilson, H. V. (1932). *Amer. Natur.* **66**, 159.
Wilson, H. V. (1937). *In* "Culture Methods for Invertebrate Animals" (J. C. Needham, ed.). Dover, New York.
Wilson, H. V., and Penney, J. T. (1928). *J. Elisha Mitchell Sci. Soc.* **44**.
Wilson, H. V., and Penney, J. T. (1930). *J. Exp. Zool.* **56**, 72.
Yazykov, A. A. (1965a). *Zh. Obsheh. Biol. (Moscow)* **26**, 690.
Yazykov, A. A. (1965b). *Zh. Obsheh. Biol. (Moscow)* **26**, 96.
Yazykov, A. A. (1967). *Zh. Obsheh. Biol. (Moscow)* **28**, 231.

AUTHOR INDEX

Numbers in italics refer to the pages on which the complete references are listed.

A

Abraham, M., 406, *407*
Acton, R. T., 180, *205*
Agrawal, N. S., 76, *108*
Agrell, I., 392, 393, 396, *407*
Agui, N., 204, *205*
Ahrens, R., 129, *138*
Aizawa, K., 29, 35, 36, *37*, 213, 223, 224, *244*, 375, *382*
Akov, S., 142, 146, 156, *165*
Alekseenko, F. M., 296, *305*
Almeida, J. D., 127, *139*
Amargier, A., 349, *360*
Anderson, N., 117, *138*
Anderson, W., 129, *138*
Andre, J., 129, *138*
Andrew, W., 178, 201, 205, *207*, 388, 399, 407, *407*, *409*
Anfinsen, C. B., 70, *110*
Ansevin, K. D., 403, *407*
Archetti, I., 258, *264*
Arvy, L., 49, *108*
Avrameas, S., 129, *138*
Aziz, P., 118, *138*

B

Babers, F. M., 45, 46, *108*
Backs, R. H., 142, 156, 158, *166*
Bailey, L., 296, *305*
Baker, F. D., 178, 201, 205, *207*, 388, 399, *409*
Ball, G. H., 37, *38*, 45, 47, 48, 51, 54, 56, 69, *108*, *109*, 183, *205*, *206*, 258, 259, *263*
Bang, F. B., 180, *205*
Barigozzi, C., 254, 255, *263*, 264
Barlow, G. H., 190, *207*, 396, 397, *409*
Barlow, J. S., 142, 155, 156, *166*
Barlow, S. S., 145, 146, *165*
Barnett, R. J., 119, *140*
Barsa, M. C., 274, *292*
Bassi, M., 308, *339*
Baumgartner, W. J., 73, *108*
Bazin, J. C., 83, *108*
Beadle, B. W., 67, *110*
Beadle, L. C., 399, *407*
Beck, S. D., 144, 145, *165*
Beckel, W. E., 47, 70, *108*, 259, *263*
Beeson, R. J., 406, *409*

411

SUBJECT INDEX

A

Abdominal ganglion, cultures of, 237

Acarians, organ cultures, 97, 99, 100

Acaratagallia sanguinolenta
tissue cultures, 310
established lines, 326

Acetone, dehydration and, 123, 124

Acheta domesticus, aseptic rearing, 143, 151–152

Acrolein, fixation and, 121

Actinomycin D, cell aggregates and, 191, 253

Acyrthosiphum pisum
aseptic rearing, 334
cell cultures, 334–336

Adenosine triphosphate, organ cultures and, 80

Aedes, see also Mosquito
organ culture, 47, 65, 69–70
tissue culture media
antibiotics and, 21
serum and, 24
vitamins in, 19

Aedes aegypti
aseptic rearing, 142, 153–156
cell lines
amphotericin B and, 236–237
clones of, 193

establishment of, 192, 260–262
polyploidy in, 200, 260
cultures, electron microscopy, 130, 136
eggs, disinfection of, 33, 145
embryonic cells, culture of, 32, 260–261
larvae, tissue cultures of, 30, 258, 259
organ cultures, 67, 70, 258–260
tissue culture media
embryo extract and, 25
hemolymph and, 22
serum and, 24

Aedes albopictus
cell lines, 192, 261, 262
tissue culture media, serum and, 24

Aedes communis, organ cultures, 70, 259–260

Aedes hexodontus, organ cultures, 70, 259–260

Aedes stephensi, tissue cultures, 262

Aeschna cyanea, organ culture, 103

Agallia constricta
aseptic rearing, 314
eggs, collection of, 312
embryonic cells, culture of, 31–32
nymphs, extraction of, 77
tissue cultures, 181–182, 309, 310, 312
establishment of, 192–193, 310, 326
main cell types, 327, 329–331

423